HENRY J. KATZ
Lt. Col., Ordnance Dept.

INTRODUCTION TO

MATHEMATICAL STATISTICS

WILEY MATHEMATICAL STATISTICS SERIES

Walter A. Shewhart, Editor

INTRODUCTION
TO
MATHEMATICAL
STATISTICS

By

PAUL G. HOEL

Associate Professor of Mathematics
University of California at Los Angeles

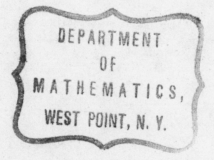

NEW YORK
JOHN WILEY & SONS, INC.
CHAPMAN & HALL, LTD.
LONDON

PREFACE

This book was designed to serve as a textbook for a two-semester course in mathematical statistics for which elementary calculus is a prerequisite. It grew out of my experiences in teaching an introductory course for junior and senior science majors. In the process of writing it, however, I attempted to keep in mind the needs of applied statisticians for a modern reference book on the fundamental methods of mathematical statistics.

The material treated was selected to give the beginner a fairly broad introduction to both classical large-sample and modern small-sample methods. A number of topics have been treated very briefly because I did not care to incorporate more material than experience indicated could be satisfactorily covered in a two-semester course. This compromise is in harmony with the view that an introduction to such a rapidly developing subject as statistics should make some attempt to survey the more important material in the field rather than concentrate heavily on a few topics. The references at the end of each chapter were designed to amplify this survey feature.

The organization of material was determined only after trying various methods of teaching the subject. For example, a systematic approach to testing hypotheses was postponed to one of the last chapters, in spite of the fact that logically it should have preceded sections in which hypotheses are tested, because it was found that science students obtained a better understanding of the subject from a more intuitive introduction. Most of the large-sample methods were placed in the first part of the book for the purpose of giving students taking only one semester of statistics a fairly unified treatment of at least the classical methods.

Since a background of elementary calculus is not sufficient for deriving much of the theory, I have not hesitated to state and use without proof essential theorems that require at least advanced calculus for their derivations. For the benefit of students with more mathematical maturity, references to such theorems will be found at the end of the chapter in which they first occur.

In conclusion, I wish to express my appreciation to Dr. W. A. Shewhart for his many helpful suggestions.

PAUL G. HOEL

Los Angeles, October, 1946

v

CONTENTS

CHAPTER I

INTRODUCTION

Statistical methods are essentially methods for dealing with data that have been obtained by a repetitive operation. For some sets of data, the operation that gave rise to the data is clearly of this repetitive type. This would be true, for example, of a set of diameters of a certain part in a mass-production manufacturing process or of a set of percentages obtained from routine chemical analyses. For other sets of data, the actual operation may not seem to be repetitive, but it may be possible to conceive of it as being so. This would be true for the ages at death of certain insurance-policy holders or for the total number of mistakes an experimental set of animals made the first time they ran a maze.

Experience indicates that many repetitive operations behave as though they occurred under essentially stable circumstances. Games of chance, such as coin tossing or dice rolling, usually exhibit this property. Many experiments in the various branches of science do likewise. Under such circumstances, it is often possible to construct a satisfactory mathematical model of the repetitive operation. This model can then be employed to study properties of the operation and to draw conclusions concerning it. Such models often prove to be useful even though the operation is not highly stable.

The mathematical model that a statistician selects for a repetitive operation is usually one that enables him to make predictions about the frequencies with which certain results can be expected in such an operation. For example, the model for studying the inheritance of color in the breeding of certain flowers might be one that predicted three times as many flowers of one color as of another color. The extent to which any such model will give valid predictions depends, of course, upon how realistic a model it is of the actual operation that produces the data.

In certain types of statistical work, the data to be investigated are classified into a number of groups and interest is then centered on the number of observations in each group. When data have been so arranged, they are said to form a frequency distribution. The mathematical model, then, often consists of a theoretical frequency distribution which is thought of as corresponding to a *population* of possible observations, and the data at hand are thought of as a *sample* extracted from this population.

1

Because of the nature of statistical data and models, it is only natural that probability should be the fundamental tool in statistical theory. From the statistician's point of view, it is convenient to treat probability as equivalent to theoretical relative frequency. Thus, the statement that the probability is $\frac{1}{5}$ that A will win at a pinball machine is assumed to imply that, if A could play this machine indefinitely, the relative frequency of wins would approach $\frac{1}{5}$. The nature of this approach and the philosophical questions arising from this or any other view of probability will not be discussed here. Such questions are not elementary, and their consideration would detract from the explanation of statistical theory at this level. It will merely be assumed that the basic laws of probability may be applied to the frequency problems that will be considered.

The science student will quickly discover the similarity between statistical procedure and common scientific procedure in which a hypothesis is set up, an experiment conducted, and the hypothesis tested by means of the experimental results. Beginning with the third chapter and continuing throughout the remainder of the book, statistical hypotheses are set up and tested by means of samples. The last two chapters in particular are intended to assist the science student toward designing his experiments more efficiently by the application of certain statistical principles.

The topics in the first seven chapters of this book are largely concerned with the theory of certain classical large-sample methods in statistical theory. They have been arranged according to the number of variables being studied. First, problems dealing with one variable are considered, then problems dealing with the relationship between two variables, and finally problems dealing with more than two variables. In each problem the descriptive methods of treating data are considered first, after which the theoretical counterpart, or mathematical model, is considered. With more than two variables, the theoretical model becomes somewhat complicated and therefore will not be treated here.

The topics in the last five chapters are largely concerned with the theory of certain modern methods in statistics, including in particular some of the important small-sample methods.

REFERENCES

A fuller discussion of some of the preceding ideas may be found in the following two books:

WILKS, S. S., *Mathematical Statistics*, Princeton University Press, pp. 1–4.
KENDALL, M. G., *The Advanced Theory of Statistics*, Griffin and Company. pp. 164–166.

CHAPTER II

FREQUENCY DISTRIBUTIONS OF ONE VARIABLE

CLASSIFICATION OF DATA

Since the statistical methods in this book are methods for dealing with repetitive data, it is essential to know what properties of such data will prove to be useful. The particular properties that will be considered, and hence the types of information that need to be extracted from a set of data, depend upon the nature of the data and upon the mathematical model that is to be chosen.

In considering the nature of the data, it is particularly important to distinguish between those sets of data for which the order in which the observations were obtained yields useful information and those sets for which it does not. For example, if one were interested in studying weather phenomena from day to day, the order might be very important. Industrial experience indicates that the information obtained from considering the order in which articles are manufactured is indispensable for efficient production. However, if one were interested in studying certain characteristics of college students and had selected a set of students by choosing every twentieth name in a college directory, he would hardly expect the order in which the names were obtained to be of any value in the study.

Methods for dealing with data for which order is important will be considered in later chapters. In this chapter the emphasis will be upon techniques that do not use order information. The material in these later chapters will enable the investigator to decide whether he is justified in assuming that he may ignore the order information present in his data.

The problem of determining what kind of information is most useful for any given mathematical model is not simple and will not be considered in this chapter. It will be assumed in this chapter that the model is one for which the methods about to be presented are appropriate.

For data of the type being considered, and for certain types of models, the information that is particularly useful is often in the form of various kinds of averages. These averages are employed to describe the data

3

and to test hypotheses concerning the population from which the data were assumed drawn. For large amounts of data, the computation of these averages becomes tedious; consequently, in order to shorten the computational time, it is desirable to classify the data into a frequency table. For example, suppose one had a record of the weights of 1,000 college men and desired their mean weight. Much time would be saved and very little accuracy lost if these weights were classified into, say, 10-pound classes and the mean weight of the classified data computed, all men in a given class being treated as though they possessed the same weight.

If the data are for a discrete variable, there is usually no need for classification. Thus, data on the number of petals on flowers of a given species, or the number of yeast cells on a square of a hemacytometer, are naturally classified. There is usually little difficulty in performing the classification when there appears to be a need for it.

If the data are for a continuous type of variable such as length, or weight, or time, they are recorded to a certain digit or decimal accuracy. For example, if the diameter of a steel rod is measured to the nearest thousandth of an inch, a diameter of 0.431 inch assumes that the "true" value lies between 0.4305 and 0.4315 inch.

In classifying data for a continuous variable, experience indicates that for most data it is desirable to use from 10 to 20 classes. With less than 10 classes, too much accuracy is lost, whereas with more than 20 classes the computations become unnecessarily tedious. In order to determine boundaries for the various class intervals, it is merely necessary to know the smallest and largest observations of the set. As an illustration, suppose that 200 steel rods were measured and it was found that the smallest and largest diameters were respectively 0.431 and 0.503 inch. Since the range of values, which is 0.072 inch here, is to be divided into 10 to 20 equal intervals, the class interval should be chosen as some convenient number between 0.0036 and 0.0072. A class interval of 0.005 inch will evidently be convenient. Since the first class interval should contain the smallest measurement of the set, it must begin at least as low as 0.4305. Furthermore, in order to avoid having measurements fall on the boundary of two adjacent class intervals, it is convenient to choose class boundaries to $\frac{1}{2}$ a unit beyond the accuracy of the measurements. Thus, in this problem it would be convenient to choose the first class interval as 0.4305–0.4355. The remaining class boundaries are then determined by merely adding the class interval 0.005 repeatedly until the largest measurement is enclosed in the final interval. If 0.4305–0.4355 is chosen as the first class interval, there will be 15 class intervals and the last class interval will be 0.5005–0.5055. When the class boundaries have been determined, it is a simple matter to list each measurement of the set in its proper class interval by merely recording a short vertical bar to represent it. When the number of bars corresponding to each class interval has been recorded, the data are said to have been classified into a frequency table. It is assumed in such a classification that all measurements in a given class interval, say the ith interval, have the value at the midpoint of the interval. This value is called the *class mark* and is denoted by x_i. Thus, $x_1 = 0.433$ and $x_{15} = 0.503$ in the example just considered. The number of measurements found in the ith class interval is denoted by f_i, while the total number of measurements is denoted by n. Table 1 illustrates the tabulation and resulting frequency table for the set of steel rods mentioned previously.

TABLE 1

Class boundaries	Frequencies	Class marks: x	Frequencies: f
0.4305–0.4355	//	0.433	2
.4355– .4405	卌	.438	5
.4405– .4455	卌 //	.443	7
.4455– .4505	卌 卌 ///	.448	13
.4505– .4555	卌 卌 卌 ////	.453	19
.4555– .4605	卌 卌 卌 卌 卌 //	.458	27
.4605– .4655	卌 卌 卌 卌 卌 ////	.463	29
.4655– .4705	卌 卌 卌 卌 卌	.468	25
.4705– .4755	卌 卌 卌 卌 ///	.473	23
.4755– .4805	卌 卌 ////	.478	14
.4805– .4855	卌 卌 卌	.483	15
.4855– .4905	卌 ////	.488	9
.4905– .4955	卌 /	.493	6
.4955– .5005	////	.498	4
.5005– .5055	//	.503	2

It is a common practice for many applied statisticians to indicate class intervals in a slightly different form from that suggested above. They record not actual class interval boundaries but rather non-contiguous boundaries. Thus, they would indicate the first three class intervals by 0.431–0.435, 0.436–0.440, and 0.441–0.445. When interval boundaries are so indicated, the true boundaries are ordinarily halfway between the upper and lower recorded boundaries of adjacent intervals. Another common method of recording class intervals is to employ common boundaries but to agree that an interval includes measurements up to but not including the upper boundary. Then the first three class intervals above would be indicated by 0.431–0.436, 0.436–0.441, and 0.441–0.446. A measurement that falls on a boundary is placed in the higher of the two intervals. If one knows the accuracy of measurement of the variable, there is little difficulty in determining the true class boundaries and class marks for these two methods of classification. It is important to use the exact class marks; otherwise a systematic error will be introduced in many of the computations to follow.

GRAPHICAL REPRESENTATION OF FREQUENCY DISTRIBUTIONS

A type of graph called a *histogram* is convenient for displaying the form of a frequency table. Curves are ordinarily reserved for display-

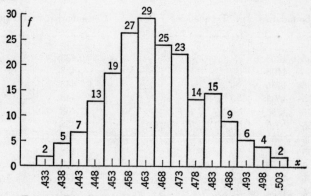

FIG. 1.   Distribution of the diameters of 200 steel rods.

ing theoretical frequency distributions. Figure 1, which is the histogram for the frequency distribution of Table 1, illustrates the nature of this type of graph. It is to be noted that the relative frequency with which x occurred in a given interval is given by the ratio of the area of the rectangle surmounting this interval to the total area of the histogram. This correspondence between frequency and area is one of the principal advantages of the histogram for graphing purposes. It should also be noted that the values of x indicated in Fig. 1 are the class marks and are located at the midpoints of the intervals.

Fortunately, many important frequency distributions to be found in nature and industry are of a relatively simple form. They usually range from a bell-shaped distribution, like that in Fig. 1, to something resembling the right half of a bell-shaped distribution. A distribution of the latter type is said to be heavily skewed, *skewness* meaning lack

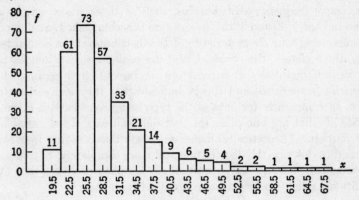

FIG. 2. Distribution of 302,000 marriages classified according to the age of the bridegroom.

of symmetry with respect to a vertical axis. It will be found, for example, that the following variables have frequency distributions that possess such forms in approximately increasing degrees of skewness:

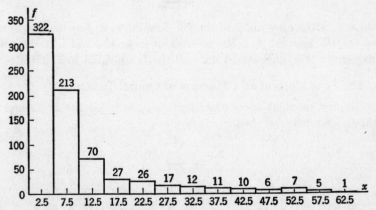

FIG. 3. Distribution of 727 deaths from scarlet fever classified according to age.

stature, many industrial measurements, weight, age at marriage, mortality age for certain diseases, wealth. Figures 1, 2, and 3 represent three such typical distributions with increasing degrees of skewness.

ARITHMETICAL REPRESENTATION OF FREQUENCY DISTRIBUTIONS

A histogram gives very little accurate quantitative information about data; consequently an arithmetical description of the data is desirable. For simple frequency distributions, such as those whose graphs are given in Figs. 1, 2, and 3, this description is accomplished satisfactorily by measuring four characteristics of the distribution: the *central tendency*, the *variation*, the *skewness*, and the *peakedness*. Although there are various quantities in current use for measuring these four characteristics, experience and theory indicate that the most satisfactory set of such measures for data of the type being considered is given by means of what are known as the first four *moments* of the variable or distribution. Theoretically, higher moments than the first four could be used to describe the distribution still more completely, but actually these higher moments are so unstable in sampling problems that little additional reliable information is obtained from them.

MOMENTS

For data that have been classified, the kth moment about the origin is defined by

$$(1) \qquad m_k' = \frac{1}{n} \sum_{i=1}^{h} x_i^k f_i$$

where x_i is the class mark of the ith class interval, f_i is the frequency for the ith interval, h is the number of intervals, and n is the total frequency. For unclassified data all the f_i are equal to 1 and $h = n$.

1. The First Moment as a Measure of Central Tendency

The first moment about the origin, m_1', is called the *mean* and is usually denoted by $\bar{x}$; hence

$$(2) \qquad \bar{x} = \frac{1}{n} \sum_{i=1}^{h} x_i f_i$$

For unclassified data, $\bar{x}$ reduces to the familiar formula for the average of a set of numbers. Formula (2) is sometimes spoken of as the formula for the weighted mean; however, it is merely a variation of the familiar form adapted to classified data. Geometrically, the mean represents the point on the x axis where a sheet of metal in the shape of the histogram would balance on a knife edge. For a histogram like that of Fig. 1, it is clear that $\bar{x}$ defines a measure of central tendency, that is, a value about which the data tend to concentrate. The mean is ordinarily meant when the word average is used. For example, the statement that the average weight of a group of people is 140 pounds implies that this is their mean weight.

If the x_i and f_i are not large, the value of $\bar{x}$ is easily computed from its definition, particularly if a calculating machine is available. Otherwise considerable time is saved for frequency tables having equal class intervals by using a short method based on introducing a new variable, u, which takes on only small integral values and which is defined by

$$(3) \qquad\qquad x_i = cu_i + x_0$$

where c is the class interval and x_0 is a conveniently chosen class mark. The computations are somewhat easier if x_0 is chosen as a class mark near the mean of the distribution. When this expression is substituted for x_i in (2),

$$\bar{x} = \frac{1}{n} \sum_{i=1}^{h} (cu_i + x_0)f_i$$

$$= \frac{1}{n} \sum_{i=1}^{h} (cu_if_i + x_0f_i)$$

$$= \frac{1}{n} \sum_{i=1}^{h} cu_if_i + \frac{1}{n} \sum_{i=1}^{h} x_0f_i$$

Since c and x_0 are constants with respect to these summations, they may be factored out and placed in front of the summation signs; hence

$$\bar{x} = c\frac{1}{n} \sum_{i=1}^{h} u_if_i + x_0\frac{1}{n} \sum_{i=1}^{h} f_i$$

From (2) it is clear that the coefficient of c is $\bar{u}$, while from the definition of n the coefficient of x_0 is 1; hence

$$(4) \qquad\qquad \bar{x} = c\bar{u} + x_0$$

Since the computations needed to find $\bar{u}$ are relatively easy, the value of $\bar{x}$ can be obtained quite easily without the aid of a calculating machine. This short method is illustrated in Table 2. The data for this frequency distribution are from 1,000 telephone conversations, the variable x being the length of a telephone conversation in seconds, recorded to the nearest second. Here x_0 was chosen as 449.5 because

TABLE 2

x	f	u	uf
49.5	6	−4	−24
149.5	28	−3	−84
249.5	88	−2	−176
349.5	180	−1	−180
449.5	247	0	
549.5	260	1	260
649.5	133	2	266
749.5	42	3	126
849.5	11	4	44
949.5	5	5	25
Totals	1,000		257

this choice gives rise to smaller products than other choices, although 549.5 is nearly as good.   When (4) is applied to Table 2,

$$\bar{x} = 100 \left(\frac{257}{1,000} \right) + 449.5 = 475.2$$

For certain common types of distributions, the mean is superior to other ordinary measures of central tendency, some of which will be considered briefly later. This superiority rests largely on the fact that in repeated sampling experiments from such distributions, of which the data at hand are thought of as the result of one such experiment, the mean usually tends to be more stable than these other measures of central tendency. For example, suppose one took a sample of 5 trees from a forest and calculated their mean height. Instead of the mean, one could have chosen, say, the middle height of the 5 as the measure of central tendency. Now, if one repeated this experiment a large number of times, he would usually find that the set of means would tend to be more closely clustered together than the set of middle measurements. This property of greater stability is particularly important in later work when a precise estimate of a population mean is desired. It should be clearly understood that the mean possesses these advantages only for certain types of distributions which are of particular importance and which will be considered in later chapters. There are other well-known distributions for which the mean is a very poor measure of central tendency.

2. The Second Moment as a Measure of Variation

The concept of variation is of paramount importance in statistics. Statistical methods have often been called methods for studying variation. The problem of measuring variation occurs repeatedly in the various sciences and in certain branches of industry. For example, in order to detect any lack of uniformity in the quality of a manufactured product, it is first necessary to know the variability of the product. This may be illustrated by the following problem. Suppose a purchaser of wire will not tolerate wire that does not possess a tensile strength of at least 50 pounds, and that he is considering purchasing his wire from one or the other of two firms. If equal samples taken from the product of these two firms gave frequency distributions like those shown in Fig. 4, it is clear that the product of only one of the firms would

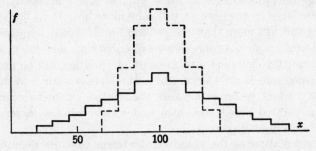

FIG. 4. Hypothetical distribution of tensile strength.

satisfy the purchaser's requirement. Since the mean tensile strength was 100 pounds in each sample, the purchaser would have had no basis for making a decision if the variation in tensile strength had been ignored.

It is customary to assume that variation means variation of the data about a measure of central tendency. Since the mean is being used as the measure of central tendency here, it is necessary to introduce moments about the mean in order to obtain a measure of variation from moments. The kth moment about the mean is defined by

$$(5) \qquad m_k = \frac{1}{n} \sum_{i=1}^{h} (x_i - \bar{x})^k f_i$$

Now it will be shown that the second moment about the mean, m_2, can be used as a measure of variation. Since it is often convenient to have a measure of variation in the same units of measurement as for the data, $\sqrt{m_2}$ is usually selected instead. This quantity is called the *standard deviation* and will be denoted by s; hence

$$(6) \qquad s = \sqrt{\frac{1}{n} \sum_{i=1}^{h} (x_i - \bar{x})^2 f_i}$$

The second moment about the mean, s^2, which is more convenient than the standard deviation as a measure of variation in certain situations, is called the *variance*. Some authors define these two quantities with n replaced by $n - 1$. Their definitions have certain advantages for later work but seem quite unnatural here.

If one considers the computation of s for two distributions of differing spread, like those whose histograms are given in Fig. 4, it should be clear that s does measure relative variation or spread. The distribution with the large tails will have a relatively larger value of s because the large deviations, $x_i - \bar{x}$, when squared and multiplied by their relatively large frequencies, f_i, will contribute heavily to the value of the sum and will more than compensate for the larger frequencies for small deviations in the concentrated distribution. The interpretation of the standard deviation as a measure of variation will be presented a few paragraphs later. At present it is merely a number in the same units as x which seems to measure the relative extent to which data are concentrated about the mean and which becomes larger as the data become more dispersed.

The calculation of the standard deviation from its definition (6) becomes inaccurate unless an accurate value of $\bar{x}$ is used, and then the computations usually become tedious. The change of variable introduced for computing the mean is also useful for obtaining a short method of computing the standard deviation for frequency tables having equal class intervals. From (3) and (4) it follows that

$$x_i - \bar{x} = c(u_i - \bar{u})$$

consequently

$$\frac{1}{n} \Sigma (x_i - \bar{x})^2 f_i = \frac{1}{n} \Sigma c^2 (u_i - \bar{u})^2 f_i$$

$$= \frac{c^2}{n} \Sigma (u_i^2 - 2u_i \bar{u} + \bar{u}^2) f_i$$

$$= c^2 \left\{ \frac{\Sigma u_i^2 f_i}{n} - 2\bar{u} \frac{\Sigma u_i f_i}{n} + \bar{u}^2 \frac{\Sigma f_i}{n} \right\}$$

$$= c^2 \left\{ \frac{\Sigma u_i^2 f_i}{n} - \bar{u}^2 \right\}$$

The short method for computing the standard deviation is therefore given by

$$(7) \qquad s = c \sqrt{\frac{\Sigma u_i^2 f_i}{n} - \bar{u}^2}$$

Hereafter, as was done in this derivation, the indicated range of summation will be omitted from the summation sign whenever the range is obvious.

For data that have not been classified, $f_i = 1$, $u_i = x_i$, and $c = 1$; consequently (7) reduces to

$$s = \sqrt{\frac{\Sigma x_i^2}{n} - \bar{x}^2}$$

This form is often more convenient than (6) for unclassified data, particularly when the x_i contain at most two digits each.

Table 3 illustrates the technique for computing s for the data of

TABLE 3

x	f	u	uf	u^2f
49.5	6	−4	−24	96
149.5	28	−3	−84	252
249.5	88	−2	−176	352
349.5	180	−1	−180	180
449.5	247	0		
549.5	260	1	260	260
649.5	133	2	266	532
749.5	42	3	126	378
849.5	11	4	44	176
949.5	5	5	25	125
Totals	1,000		257	2,351

Table 2. When (7) is applied to Table 3,

$$s = 100 \sqrt{\frac{2,351}{1,000} - (0.257)^2} = 151$$

correct to the nearest integer.

In order to interpret the standard deviation as a measure of variation, it is necessary to anticipate certain results of later work. For a set of data that has been obtained by sampling a particular type of population called a *normal* population, it will be shown that the interval $(\bar{x} - s, \bar{x} + s)$ will usually include about 68 per cent of the observations and the interval $(\bar{x} - 2s, \bar{x} + 2s)$ will usually include about 95 per cent of the observations. A sketch of a particular normal distribution is shown in Fig. 3, Chapter III.

As an illustrative example of this property, consider the data for which the standard deviation was just computed. Previous calculations gave $\bar{x} = 475$ and $s = 151$, correct to the nearest integer; consequently the above two intervals are (324, 626) and (173, 777) respectively. The number of observations lying within these intervals may be found approximately by interpolating as though the observations in a given interval were dispersed uniformly throughout the interval. This assumption implies that on the histogram any fractional part of a class interval will include the same fractional part of the frequencies in that interval. For ease of interpolation, the histogram for this frequency distribution is shown in Fig. 5. If interpolation is carried

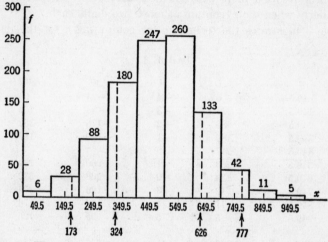

Fig. 5.   Histogram for the distribution of 1,000 telephone conversations.

to the nearest unit, it will be found that the interval (324, 626) will include $136 + 247 + 260 + 35$ measurements, which is 67.8 per cent of them. The interval (173, 777) excludes $6 + 21 + 9 + 11 + 5$ measurements, which is 5.2 per cent. For a histogram as irregular as this, these results are unusually close to the theoretical percentages. However, even for histograms possessing a considerable lack of symmetry, the actual percentages are often surprisingly close to the theoretical percentages, primarily because the large percentage of measurements in the short tail included by such an interval is compensated to a considerable extent by the small percentage of measurements in the long tail which are included.

For certain common types of data, the standard deviation is superior to other common measures of variation, some of which will be considered briefly later. The superiority rests partly on its greater stability in repeated sampling experiments and partly on its convenience for developing statistical theory. The situation with respect to other measures of variation is very much like that of the mean with respect to other measures of central tendency.

3. The Third Moment as a Measure of Skewness

As was indicated previously, skewness implies a lack of symmetry with respect to a vertical axis through the mean. Increasing degrees of skewness are well illustrated by Figs. 1, 2, and 3. Distributions with a slight amount of skewness seem to be more common in statistical applications than any other type. Now, the third moment about the mean, $\Sigma(x_i - \bar{x})^3 f_i/n$, has properties that make it useful for measuring the amount of skewness in a distribution. The third moment will be zero for a symmetrical histogram because, for each positive deviation, $x_i - \bar{x}$, there will be a corresponding negative deviation with the same frequency, f_i, so that these deviations when cubed and multiplied by f_i will cancel each other in the summation. For a histogram with a large right tail, in which the distribution is said to be skewed to the right or positively skewed, the third moment will tend to be positive because these large positive deviations when cubed and multiplied by their relatively large frequencies contribute heavily to the sum. As it stands, however, the third moment about the mean is not satisfactory as a measure of skewness because its value depends upon the units of measurement of x. To obtain a measure that is a pure number, the third moment is divided by the cube of the standard deviation. This ratio gives a measure that is not only independent of the scale of units of x but also independent of the choice of origin—a property that would not hold, for example, if the third moment had been divided by the cube of the mean. This measure of skewness being denoted by a_3,

$$a_3 = \frac{m_3}{m_2^{3/2}}$$

This measure can be zero without the distribution's being symmetrical; however, it usually serves as a highly satisfactory measure of skewness. For Figs. 1, 2, and 3, the values of a_3 are approximately -0.5, 1.8, and 2.3, respectively. The procedure for calculating a_3 will be considered in the next section.

4. The Fourth Moment as a Measure of Peakedness

Consider the two histograms in Fig. 6. They were constructed to have the same means and standard deviations but to differ considerably with respect to the peakedness of the graph in the neighborhood of the mean. If two distributions have the same standard deviations but one of them has a considerably larger percentage of its data concentrated about its mean as in Fig. 6, then that one will usually have considerably longer tails to compensate for the larger percentage of small squared deviations contributing to the total sum of squared deviations in the definition of the standard deviation. Because of the heavy contribution of the large deviations to the sum of the fourth powers of the deviations, the peaked distribution with long tails will therefore tend to have a relatively larger value of the fourth moment about the mean. It does not follow from these considerations that the more peaked of two such distributions necessarily has the larger

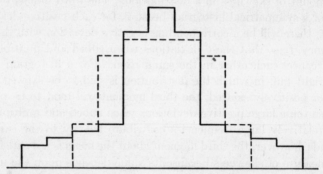

Fig. 6.   Hypothetical distributions with different "peakedness."

fourth moment. Examples can be constructed for which this is not true; nevertheless, it is convenient to treat the fourth moment as a measure of peakedness. In order to obtain a measure of peakedness that is independent of the units of measurement, the fourth moment is divided by the fourth power of the standard deviation. If a_4 denotes this measure of peakedness,

$$a_4 = \frac{m_4}{m_2{}^2}$$

It is customary in statistical literature to speak of this quantity as a measure of *kurtosis*. There seems to be little point, however, in perpetuating a Greek word to describe this property of a distribution, particularly since the property is not precisely defined.

It is customary to compare the peakedness of distributions with that of the previously mentioned normal distribution, for which this measure turns out to be 3. For Figs. 1, 2, and 3, the values of a_4 are approximately 2.85, 7.15, and 8.37, respectively. Although a comparison of the values of a_3 and a_4 for these three illustrations might indicate a relationship between these two measures, they are, nevertheless, independent measures.

Moments about the mean are tedious to compute by means of the formulas defining them. The change of variable for shortening the calculation of both the mean and the standard deviation for equal intervals can be used to advantage here also. To obtain the short method for calculating the kth moment about the mean, it is merely necessary to substitute $x_i - \bar{x} = c(u_i - \bar{u})$ in (5) and apply the binomial theorem. Thus,

$$m_k = \frac{1}{n} \Sigma c^k (u_i - \bar{u})^k f_i$$

$$= \frac{c^k}{n} \Sigma \left(u_i^k - k u_i^{k-1}\bar{u} + \frac{k(k-1)}{2} u_i^{k-2}\bar{u}^2 - \cdots + (-1)^k \bar{u}^k \right) f_i$$

$$(8) \quad = c^k \left\{ \frac{\Sigma u_i^k f_i}{n} - k\bar{u}\frac{\Sigma u_i^{k-1} f_i}{n} \right.$$

$$\left. + \frac{k(k-1)}{2} \bar{u}^2 \frac{\Sigma u_i^{k-2} f_i}{n} - \cdots + (-1)^k \bar{u}^k \right\}$$

The sums occurring in this formula are relatively easy to compute with a table of powers and a calculating machine. The technique for com-

TABLE 4

x	f	u	uf	$u^2 f$	$u^3 f$	$u^4 f$
49.5	6	−4	−24	96	−384	1,536
149.5	28	−3	−84	252	−756	2,268
249.5	88	−2	−176	352	−704	1,408
349.5	180	−1	−180	180	−180	180
449.5	247	0				
549.5	260	1	260	260	260	260
649.5	133	2	266	532	1,064	2,128
749.5	42	3	126	378	1,134	3,402
849.5	11	4	44	176	704	2,816
949.5	5	5	25	125	625	3,125
Totals	1,000		257	2,351	1,763	17,123

puting a_3 and a_4 will be illustrated on the data of Table 2. The computations are shown in Table 4. Here

$$\frac{\Sigma u_i f_i}{n} = 0.257, \quad \frac{\Sigma u_i^2 f_i}{n} = 2.351$$

$$\frac{\Sigma u_i^3 f_i}{n} = 1.763, \quad \frac{\Sigma u_i^4 f_i}{n} = 17.123$$

Therefore,

$$m_3 = 100^3\{1.763 - 3(0.257)(2.351) + 3(0.257)^2(0.257) - (0.257)^3\}$$
$$= 100^3\{-0.016\}$$
$$m_4 = 100^4\{17.123 - 4(0.257)(1.763)$$
$$+ 6(0.257)^2(2.351) - 4(0.257)^3(0.257) + (0.257)^4\}$$
$$= 100^4\{16.23\}$$

$$a_3 = \frac{-0.016}{3.45} = -0.005$$

$$a_4 = \frac{16.23}{5.22} = 3.11$$

As was to be expected from comparing Fig. 5 and Fig. 3, Chapter III, these values are close to the theoretical normal distribution values of 0 and 3 respectively.

Formula (8) is convenient for computing the moments about the mean in terms of moments about the origin. It is merely necessary to choose $c = 1$ and $u_i = x_i$, and then (8) reduces to

$$(9) \quad m_k = m_k' - km_{k-1}'m_1' + \frac{k(k-1)}{2}m_{k-2}'m_1'^2 - \cdots + (-1)^k m_1'^k.$$

OTHER DESCRIPTIVE MEASURES

Among the more common other measures of central tendency are the median, mode, and geometric mean.

For a set of measurements arranged in order of magnitude, the median is defined as the middle measurement, if there is one, otherwise as the interpolated middle value. Thus, for the set of measurements, 2, 3, 3, 4, 5, 5, 6, 6, 7, 7, 7, 9, the median is 5.5. For classified data the median is defined as the abscissa which divides the area of the histogram into two equal parts. Some workers prefer the median to the mean when the distribution is heavily skewed because they feel that it is more representative of what a measure of central tendency should be than the mean is under such circumstances. They might, for example, prefer the median when discussing the notion of average wage of a community because a few very large incomes would produce a mean wage higher than the notion of average wage implies, whereas the median wage would not be so affected.

The mode of a set of measurements is defined as the measurement with the maximum frequency, if there is one. For the set of measurements in the preceding paragraph, the mode is 7. If there is more than one measurement with the maximum frequency, no completely satisfactory definition exists. The mode is used occasionally in situations similar to those for which the median might be selected. Since the mode is of questionable value in descriptive statistics, it will not be considered further here.

The geometric mean of a set of measurements is defined as $\sqrt[n]{x_1^{f_1}x_2^{f_2}\cdots x_h^{f_h}}$. If the data are classified, x_i represents the ith class mark; otherwise it represents the ith measurement, in which event all the f_i equal 1. It will be observed that the logarithm of the geometric mean is equal to the arithmetic mean of the logarithms. This measure is used principally in working with business index numbers, for which it possesses certain advantages.

Among the more common measures of variation are the range and mean deviation.

The range, which is the difference between the largest and smallest measurement in the set, is used as a measure of variation largely because of its ease of computation. It is often applied in certain industrial engineering work. It has two important disadvantages. First, its value usually increases with n because there is a better chance of obtaining extreme measurements if a large sample of data is taken than if a small sample is taken. It is possible, however, to make allowance for this growth and thus eliminate this disadvantage of the range. Secondly, the range is usually quite unstable in repeated sampling experiments of the same size when n is large; consequently, its use is ordinarily restricted to sets of data containing less than 10 observations each. Because of its importance in various fields, the range will be studied more fully in a later chapter.

The mean deviation is defined as $\Sigma \mid x_i - \bar{x} \mid f_i/n$, where the absolute values, that is, the positive values of deviations are employed. This measure of variation is often used because it appears to be easier to calculate and understand than the standard deviation. It will be found, however, that the short method of calculating the standard deviation is about as fast as calculating the mean deviation, when n is large.

There are additional measures of skewness and peakedness in current use, but they will not be considered here. Consideration was given to these other measures of central tendency and variation only because they appear quite often in certain fields of application and a student of statistical methods should be acquainted with them. However, for the present, moments will be selected as the preferred set of descriptive measures unless there are valid reasons for doing otherwise.

REFERENCES

A more detailed discussion of moments and other descriptive measures will be found in the following books:

KENNEY, J. F., *Mathematics of Statistics*, Part 1, D. Van Nostrand Company.

RICHARDSON, C. H., *An Introduction to Statistical Analysis*, Revised, Harcourt, Brace and Company.

YULE and KENDALL, *Introduction to the Theory of Statistics*, Griffin and Company.

An interesting example of a mathematical model for which moments are a poor choice of descriptive measures is the theoretical distribution given by

$$f(x) = \frac{1}{\pi[1 + (x - m)^2]}$$

For this distribution, which is called the Cauchy distribution, it turns out that the mean of a sample of n observations is no better than a single observation for estimating the value of m; the median is a far better measure of central tendency.

EXERCISES

1. Weights of 300 entering freshmen ranged from 98 to 226 pounds, correct to the nearest pound.   Determine class boundaries and class marks for the first and last class intervals.

2. The thickness of 400 washers ranged from 0.421 to 0.563 inch.   Determine class boundaries and class marks for the first and last class intervals.

3. If the weights in problem 1 had been recorded to the nearest quarter of a pound, what change if any would you make in your classification?

4. Given the following frequency table of the heights in centimeters of 1,000 students, draw its histogram, indicating the class marks.

x	155–157	158–160	161–163	etc.										
f	4	8	26	53	89	146	188	181	125	92	60	22	4	1	1

5. Given the following frequency table of the diameters in feet of 56 shrubs from a common species: (*a*) draw its histogram; (*b*) guess by merely inspecting the histogram, the values of $\bar{x}$, s, a_3, and a_4.

x	1	2	3	4	5	6	7	8	9	10	11	12
f	1	7	11	16	8	4	5	2	1	0	0	1

6. Given the following frequency table on the number of petals per flower for ranunculus: (a) draw its histogram; (b) guess, by merely inspecting the histogram, the values of $\bar{x}$, s, a_3, and a_4.

x	5	6	7	8	9	10
f	133	55	23	7	2	2

7. Give one illustration each of types of data for which you would expect the frequency distribution to be (a) fairly symmetrical, (b) slightly skewed, (c) heavily skewed, (d) J shaped.

8. For the data of problem 5 calculate $\bar{x}$ by (a) definition, (b) the short method.

9. For the data of problem 5 find (a) the crude median and mode, (b) the median by interpolation.

10. For the data of problem 5, calculate s by (a) definition, (b) the short method.

11. For the data of problem 5 find the range and mean deviation.

12. For the data of problem 5 calculate a_3 and a_4 by the short method.

13. Show that $\sum_{i=1}^{h} (x_i - \bar{x})f_i = 0$.

14. Show that $\overline{X} = \dfrac{N_1\overline{X}_1 + N_2\overline{X}_2}{N}$ if $N_1 + N_2 = N$ and $\overline{X}_1$ and $\overline{X}_2$ are two means of different data which are to be combined into one set.

15. Use the formula of problem 14 to find $\overline{X}$ for the following data on tuberculosis deaths by ages in which the intervals are not all equal. Use the short method for computing $\overline{X}_1$ and $\overline{X}_2$.

x	0–4	5–9	10–14	etc.				35–44	45–54	etc.		
f	1,356	537	1,278	6,300	10,911	10,349	8,776	15,456	11,060	7,455	4,788	1,866

16. For the histogram of problem 5, (a) find what percentage of the data lies within the intervals $\bar{x} \pm s$ and $\bar{x} \pm 2s$; (b) compare these percentages with normal curve values, indicating whether the agreement is about what might be expected here.

17. Show that $s^2 = \dfrac{N_1s_1^2 + N_2s_2^2}{N} + \dfrac{N_1N_2}{N^2} (\overline{X}_1 - \overline{X}_2)^2$ for a situation like that of problem 14.

18. Use the formula of problem 17 on the data of problem 15 to find s^2, using the short method to find s_1^2 and s_2^2.

19. Would the standard deviation of tree diameters selected at random from a given forest increase, decrease, or remain about the same as you took larger and larger samples?

CHAPTER III

THEORETICAL FREQUENCY DISTRIBUTIONS OF ONE VARIABLE

CONTINUOUS FREQUENCY DISTRIBUTIONS

1. General Distribution Functions

In order to obtain statistical methods that will be sufficiently versatile to handle a wide variety of practical problems, it is necessary to work mathematically with theoretical frequency distributions which represent actual distributions satisfactorily. For a continuous variable this implies working with curves rather than with histograms.

In certain types of statistical work, a set of data is thought of as a sample that has been taken from some theoretical frequency distribution, or population. Thus, data giving the diameters of 100 trees may be thought of as having been obtained by selecting 100 trees at random from some forest. By *random sampling* from a practical point of view is ordinarily meant a mechanical method of sampling like that for games of chance. For example, if each tree of a forest were assigned a number on a slip of paper and these slips of paper were thoroughly mixed in a container, then drawing from this container would be considered to give random sampling of the forest. However, the following game-of-chance procedure would not be considered random sampling of the forest. Suppose that the forest is in the form of a square and that it is thought of as having been divided into a large number of equal squares by means of equally spaced lines parallel to the sides. Then a square may be selected by numbering the squares and drawing a number by means of slips of paper as before. After a square has been selected, a tree may be selected from the square in a similar manner. For this sampling procedure it might happen that one of the small squares had a single tree in it while another square had 10 trees; consequently the single tree would be sampled 10 times as often on the average as any one of the 10 trees. Although the sampling in both procedures is based upon games of chance, the second does not allow the game of chance to operate upon the individual of the population. If each square contained the same number of trees, however, the second procedure would be considered random sampling.

It is to be noted that random sampling from this point of view implies a finite population, although the population may be thought of as extremely large. In sampling from a finite population, it will be assumed that the individual selected is returned to the population so that the population remains of constant size.

In order to apply calculus methods to populations, it is convenient to conceive of them as infinite in size and to represent their frequency distributions by curves. A mathematical definition of random sampling for such idealized infinite populations will be considered later. One need not be concerned about the lack of reality in the assumption of an infinite population and the method of sampling randomly from it

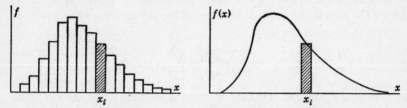

FIG. 1. Hypothetical observed and theoretical frequency distributions.

since such artificial devices are merely part of a mathematical theory, or model, and in practice there is not much difficulty in applying the resulting theory to finite reality.

Properties. A theoretical distribution function of a continuous variable x will be denoted by $f(x)$. It is defined as that function for which

$$(1) \qquad \int_{\alpha}^{\beta} f(x)\,dx = P[\alpha < x < \beta]$$

where $\alpha < \beta$ are any two values of x and the expression on the right indicates the probability, that is, the theoretical relative frequency, with which x will fall between α and β in random sampling.

For the purpose of explaining the reasoning behind this definition, consider the histogram and curve of Fig. 1, in which the total area under each is equal to 1. The curve is to be thought of as the graph of $f(x)$, and the histogram is to be thought of as the graph of the observed frequency distribution of a random sample of size n extracted from the population represented by $f(x)$. Now, the area of the shaded rectangle of the histogram must be f_i/n, since the ordinates are proportional to the observed frequencies and $\Sigma f_i/n = 1$. Thus, the area under the histogram above the ith interval is equal to the relative frequency with which x occurred in the ith class interval. The analogous geometrical property for the curve would require that the area under the curve above the ith interval be equal to the theoretical relative frequency with which x will occur in that interval. Since this property should not depend upon the classification of data, it should hold for any interval (α, β) as in (1).

It follows from (1) that the total area under the graph of $f(x)$ which lies above the x axis must equal 1 and that $f(x) \geq 0$ if it is a continuous function; consequently many functions could not serve as mathematical models for observed distributions.

Moments. Moments for theoretical distributions may be defined by considering the limit of the sum which defines moments of observed distributions. Consider the problem geometrically by means of Fig. 1. Since the area of the shaded rectangle of the histogram is f_i/n, it follows from (1), Chapter II, that

$$m_k' = \sum_{i=1}^{h} x_i^k \frac{f_i}{n} = \sum_{i=1}^{h} x_i^k y_i \, \Delta x$$

where y_i denotes the ordinate of the ith rectangle and Δx the class interval. For the curve corresponding to this histogram, the natural procedure would be to define the kth moment as the limit of this sum with y_i replaced by $f(x_i)$ as Δx approached zero. Hence, the theoretical kth moment about the origin, which will be denoted by μ_k', is defined by

$$(2) \qquad \mu_k' = \int_a^b x^k f(x) \, dx$$

where (a, b) is the interval over which $f(x)$ is defined. The corresponding kth moment about the mean, by analogy with (5), Chapter II, is defined by

$$(3) \qquad \mu_k = \int_a^b (x - \mu_1')^k f(x) \, dx$$

Throughout this book corresponding Greek and Roman letters will be used to represent corresponding theoretical and data quantities. Thus, μ_k' represents the theoretical or population kth moment for which m_k' is the corresponding observed or sample value. Then m_k' is thought of as an approximation to μ_k' based upon a random sample of size n. There will be two exceptions to this rule because of tradition. The first is that $\bar{x}$ and m will be used to represent a sample and population mean respectively in place of m_1' and μ_1'. The second is that p' and p will represent a sample and population percentage respectively in place of p and π. A third change in notation because of tradition, but one which does not contradict the above rule, is that s and σ will represent a sample and population standard deviation respectively in place of $\sqrt{m_2}$ and $\sqrt{\mu_2}$. With these changes in notation, the four descriptive quantities, based upon moments, for data and theory are $\bar{x}$, s, a_3, a_4 and m, σ, α_3, α_4, respectively.

As an illustration of how to find these descriptive quantities for a theoretical distribution, consider the function

$$f(x) = ce^{-x}$$

defined only for non-negative values of x. This function can serve as a distribution function provided that c is chosen properly. Since the area under the graph of $f(x)$ must equal 1,

$$1 = \int_0^\infty ce^{-x}\, dx = c$$

and hence $f(x) = e^{-x}$. To find the four descriptive quantities for this distribution, it is convenient to find the kth moment about the origin. If (2) is applied,

$$\mu_k' = \int_0^\infty x^k e^{-x}\, dx$$

The value of this definite integral is found in any standard table of integrals, or it may be evaluated by repeated integration by parts. This integral is the integral defining the *gamma*, or factorial, function. More precisely,

$$\Gamma(k + 1) = \int_0^\infty x^k e^{-x}\, dx$$

When k is a positive integer, $\Gamma(k + 1) = k!$. Since k is a positive integer in this problem, $\mu_k' = k!$; consequently $\mu_1' = 1$, $\mu_2' = 2$, $\mu_3' = 6$, and $\mu_4' = 24$. Then, since formula (9), Chapter II, for find-

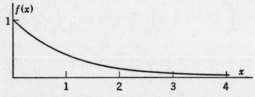

FIG. 2. The distribution function $f(x) = e^{-x}$, $x \geq 0$.

ing the moments about the mean in terms of moments about the origin holds for theoretical moments also, $m = 1$, $\mu_2 = 1$, $\mu_3 = 2$, and $\mu_4 = 9$; consequently $m = 1$, $\sigma = 1$, $\alpha_3 = 2$, and $\alpha_4 = 9$. The graph of this distribution is shown in Fig. 2. Although this function was selected merely for illustration of methods, it might conceivably prove useful as a mathematical model for histograms similar to the one in Fig. 3, Chapter II.

Moment-generating function. Although the direct computation of a theoretical moment from its integral definition may be relatively easy with the aid of a table of integrals, it is convenient for later theory to be able to compute moments indirectly by another method. This method will be introduced here and used throughout several chapters for deriving formulas. It involves finding what is known as the *moment-generating function*. As the name implies, the moment-generating function is a function that generates moments. It is defined by

$$(4) \qquad M_x(\theta) = \int_a^b e^{\theta x} f(x)\, dx$$

This integral is a function of the parameter θ only, but the subscript x is placed on $M(\theta)$ to show what variable is being considered. The parameter θ has no real meaning here; it is merely a mathematical tool for aiding in the determination of moments. To see how $M_x(\theta)$ does generate moments, assume that $f(x)$ is a distribution function for which this integral exists. Then $e^{\theta x}$ may be expanded in a power series and the integrations may be performed term by term. Since the power series for e^z is

$$e^z = 1 + z + \frac{z^2}{2!} + \frac{z^3}{3!} + \cdots$$

it follows that

$$M_x(\theta) = \int_a^b [1 + \theta x + \frac{\theta^2 x^2}{2!} + \frac{\theta^3 x^3}{3!} + \cdots] f(x)\, dx$$

$$= \int_a^b f(x)\, dx + \theta \int_a^b x f(x)\, dx + \frac{\theta^2}{2!} \int_a^b x^2 f(x)\, dx + \cdots$$

$$(5) \qquad = \mu_0' + \mu_1'\, \theta + \mu_2' \frac{\theta^2}{2!} + \mu_3' \frac{\theta^3}{3!} + \cdots$$

It will be observed that the coefficient of $\theta^k/k!$ in this expansion is the kth moment about the origin; consequently, if the moment-generating function can be found for a variable x and can be expanded into a power series in θ, the moments of the variable are readily obtained by merely inspecting the expansion. If a particular moment is desired, it may be more convenient to evaluate it by computing the proper derivative of $M_x(\theta)$ at $\theta = 0$, since repeated differentiation of (5) shows that

$$(6) \qquad \mu_k' = \frac{d^k M}{d\theta^k}\bigg|_{\theta = 0}$$

There are distribution functions that do not possess moments of all orders; consequently this method cannot be applied to them. For example, if $f(x)$ is defined for $x \geq 0$ by

$$f(x) = \frac{c}{1 + x^4}$$

it will be found by direct integration that no moment higher than the second exists.

As an illustration of the moment-generating-function technique for finding moments, consider the function of the preceding section that illustrated the direct computation of moments from their integral definition. Here $f(x) = e^{-x}$. Then, by (4),

$$M_x(\theta) = \int_0^\infty e^{\theta x} \cdot e^{-x}\, dx = \int_0^\infty e^{x(\theta-1)}\, dx = \frac{e^{x(\theta-1)}}{\theta - 1}\bigg|_0^\infty$$

Since θ is a parameter that can be chosen as small as desired, this moment-generating function will exist provided that $\theta < 1$. Then

$$\frac{e^{x(\theta-1)}}{\theta - 1}\bigg|_0^\infty = \frac{e^{-x(1-\theta)}}{\theta - 1}\bigg|_0^\infty = \frac{1}{1 - \theta}$$

For $|\theta| < 1$,

$$M_x(\theta) = \frac{1}{1 - \theta} = 1 + \theta + \theta^2 + \theta^3 + \cdots$$

$$= 1 + \theta + 2!\frac{\theta^2}{2!} + 3!\frac{\theta^3}{3!} + \cdots$$

Since the coefficient of $\theta^k/k!$ is $k!$, it follows that $\mu_k' = k!$, which is the result obtained by direct integration in the preceding section.

Although the kth moment, μ_k', and the moment-generating function, $M_x(\theta)$, were defined for the variable x only, the definitions can be generalized to hold for the variable $g(x)$, where $g(x)$ is any function of x. For example, if $g(x) = x - m$, the kth moment of $g(x)$ would be the kth moment of x about its mean, and the moment-generating function of $g(x)$ would yield moments about the mean for x. Thus, general definitions in terms of $g(x)$ enable one to shift easily from moments about the origin to moments about the mean. In addition, such general definitions enable one to consider various other useful changes of variable. These general definitions are the following:

$$(7) \qquad \mu_{k:g}{}' = \int_a^b g^k(x)f(x)\,dx$$

$$(8) \qquad M_g(\theta) = \int_a^b e^{\theta g(x)}f(x)\,dx$$

When $g(x) = x$, these definitions reduce to (2) and (4). When $g(x) = x - m$, definition (7) reduces to (3).

Two useful properties of the moment-generating function are easily obtained. Let c be any constant, and let $G(x)$ be a function of x for which the moment-generating function exists. Then, since $g(x)$ in (8) represents an arbitrary function, $g(x)$ may be chosen as $g(x) = cG(x)$; consequently

$$(9) \qquad M_{cG}(\theta) = \int_a^b e^{\theta cG(x)}f(x)\,dx = M_G(c\theta)$$

The other property is obtained by choosing $g(x) = G(x) + c$. Then

$$(10) \quad M_{G+c}(\theta) = \int_a^b e^{\theta[G(x)+c]}f(x)\,dx = e^{\theta c}\int_a^b e^{\theta G(x)}f(x)\,dx = e^{c\theta}M_G(\theta)$$

These two properties enable one to dispose of a bothersome constant, c, which is a factor of, or is added to, a function, $G(x)$. Applications of these two properties will be made in later sections.

2. Normal Distribution

A normal-distribution function is defined as a function of the form

$$(11) \qquad f(x) = ce^{-\frac{1}{2}\left(\frac{x-a}{b}\right)^2}$$

where a, b, and c are parameters so restricted that $f(x)$ has the essential properties of a distribution function. For example, c must be such that the area under the normal curve is equal to 1. Normal distributions are very useful as mathematical models for many frequency distributions found in nature and industry. Thus, a great many measurements made on manufactured articles possess distributions that can be approximated well by normal distributions. As was indicated in the preceding chapter, the same is also true of many biological measurements. Figures 1 and 5, Chapter II, illustrate histograms which it will be found could be approximated well by means of normal curves.

Even if there were few natural distributions of this form, the normal distribution would still be extremely important because of its place in theoretical work. Thus, it will be shown later that under mild restrictions a sample mean approximately follows a normal distribution even though the basic variable does not.

Properties. The characteristic properties of a normal distribution may be obtained by studying the four descriptive quantities defined in the preceding chapter. Since these quantities are defined in terms of moments, consider the moment-generating function of a normal variable. It is convenient here to work with the variable $x - a$ rather than with x.

If definition (8) with $g(x) = x - a$ is applied to (11),

$$M_{x-a}(\theta) = \int_{-\infty}^{\infty} e^{\theta(x-a)} f(x) \, dx$$

$$= c \int_{-\infty}^{\infty} e^{\theta(x-a) - \frac{1}{2}\left(\frac{x-a}{b}\right)^2} dx$$

Let $z = (x - a)/b$; then $dx = b \, dz$ and

$$M_{x-a}(\theta) = bc \int_{-\infty}^{\infty} e^{\theta b z - \frac{z^2}{2}} dz$$

Complete the square in the exponent as follows:

$$\theta b z - \frac{z^2}{2} = -\frac{1}{2}(z - \theta b)^2 + \frac{1}{2}\theta^2 b^2$$

Then,

$$M_{x-a}(\theta) = bc e^{\frac{1}{2}\theta^2 b^2} \int_{-\infty}^{\infty} e^{-\frac{1}{2}(z-\theta b)^2} dz$$

If $t = z - \theta b$, then $dz = dt$ and

$$M_{x-a}(\theta) = bc e^{\frac{1}{2}\theta^2 b^2} \int_{-\infty}^{\infty} e^{-\frac{t^2}{2}} dt$$

The value of this integral can be found in any standard table of integrals. Or it may be evaluated directly by the following device. Let

$$I = \int_{0}^{\infty} e^{-\frac{t^2}{2}} dt$$

Then

$$I^2 = \int_{0}^{\infty} e^{-\frac{x^2}{2}} dx \int_{0}^{\infty} e^{-\frac{y^2}{2}} dy$$

$$= \int_{0}^{\infty} \int_{0}^{\infty} e^{-\frac{x^2+y^2}{2}} dx \, dy$$

In polar coordinates,

$$I^2 = \int_0^{\frac{\pi}{2}} \int_0^{\infty} e^{-\frac{r^2}{2}} r \, dr \, d\theta$$

$$= \int_0^{\frac{\pi}{2}} -e^{-\frac{r^2}{2}} \Big|_0^{\infty} d\theta$$

$$= \int_0^{\frac{\pi}{2}} d\theta = \frac{\pi}{2}$$

Hence,

$$\int_{-\infty}^{\infty} e^{-\frac{t^2}{2}} dt = \sqrt{2\pi}$$

and

(12) $$M_{x-a}(\theta) = \sqrt{2\pi} bc e^{\frac{1}{2}\theta^2 b^2}$$

If this exponential is expanded in a power series,

$$M_{x-a}(\theta) = \sqrt{2\pi} bc \left[1 + b^2 \frac{\theta^2}{2} + b^4 \frac{\theta^4}{8} + \cdots \right]$$

Since the constant term is the moment of zero order, which is merely the area under the curve, and since this area is always equal to 1 for a distribution function, it follows that $\sqrt{2\pi} bc = 1$ and that

$$M_{x-a}(\theta) = 1 + b^2 \frac{\theta^2}{2} + b^4 \frac{\theta^4}{8} + \cdots$$

The coefficient of θ is zero; consequently the mean of the variable $x - a$ must be zero, and hence the mean of x must be a. The mean of a variable x is usually denoted by m, so that $a = m$. Since $x - a = x - m$ and the above generating function gives moments of $x - a$, the above expansion must give moments of x about its mean. It therefore follows that all odd moments of a normally distributed variable about its mean are zero. This was to be expected because from (11) it is clear that the normal curve is symmetrical with respect to the line $x = a$. Now the coefficient of $\theta^2/2$ is the second moment, while that of $\theta^4/24$ is the fourth moment; hence

$$\sigma^2 = \mu_2 = b^2$$

$$\alpha_3 = \frac{\mu_3}{\mu_2^{3/2}} = 0$$

$$\alpha_4 = \frac{\mu_4}{\mu_2^2} = 3$$

Since, from above, $a = m$, $b = \sigma$, and $\sqrt{2\pi}bc = 1$, the parameters a, b, and c may be solved for in terms of the familiar statistical parameters m and σ and inserted in (11) to give

$$(13) \qquad f(x) = \frac{1}{\sigma\sqrt{2\pi}}\, e^{-\frac{1}{2}\left(\frac{x-m}{\sigma}\right)^2}$$

Thus, a normal distribution is completely determined by specifying its mean and standard deviation. It should be noted that the only

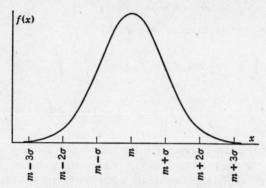

Fig. 3. Typical normal distribution.

difference between (11) and (13) is that the parameters in (11) have now been reduced to two independent parameters which have been given statistical meaning. It should also be noted that all normal distributions possess the same amount of peakedness as measured by moments, namely that expressed by $\alpha_4 = 3$.

The graph of a normal distribution function is shown in Fig. 3.

For the purpose of interpreting the standard deviation geometrically, consider the points of inflection of a normal curve. When (13) is differentiated twice,

$$f' = -\frac{1}{\sigma^2}(x - m)f$$

$$f'' = -\frac{1}{\sigma^2}\left[1 - \left(\frac{x - m}{\sigma}\right)^2\right]f$$

From the first derivative it is clear that there is but one maximum point, which occurs at $x = m$. From the second derivative it follows that points of inflection occur at $x = m \pm \sigma$. Geometrically, then, the standard deviation is the distance from the axis of symmetry to a point of inflection.

In the preceding chapter, meaning was given to the standard deviation as a measure of variation by stating that, for histograms approximating a normal curve, the interval $\bar{x} \pm s$ included about 68% of the data while $\bar{x} \pm 2s$ included about 95% of the data. This property will now be verified.

From (1), the relative frequency with which x will fall in the interval $m \pm \sigma$ is given by

$$\int_{m-\sigma}^{m+\sigma} \frac{1}{\sigma\sqrt{2\pi}} e^{-\frac{1}{2}\left(\frac{x-m}{\sigma}\right)^2} dx$$

When $t = (x - m)/\sigma$, then $dx = \sigma\, dt$ and

$$\int_{m-\sigma}^{m+\sigma} \frac{1}{\sigma\sqrt{2\pi}} e^{-\frac{1}{2}\left(\frac{x-m}{\sigma}\right)^2} dx = \frac{1}{\sqrt{2\pi}} \int_{-1}^{1} e^{-\frac{t^2}{2}} dt$$

$$= 2\frac{1}{\sqrt{2\pi}} \int_{0}^{1} e^{-\frac{t^2}{2}} dt$$

The value of the last integral and the factor $1/\sqrt{2\pi}$ may be found in Table II in the back to be 0.3413. Hence the value of the desired integral is 0.68, correct to two digits. For the limits $m \pm 2\sigma$, one may verify that $t = \pm 2$ and that the area between is 0.95. The unit of measurement given by $t = (x - m)/\sigma$ is called a *standard unit*. Table II is therefore a table of the normal distribution in standard units, that is, of a normal distribution with zero mean and unit standard deviation.

Fitting to histograms. Consider the problem of fitting a normal curve to a histogram. If one has reasons for believing that a set of data represents a random sample from some normal population, then the fitted normal curve would serve as an approximation to the population curve. Since a normal distribution is completely determined by its mean and standard deviation and these quantities can be rather accurately estimated for n fairly large, one would have considerably more confidence in the fitted normal curve as representing the population distribution than in the histogram of the data as doing so. There is not much occasion to fit normal curves to histograms. Frequency curve fitting is important in some statistical fields; however, for most statistical purposes it is more of an exercise to acquaint the student with the normal curve and with the extent to which normal data are found in statistical practice.

As an illustration of the technique of fitting a normal curve to a histogram, consider once more the data of Table 2, Chapter II, for which the four descriptive quantities were calculated previously and whose histogram is shown in Fig. 5, Chapter II. Here $\bar{x} = 475$, $s = 151$, $a_3 = -0.005$, and $a_4 = 3.11$. It appears that the values of a_3 and a_4 are close to the theoretical values of $\alpha_3 = 0$ and $\alpha_4 = 3$ for a normal distribution; consequently a normal curve might be expected to fit fairly well. Now choose $m = \bar{x}$ and $\sigma = s$. Then by (13) the resulting normal distribution is

$$(14) \qquad f(x) = \frac{1}{151\sqrt{2\pi}} e^{-\frac{1}{2}\left(\frac{x-475}{151}\right)^2}$$

The graph of this function, of course, has unit area and hence must be multiplied by the total area of the histogram if it is to fit the histogram. However, except for the purpose of seeing how well the curve fits the histogram, it is not necessary to calculate ordinates, since the agreement between the fitted curve and the histogram will be determined by comparing the corresponding areas under the curve and the histogram for the various class intervals. In the fitting technique it is therefore convenient to work with percentage areas under the normal curve. These percentage areas for the various class intervals of the histogram are calculated systematically by starting with the first class interval. Now to any value of x for the curve (14) there corresponds a value of $t = (x - 475)/151$ for the *standard normal curve*

$$(15) \qquad f(t) = \frac{1}{\sqrt{2\pi}} e^{-\frac{t^2}{2}}$$

such that the percentage of area to the left of x in (14) is the same as the percentage of area to the left of t in (15). For, since $t = (x - 475)/151$, then $dx = 151\,dt$ and

$$\int_{-\infty}^{x} \frac{1}{151\sqrt{2\pi}} e^{-\frac{1}{2}\left(\frac{x-475}{151}\right)^2} dx = \int_{-\infty}^{t} \frac{1}{\sqrt{2\pi}} e^{-\frac{t^2}{2}} dt$$

The value of this integral can be obtained from Table II. The procedure for finding these normal curve frequencies is illustrated in Table 1.

The agreement seems to be excellent except for the rather large difference between 230.3 and 260. The extent of such discrepancies is more readily realized by comparing the graphs of the histogram and the fitted normal curve as shown in Fig. 4. The problem of whether or not the fit may be considered satisfactory will be considered in a later chapter.

Applications. The interesting and important applications of normal distributions will be considered in later chapters after further essential

TABLE 1

Class boundaries x	$\dfrac{x-475}{151}$ t	Area to left of t A	Area of interval to left of t ΔA	Theoretical frequency $n\,\Delta A$	Observed frequency
99.5	−2.49	0.0064	0.0064	6.4	6
199.5	−1.82	.0344	.0280	28.0	28
299.5	−1.16	.1230	.0886	88.6	88
399.5	−0.50	.3085	.1855	185.5	180
499.5	0.16	.5636	.2551	255.1	247
599.5	0.82	.7939	.2303	230.3	260
699.5	1.49	.9319	.1380	138.0	133
799.5	2.15	.9842	.0523	52.3	52
899.5	2.81	.9975	.0133	13.3	11
999.5	3.47	.9997	.0022	2.2	5

theory has been developed. Here, only two simple illustrations of its direct applicability will be given.

Many college instructors of large classes assign letter grades on examinations by means of the normal distribution. The procedure followed is to ignore that part of the distribution lying outside of the interval $m \pm 2.5\sigma$, or $m \pm 3\sigma$, and then divide this interval into five equal parts corresponding to the letter grades F, D, C, B, and A. If

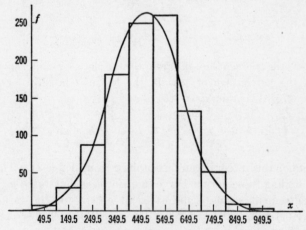

Fig. 4.   Normal curve fitted to histogram.

$m \pm 2.5\sigma$ is used, each interval will be σ units in length; consequently the six values of x determining these five intervals will be $m - 2.5\sigma$, $m - 1.5\sigma$, $m - 0.5\sigma$, $m + 0.5\sigma$, $m + 1.5\sigma$, and $m + 2.5\sigma$. The corresponding values of $t = (x - m)/\sigma$ will be -2.5, -1.5, -0.5, 0.5, 1.5, and 2.5. From Table II it will be found that the areas within these five intervals are respectively 0.06, 0.24, 0.38, 0.24, and 0.06. Since these percentages do not total 100%, it is customary to allow the two end intervals to extend to infinity. Then the percentages of students who will be assigned the corresponding letter grades are 7% F, 24% D, 38% C, 24% B, and 7% A.

As a second illustration, consider the following problem. If skulls are classified into three categories, corresponding to a length-breadth index being less than 75, between 75 and 80, or greater than 80, and if this index is assumed to be normally distributed, determine the approximate mean and standard deviation for a set of skulls for which 58%, 38%, and 4%, respectively, were found in these categories. From Table II, the value of $t = (75 - m)/\sigma$ corresponding to an area of 0.58 to the left of $x = 75$ is $t = 0.20$. Similarly, the value of $t = (80 - m)/\sigma$ corresponding to an area of 0.04 to the right of $x = 80$ is $t = 1.75$. The value of m and σ may now be determined by solving the equations

$$\frac{75 - m}{\sigma} = 0.20$$

$$\frac{80 - m}{\sigma} = 1.75$$

The solution of these equations is $m = 74.4$ and $\sigma = 3.2$.

DISCRETE FREQUENCY DISTRIBUTIONS

The only discrete variables that will be considered here are those which take on non-negative integral values. For example, the variable might be the number of heads obtained in tossing 20 coins, or the number of accidents a car owner has per year.

1. Moments

From analogy with (1), Chapter II, the kth moment of a theoretical discrete frequency distribution will be defined by

$$(16) \qquad \mu_k' = \sum_{x=0}^{\infty} x^k P(x)$$

where $P(x)$ is the probability that the variable takes on the value x. It should be clear that this is merely (1), Chapter II, with the sample relative frequency f_i/n replaced by its theoretical value. Similarly, the kth moment of the variable $g(x)$ is defined by

$$(17) \qquad \mu_{k:g}' = \sum_{x=0}^{\infty} g^k(x)P(x)$$

Finally, the moment-generating function of $g(x)$ is defined by

$$(18) \qquad M_g(\theta) = \sum_{x=0}^{\infty} e^{\theta g(x)}P(x)$$

For the purpose of verifying that this function does generate moments, expand $e^{\theta g(x)}$ and sum term by term.   Thus

$$M_g(\theta) = \sum_{x=0}^{\infty} \left[1 + \theta g(x) + \frac{\theta^2}{2} g^2(x) + \cdots \right] P(x)$$

$$= \sum_{x=0}^{\infty} P(x) + \theta \sum_{x=0}^{\infty} g(x)P(x) + \frac{\theta^2}{2!} \sum_{x=0}^{\infty} g^2(x)P(x) + \cdots$$

$$= \mu_{0:g}' + \mu_{1:g}'\theta + \mu_{2:g}' \frac{\theta^2}{2} + \cdots$$

2. Basic Rules of Probability

Before considering particular discrete distributions, it is desirable to review briefly the basic rules of discrete probability. Most college algebra books introduce these rules and apply them to simple games of chance.

If $P(A)$ is the probability that the event A will occur and $P(B)$ is the probability that the event B will occur, then the addition rule of probability,

$$(19) \qquad P = P(A) + P(B)$$

gives the probability that either A or B will occur, provided that A and B are mutually exclusive events. For example, if $P(A) = \frac{1}{4}$ is the probability that an individual will win a \$1.00 prize at a punch board and $P(B) = \frac{1}{12}$ is the probability that he will win a \$5.00 prize at this same punch board, then $P = \frac{1}{4} + \frac{1}{12} = \frac{1}{3}$ is the probability that he will win either a \$1.00 prize or a \$5.00 prize in a single punch at the punch board.

If $P(A, B)$ denotes the probability that both A and B will occur and $P_A(B)$ denotes the conditional probability that the event B will occur when A is known to have occurred, then the multiplication rule of probability,

$$(20) \qquad P(A, B) = P(A)P_A(B)$$

gives the probability that both A and B will occur. As an illustration, consider the probability of drawing 2 spades from a deck of cards in 2 draws. Here both A and B correspond to the event of drawing a spade; hence $P(A) = \frac{13}{52}$, $P_A(B) = \frac{12}{51}$, and $P(A, B) = \frac{13}{52} \cdot \frac{12}{51} = \frac{1}{17}$.

If the events A and B are independent, (20) reduces to

$$(21) \qquad P(A, B) = P(A)P(B)$$

As an illustration, consider the preceding problem in which the first card drawn is returned to the deck before the second drawing. Then $P(A) = \frac{13}{52}$, $P(B) = \frac{13}{52}$, and $P(A, B) = (\frac{13}{52})^2 = \frac{1}{16}$. As another illustration, if $P(A) = \frac{1}{3}$ is the probability that an individual will win a prize at a punch board and $P(B) = \frac{1}{4}$ is the probability that he will win a prize at a pinball machine, then $P = \frac{1}{3} \cdot \frac{1}{4} = \frac{1}{12}$ is the probability that he will win at both games if he takes 1 chance at each.

These three rules of probability suffice for direct derivations of several important discrete distributions and for the solution of many important practical probability problems.

As an exercise to develop familiarity with the manipulation of these formulas, consider the following problem. An urn contains 2 white and 3 black balls, while a second urn contains 4 white balls and 1 black ball. If an urn is selected at random and a single ball is drawn, what is the probability that it will be white? The probability that the first urn will be selected is $\frac{1}{2}$, in which event the probability of drawing a white ball is $\frac{2}{5}$; therefore by (20) the probability of both events occurring is $\frac{1}{2} \cdot \frac{2}{5} = \frac{1}{5}$. The probability that the second urn will be selected is likewise $\frac{1}{2}$, in which event the probability of drawing a white ball is $\frac{4}{5}$; therefore the probability of both of these events occurring is $\frac{1}{2} \cdot \frac{4}{5} = \frac{2}{5}$. Since these two possibilities constitute mutually exclusive events, by (19) the probability of one or the other of these possibilities occurring is $\frac{1}{5} + \frac{2}{5} = \frac{3}{5}$, which is therefore the desired probability.

3. Binomial Distribution

Let p be the probability that an event will occur at a single trial, and let $q = 1 - p$ denote the probability that it will fail to occur. If the event occurs at a given trial, it will be called a success, otherwise a failure. Let n independent trials be made, and denote by x the number of successes observed in the n trials. Then consider the problem of determining the probability of obtaining precisely x successes in n trials.

First, determine the probability of obtaining x consecutive successes, followed by $n - x$ consecutive failures. These n events are independent; therefore by (21) this probability is

$$\overbrace{p \cdot p \cdots p}^{x} \cdot \overbrace{q \cdot q \cdots q}^{n-x} = p^x q^{n-x}$$

The probability of obtaining precisely x successes and $n - x$ failures in some other order of occurrence is the same as for this particular order because the p's and q's are merely rearranged to correspond to the other order. In order to solve the problem, it is therefore necessary to count the number of such orders.

The number of orders is the number of permutations possible with n letters of which x are alike (p's) and the remaining $n - x$ are alike (q's). Now a familiar college algebra formula states that the number of permutations of n things of which n_1 are alike, n_2 are alike, $\cdots$, and n_k are alike is given by

$$(22) \qquad \frac{n!}{n_1! n_2! \cdots n_k!}$$

A direct application of this formula shows that the number of permutations of the p's and q's is equal to

$$(23) \qquad \frac{n!}{x!(n - x)!}$$

Now by (19) the probability that one or the other of a set of mutually exclusive events will occur is the sum of their separate probabilities; consequently it is necessary to add $p^x q^{n-x}$ as many times as there are different orders in which the desired result can occur. Since (23) gives the number of such orders, it follows that the probability of obtaining x successes in n independent trials of an event, for which p is the probability of success in a single trial, is given by

$$(24) \qquad P(x) = \frac{n!}{x!(n - x)!} p^x q^{n-x}$$

This function is called the *binomial* or *Bernoulli* distribution function. The name binomial comes from the relationship of (24) to the following binomial expansion:

$$(q + p)^n = q^n + nq^{n-1}p + \frac{n(n - 1)}{2} q^{n-2}p^2 + \cdots + p^n$$

$$(25) \qquad = \sum_{x=0}^{n} \frac{n!}{x!(n - x)!} p^x q^{n-x}$$

From (24) it is clear that (25) may be written

$$(q + p)^n = \sum_{x=0}^{n} P(x)$$

Thus the terms in this binomial expansion give the probabilities of the various possible results in their natural order.

The binomial distribution can be used to solve many practical problems related to repeated trials of an event. Such problems will be considered later; however, to illustrate the nature of formula (24), consider two simple problems related to the rolling of a die. If a true die is rolled 5 times, what is the probability that precisely 2 of the rolls will show ones? Here success consists of obtaining a one; hence $p = \frac{1}{6}$, $q = \frac{5}{6}$, and $n = 5$. When (24) is applied, the solution is

$$P(2) = \frac{5!}{2!3!} \left(\frac{1}{6}\right)^2 \left(\frac{5}{6}\right)^3 = 0.16$$

If the die is rolled 5 times, what is the probability of obtaining at most 2 ones? To answer this question it is necessary to compute the probabilities of obtaining precisely 0 ones, 1 one, and 2 ones. Applying (24),

$$P(0) = \frac{5!}{0!5!} \left(\frac{1}{6}\right)^0 \left(\frac{5}{6}\right)^5 = 0.40$$

$$P(1) = \frac{5!}{1!4!} \left(\frac{1}{6}\right)^1 \left(\frac{5}{6}\right)^4 = 0.40$$

Since these three possibilities are mutually exclusive events, formula (19) may be applied to give

$$P(x \leq 2) = P(0) + P(1) + P(2) = 0.96$$

Binomial moments. If the number of trials, n, of an event is large, the computation of probabilities by means of (24) becomes burdensome. Since most practical problems related to repeated trials of an event involve a large number of trials, it is important to find fast approximate methods for computing such probabilities. Fortunately, the histogram representing the binomial distribution can be approximated very well by means of the proper normal curve when n is large;

consequently normal curve methods can be employed to calculate these probabilities. Before investigating this property in general, consider a numerical example.

Determine the graph of the binomial distribution for which $p = \frac{1}{3}$ and $n = 12$. This is hardly a large value of n, so that a good normal approximation is not to be expected here. Since $P(x)$ is to be computed for all values of x from 0 to 12, it is easier to compute each value, after

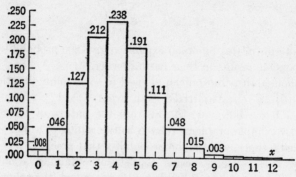

Fig. 5.   Binomial distribution, $p = \frac{1}{3}$, $n = 12$.

the first, from the preceding one rather than to compute each value by itself.   Here, by (24),

$$P(x) = \frac{12!}{x!(12 - x)!}\left(\frac{1}{3}\right)^{x}\left(\frac{2}{3}\right)^{12-x}$$

It is easily verified that

$$P(k + 1) = \frac{12 - k}{k + 1}\frac{1}{2}P(k)$$

After $P(0)$ was computed, this relationship was used to obtain the following values:

$$
\begin{aligned}
P(0) &= & 0.007707 \qquad & P(7) &= \tfrac{3}{7}P(6) &= 0.047687 \\
P(1) &= 6P(0) &= 0.046242 \qquad & P(8) &= \tfrac{5}{16}P(7) &= 0.014902 \\
P(2) &= \tfrac{11}{4}P(1) &= 0.127166 \qquad & P(9) &= \tfrac{2}{9}P(8) &= 0.003312 \\
(26)\quad P(3) &= \tfrac{5}{3}P(2) &= 0.211943 \qquad & P(10) &= \tfrac{3}{20}P(9) &= 0.000497 \\
P(4) &= \tfrac{9}{8}P(3) &= 0.238436 \qquad & P(11) &= \tfrac{1}{11}P(10) &= 0.000045 \\
P(5) &= \tfrac{4}{5}P(4) &= 0.190749 \qquad & P(12) &= \tfrac{1}{24}P(11) &= 0.000002 \\
P(6) &= \tfrac{7}{12}P(5) &= 0.111270 & & &
\end{aligned}
$$

Since $P(0)$ was computed correct to four digits only, the remaining values would not be expected to be correct to more than four digits, even though they have been recorded to six decimals for the sake of appearances. The graph of this binomial distribution is shown in Fig. 5. It appears that this histogram could be fitted quite well by the proper normal curve.

In order to determine what normal curve should be used to fit any given binomial-distribution histogram, it is necessary to determine the mean and standard deviation of the general binomial distribution. This will be accomplished by means of its moment-generating function. When definition (18) is applied to (24),

$$M_x(\theta) = \sum_{x=0}^{n} e^{\theta x} \frac{n!}{x!(n-x)!} p^x q^{n-x}$$

$$= \sum_{x=0}^{n} \frac{n!}{x!(n-x)!} (pe^\theta)^x q^{n-x}$$

But from (25) this sum can be written as a binomial raised to the nth power because the expansion is purely algebraic and need not be interpreted in terms of probabilities. Hence

(27) $$M_x(\theta) = (q + pe^\theta)^n$$

The desired moments may be obtained by applying (6). If (27) is differentiated twice,

$$M'(\theta) = npe^\theta(q + pe^\theta)^{n-1}$$

and

$$M''(\theta) = npe^\theta(q + pe^\theta)^{n-2}(q + npe^\theta)$$

The values of these derivatives at $\theta = 0$ are np and $npq + n^2p^2$, respectively; hence these are the values of μ_1' and μ_2', respectively. From formula (9), Chapter II, and these results, it follows that $\mu_2 = \mu_2' - \mu_1'^2 = npq$; consequently the general binomial distribution has its mean and standard deviation given by the formulas

$$m = np$$

(28)

$$\sigma = \sqrt{npq}$$

Thus, if a normal curve is to be fitted to a binomial histogram, it is merely necessary to use formulas (28) and the technique previously illustrated in Table 1.

If the third and fourth derivatives are evaluated at $\theta = 0$ and formula (9), Chapter II, is applied to give moments about the mean, it will be found that

(29)

$$\alpha_3 = \frac{q - p}{\sqrt{npq}}$$

$$\alpha_4 = 3 + \frac{1 - 6pq}{\sqrt{npq}}$$

From these formulas it is clear that the skewness of any binomial distribution as measured by α_3 approaches zero with increasing n, and that its peakedness as measured by α_4 approaches that of a normal distribution. Although these are indications that the normal approximation will be good for large n, it is necessary to show that all the moments of the binomial distribution approach those of some normal distribution before one can be certain of the fact. A demonstration of this property will be given in the next section.

As an illustration of how to use formulas (28) and normal curve methods for approximating probabilities of repeated trials of an event, consider a die problem related to Fig. 5. If a die is rolled 12 times and the appearance of either a one or a two is classified as a success, what is the probability of obtaining at least 6 successes? Since $p = \frac{1}{3}$ and $n = 12$ here, the exact answer correct to three decimals is given by adding the probabilities in (26) from $P(6)$ through $P(12)$. Hence,

$$P(x \geq 6) = 0.178$$

Geometrically, this answer is the area of that part of the histogram in Fig. 5 lying to the right of $x = 5.5$. Therefore, to approximate this probability by normal curve methods, it is merely necessary to find the area under that part of the fitted normal curve which lies to the right of 5.5. If (28) is applied,

$$m = 12 \cdot \tfrac{1}{3} = 4$$

$$\sigma = \sqrt{12 \cdot \tfrac{1}{3} \cdot \tfrac{2}{3}} = 1.63$$

Consequently,

$$t = \frac{x - m}{\sigma} = \frac{5.5 - 4}{1.63} = 0.92$$

But from Table II the area to the right of $t = 0.92$ is 0.179, which, compared to the correct value of 0.178, is in error by only about 0.5%.

To test the accuracy of normal curve methods over a shorter interval, consider the probability of obtaining precisely 6 successes in the 12 rolls of the die. From (26) the answer correct to three decimals is

$$P(6) = 0.111$$

To approximate this answer, it is merely necessary to find the area under the fitted normal curve between $x = 5.5$ and $x = 6.5$. Thus,

$$t_2 = \frac{6.5 - 4}{1.63} = 1.53, \quad A_2 = 0.4370$$

$$t_1 = \frac{5.5 - 4}{1.63} = 0.92, \quad A_1 = 0.3212$$

Therefore the required area is 0.116, which is in error by about 5%. From these two examples it appears that normal curve methods are quite accurate, even for some situations such as the one considered here in which n is not very large.

Normal curve approximation. Thus far the fact that the binomial distribution can be approximated well for large n by the normal distribution with $m = np$ and $\sigma = \sqrt{npq}$ has been made plausible by numerical examples and by inspecting α_3 and α_4. Now consider the verification of this fact by means of the moment-generating function. Here it is convenient to use the variable

$$\frac{x - np}{\sqrt{npq}} = \frac{x - m}{\sigma} = t$$

From properties (9) and (10), and (27), it follows that

$$M_t(\theta) = M_{x-m}\left(\frac{\theta}{\sigma}\right)$$

(30)
$$= e^{-\frac{m\theta}{\sigma}} M_x\left(\frac{\theta}{\sigma}\right)$$

$$= e^{-\frac{m\theta}{\sigma}} (q + pe^{\frac{\theta}{\sigma}})^n$$

Taking the logarithm of both sides to the base e gives

$$\log M_t(\theta) = -\frac{m\theta}{\sigma} + n \cdot \log (q + pe^{\frac{\theta}{\sigma}})$$

Expanding $e^{\frac{\theta}{\sigma}}$ and replacing $q + p$ by 1 yields

$$\log M_t(\theta) = -\frac{m\theta}{\sigma} + n \log \left\{ 1 + p \left[\left(\frac{\theta}{\sigma}\right) + \frac{1}{2!}\left(\frac{\theta}{\sigma}\right)^2 + \frac{1}{3!}\left(\frac{\theta}{\sigma}\right)^3 + \cdots \right] \right\}$$

The logarithm on the right may be treated as of the form $\log \{1 + z\}$. If $|\theta|$ is chosen sufficiently small, the expansion

$$\log \{1 + z\} = z - \frac{z^2}{2} + \frac{z^3}{3} - \frac{z^4}{4} + \cdots$$

may be applied to give

(31) $\log M_t(\theta) = -\dfrac{m\theta}{\sigma}$

$$+ n \left\{ p \left[\left(\frac{\theta}{\sigma} \right) + \frac{1}{2!} \left(\frac{\theta}{\sigma} \right)^2 + \cdots \right] - \frac{p^2}{2} \left[\left(\frac{\theta}{\sigma} \right) + \frac{1}{2!} \left(\frac{\theta}{\sigma} \right)^2 + \cdots \right]^2 + \cdots \right\}$$

Collecting terms in powers of θ gives

$$\log M_t(\theta) = \left(-\frac{m}{\sigma} + \frac{np}{\sigma} \right) \theta + n \left(\frac{p}{\sigma^2} - \frac{p^2}{\sigma^2} \right) \frac{\theta^2}{2!} + \cdots$$

But, since $np = m$ and $\sigma^2 = npq$, the coefficient of θ vanishes and the coefficient of $\theta^2/2!$ reduces to 1; consequently

$$\log M_t(\theta) = \frac{\theta^2}{2} + \text{terms in } \theta^k, \quad k = 3, 4, \cdots$$

From an inspection of (31), which shows how terms in θ^k arise, it is clear that all terms in θ^k contain n/σ^k as a common factor. The other factor for each such term is a constant times a power of p. Since this other factor does not involve n and since

$$\frac{n}{\sigma^k} = \frac{n}{(npq)^{\frac{k}{2}}}$$

with $k \geq 3$ here, all such terms will approach zero as n becomes infinite. This implies that

$$\lim_{n \to \infty} \log M_t(\theta) = \frac{\theta^2}{2}$$

which in turn implies that

(32) $$\lim_{n \to \infty} M_t(\theta) = e^{\frac{\theta^2}{2}}$$

A justification of the above expansions and limits would require a knowledge of advanced calculus methods and therefore will not be considered here.

Now compare (32) and the normal moment-generating function given by (12). From the discussion immediately following (12), it is clear that for a normal variable x

$$(33) \qquad M_{x-m}(\theta) = e^{\frac{\sigma^2\theta^2}{2}}$$

Since the first equality of (30) holds for any variable, it may be applied to (33) to give

$$M_{\frac{x-m}{\sigma}}(\theta) = M_{x-m}\left(\frac{\theta}{\sigma}\right) = e^{\frac{\theta^2}{2}}$$

A comparison of this result and (32) shows that the binomial variable $t = (x - np)/\sqrt{npq}$ has a moment-generating function which approaches the moment-generating function of the normal variable whose mean is zero and whose standard deviation is 1. This implies that all the moments of this binomial variable approach those of the standard normal variable.

In order to complete this discussion, it is necessary to introduce two very important theorems of advanced theoretical statistics. The first theorem states that a distribution function is uniquely determined by its moment-generating function. For example, if the moment-generating function of a variable z is known to be $e^{\frac{\theta^2}{2}}$, then z must be the standard normal variable. The second theorem states that, if one distribution function has a moment-generating function which approaches the moment-generating function of a second distribution function, then the first distribution function approaches the second distribution function. This theorem insures that the binomial variable being studied approaches the standard normal variable, because by (32) its moment-generating function approaches the moment-generating function of the standard normal variable. A precise statement of these two theorems, including conditions when they hold, will not be made here; nevertheless frequent use will be made of them. A direct application of these theorems to (32) yields the following theorem.

Theorem I. *If x represents the number of successes in n independent trials of an event for which p is the probability of success in a single trial, then the variable $(x - np)/\sqrt{npq}$ has a distribution which approaches the normal distribution with mean zero and standard deviation 1 as the number of trials becomes increasingly large.*

This theorem justifies the previous use of normal curve methods for approximating probabilities related to successive trials of an event when n is large. Experience indicates that the approximation is fairly good as long as, for $p \leq \frac{1}{2}$, $np > 5$ at least. Obviously, a very small value of p together with a moderately large value of n would yield a small mean and thus produce a skewed distribution; hence the necessity for including p in this empirical rule. Figures 6 and 7 indicate how rapidly the distribution of the variable $(x - np)/\sqrt{npq}$ approaches normality when $p = \frac{1}{3}$ and $n = 24$ and 48, respectively. The common y scale for these two graphs is approximately 17 times that for the x axis.

There are numerous occasions when it is more convenient to work with the percentage of successes in n trials than with the actual number of successes. Since

$$(34) \qquad \frac{x - np}{\sqrt{npq}} = \frac{\dfrac{x}{n} - p}{\sqrt{\dfrac{pq}{n}}}$$

it follows as a corollary of Theorem I that the percentage of successes, x/n, is approximately normally distributed with mean p and standard deviation $\sqrt{pq/n}$, provided that n is sufficiently large. The word percentage will be used here and later to mean the decimal ratio.

Applications. Certain types of practical problems dealing with percentages can be solved by means of this normal approximation. As a first illustration, consider the following simple genetics problem. According to Mendelian inheritance, certain crosses of peas should give yellow and green peas in the ratio of 3:1. In an experiment, 176 yellow and 48 green peas were obtained. Do these results conform to theory?

Here the 224 peas may be treated as 224 trials of an event for which the probability of obtaining a yellow pea in a single trial is $\frac{3}{4}$. Then

$$p = \tfrac{3}{4}, \quad n = 224, \quad m = np = 168, \quad \sigma = \sqrt{npq} = 6.5$$

From the experimenter's point of view, an experiment corroborates theory if its results are sufficiently close to expectation. In this problem it is therefore a question of deciding whether 176 is sufficiently close to 168. Since poor experimental results correspond to large deviations from the mean, whether positive or negative, it is a question of how large a deviation numerically should be tolerated before the experiment will be judged as not conforming to theory. It is customary for many statisticians to determine a *critical* deviation such that the probability is 0.05 (or 0.01) of obtaining a deviation larger numerically than the critical deviation and to declare an experimental result as not conforming unless its deviation is less numerically than the critical one. In order to determine the 0.05 critical deviation, it would be necessary to calculate and sum the probabilities of the binomial distribution corresponding to this problem beginning at the mean and expanding symmetrically until a total probability of 0.95 had been

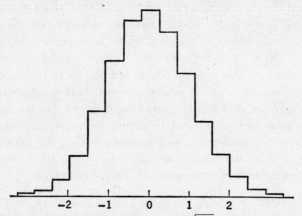

FIG. 6. Binomial distribution of $(x - np)/\sqrt{npq}$ for $p = \frac{1}{3}$ and $n = 24$.

obtained. However, this critical deviation can be determined approximately very easily by using the normal approximation to this binomial distribution. Because $|t| = 2$ corresponds to an interval of 2 standard

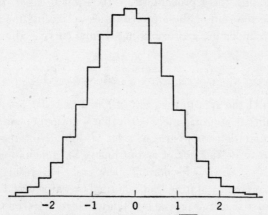

FIG. 7. Binomial distribution of $(x - np)/\sqrt{npq}$ for $p = \frac{1}{3}$ and $n = 48$.

deviations on both sides of the mean and this interval includes about 95% of the normal curve area, it is customary to choose $|t| = 2$ as the critical value of $|t|$ rather than the more accurate Table II value of $|t| = 1.96$. For this problem, therefore, an experimental result would be declared to conform to theory if it fell within the interval

$$m \pm 2\sigma = 168 \pm 13$$

Since 176 falls well within this interval, there is no reason on this basis for doubting that Mendelian inheritance is operating here.

As a second illustration, consider the following problem. From past experience the manufacturer of parts finds that when a machine is functioning properly 5% of the parts are defective on the average. During the course of a day's operation by a new operator, 400 parts are turned out, 30 of which are defective. Is the operator satisfactory?

The answer to this question depends upon what is meant by the word satisfactory. Here it will be assumed that satisfactory means that the number of defective parts should not be greater than what could be reasonably attributed to chance for a normal operator. If this operator is considered to be a normal operator, the 400 parts may be thought of as 400 trials of an event for which the probability of obtaining a defective part in a single trial is 0.05; hence

$$p = 0.05, \quad n = 400, \quad m = np = 20, \quad \sigma = \sqrt{npq} = 4.36$$

By means of the binomial distribution corresponding to this problem, it is possible to calculate the probability of obtaining 30 or more defective parts. This probability could be obtained by using (24) to calculate the successive probabilities of obtaining 30, 31, $\cdots$, 400 defectives and then adding these probabilities. It is much easier, however, to approximate the sum of these probabilities by finding the area to the right of 29.5 under the approximating normal curve. Here

$$t = \frac{x - m}{\sigma} = \frac{29.5 - 20}{4.36} = 2.18$$

From Table II the area to the right of $t = 2.18$ is 0.015; consequently the probability is approximately 0.015 that a normal operator will turn out 30 or more defective parts in a lot of 400. Now this one day's experience may be thought of as but one of an indefinite sequence of similar day's experiences for normal operators. This result may therefore be interpreted by stating that a normal operator would have a day as bad or worse than this only about 3 days in every 200 on the average. From the manufacturer's point of view, this operator has undoubtedly turned out more defective parts than can be reasonably attributed to chance; consequently he would be judged unsatisfactory from this point of view.

The reasonableness of this decision depends upon the extent to which the mathematical model used here represents the actual situation. If the successive parts turned out by normal operators do not behave like random samples from a binomial population, then one is not justified in applying these methods. It might happen as it often does, for example, that the variability of normal operators is much larger than that given by $\sigma = \sqrt{npq}$, or that the percentage of defective parts varies with the day of the week or the condition of the machine.

As a third illustration, consider the problem just alluded to of determining whether daily percentages of defectives may be treated as random samples from a binomial population. Industrial experience has shown that most production processes do not behave in this idealized manner and that much valuable information is obtained concerning the process if the order in which data are obtained is

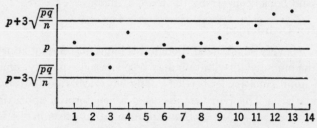

FIG. 8.   Control chart for fraction defective.

preserved. A simple graphical method, called a *quality control chart*, has been found highly useful for assisting in the solution of this problem. Such a chart for the percentage of defectives is illustrated in Fig. 8. The middle line is thought of as corresponding to the process percentage defective, although it is usually merely the mean of past daily percentages. The other two lines serve as control limits for daily percentages of defectives. From (34) it will be observed that these two control lines are spaced three standard deviations from the mean line. Along the x axis are recorded the time units for successive samples. If now the production process behaves in the idealized manner and if the normal approximation to the binomial distribution may be used, the probability that a daily percentage point when plotted on this chart will fall outside the control band is approximately equal to the probability that a normal variable will assume a value more than three standard deviations away from its mean, which from Table II is 0.003. Because of this small probability, it is reasonable to assume that the production process is no longer behaving properly when a point falls outside of the control band; consequently the production engineer checks over the various steps in the process when this event occurs. From an inspection of Fig. 8, it will be observed that the process in question went out of control on the twelfth day.

Industrial experience shows that only rarely does a production process behave in this idealized manner when the control-chart technique is first applied. Nevertheless, the technique is highly useful because it enables one to discover causes of a lack of control and thus to improve on the production process until gradually statistical control has been obtained.

This illustration and discussion of a quality control chart gives a very incomplete picture of how quality control methods operate. Such methods constitute an extensive field of applied statistics, and numerous articles and books concerning them are available.

4. Poisson Distribution

When p is very small, even though n is large, the normal approximation to the binomial distribution may be poor; consequently some other form of approximation is needed. The empirical rule that was suggested just after Theorem I implies that a new form of approximation is needed when $np < 5$. Such an approximation exists in the form of the Poisson distribution function, which is defined by

$$(35) \qquad P(x) = \frac{e^{-m}m^x}{x!}$$

Poisson approximation to the binomial. To verify the fact that (35) does serve as a good approximation to the binomial for very small p and very large n, consider the binomial distribution as p approaches zero and n becomes infinite in such a manner that $m = np$ remains fixed. For this purpose it is convenient to compare the moment-generating functions of these two distributions.

From (18) and (35) the moment-generating function of the Poisson distribution is given by

$$M_x(\theta) = \sum_{x=0}^{\infty} e^{\theta x} \frac{e^{-m}m^x}{x!} = e^{-m} \sum_{x=0}^{\infty} \frac{(me^\theta)^x}{x!}$$

But this last sum is merely the expansion of e^{me^θ}; consequently

$$(36) \qquad M_x(\theta) = e^{m(e^\theta - 1)}$$

Now the moment-generating function of the binomial distribution is given by (27). Let it be denoted by $M_x'(\theta)$; it may be manipulated as follows into a form resembling (36).

$$M_x'(\theta) = [q + pe^\theta]^n$$

$$= e^{n \log [q + pe^\theta]}$$

$$= e^{n \log [1 + p(e^\theta - 1)]}$$

$$= e^{np(e^\theta - 1) \log [1 + p(e^\theta - 1)]^{\frac{1}{p(e^\theta - 1)}}}$$

$$(37) \qquad = e^{m(e^\theta - 1) \log [1 + p(e^\theta - 1)]^{\frac{1}{p(e^\theta - 1)}}}$$

Since e may be defined by

$$\lim_{z \to 0} [1 + z]^{\frac{1}{z}} = e$$

it will be observed that the expression in (37) whose logarithm is being taken will play a similar role as p approaches zero. Thus,

$$\lim_{p \to 0} [1 + p(e^\theta - 1)]^{\frac{1}{p(e^\theta - 1)}} = e$$

Consequently,

$$(38) \qquad \lim_{p \to 0} \log [1 + p(e^\theta - 1)]^{\frac{1}{p(e^\theta - 1)}} = 1$$

Since $np = m$ is being held fixed, it is clear from (37), (38), and (36) that

$$\lim_{p \to 0} M_x'(\theta) = M_x(\theta)$$

By the same argument as that given before Theorem I, this limit implies that the binomial distribution approaches the Poisson distribution under the given conditions. This demonstrates the following theorem.

Theorem II. *If the probability of success in a single trial, p, approaches zero while the number of trials, n, becomes infinite in such a manner that np = m remains fixed, the binomial distribution approaches the Poisson distribution.*

Figures 9 and 10 indicate how rapidly the binomial distribution approaches the Poisson distribution. The dotted lines represent the fixed Poisson histogram for $m = 4$, and the solid lines the binomial histogram for $p = \frac{1}{3}$ and $p = \frac{1}{24}$, respectively.

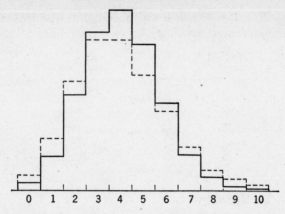

FIG. 9.   Binomial (—) and Poisson (---) distributions for $m = 4$ and $p = \frac{1}{3}$.

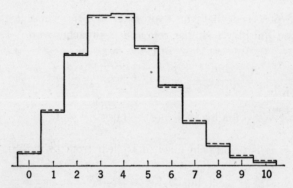

FIG. 10.   Binomial (—) and Poisson (---) distributions for $m = 4$ and $p = \frac{1}{24}$.

Applications.   As an illustration of a distribution that may be thought of as possessing Poisson characteristics, consider the data of Table 2 on the distribution of yeast cells in the 400 squares of a hemacytometer.

TABLE 2

No. cells (x) per square	0	1	2	3	4	5	6	7	8	9	10
Observed frequency	103	143	98	42	8	4	2	0	0	0	0
Expected frequency	107	141	93	41	14	4	1	0	0	0	0

The procedure for obtaining the observed frequencies consists in diluting the yeast cells in a liquid, thoroughly mixing the dilution, filling a counting chamber that has been ruled into 400 squares with the mixture, and then counting the number of yeast cells on each square under a microscope. If the mixture is thought of as consisting of yeast cells and groups of molecules of the liquid about equal in size to the yeast cells, the yeast cells will constitute only a very small percentage of such units of volume; nevertheless the total number of such units on one square of the hemacytometer is so large that several yeast cells may be found among them. The number of trials here corresponds to the total number of units on a square, and the number of successes corresponds to the number of yeast cells on the square. If the mixing has been thorough, one would expect the yeast cells to be distributed at random in the mixture and the units on a square to constitute a set of independent trials.

The mean of x for Table 2 will be found to be $\bar{x} = 1.32$. If it is assumed on the basis of the preceding discussion that x possesses a Poisson distribution and if the value of m is approximated well by $\bar{x}$, the theoretical or expected frequencies may be obtained from (35) by computing the successive values of

$$400 \frac{e^{-1.32}(1.32)^x}{x!}$$

These frequencies are readily computed by computing each frequency, after the first, from the preceding frequency. The results of these computations correct to the nearest unit are given in Table 2. There appears to be excellent agreement here.

If there had been poor agreement between the observed and expected frequencies, it might have been caused by the lack of realism in the mathematical model, or by the lack of randomness in the distribution of yeast cells because of poor experimental technique. It is customary in work of this type to use the lack of agreement as evidence of poor technique rather than to question the reality of the Poisson assumption.

5. Multinomial Distribution

The binomial distribution is applicable to a discrete variable that assumes only one or the other of two values. For situations in which more than two values are possible and desirable, a generalization of the binomial distribution is needed. This generalization is known as the multinomial distribution. It will be of particular value in later theory. Strictly speaking, the multinomial distribution is a distribution function of several variables; nevertheless it will be included here because of its intimate relation to the binomial distribution and because it arises from considering a single variable which can assume only a discrete set of values.

Consider a discrete variable x which at any trial of the event can assume one and only one of the values $x_1, x_2, \cdots, x_k$. Let the probability that x will assume the value x_i be denoted by p_i. Then, in n trials of the event, the probability that x_i will be assumed n_i times $(i = 1, 2, \cdots, k)$, where $\sum_1^k n_i = n$, can be obtained in the following manner.

Consider the particular sequence of events given by

$$\overbrace{x_1, \cdots, x_1}^{n_1}, \overbrace{x_2, \cdots, x_2}^{n_2}, \cdots, \overbrace{x_k, \cdots, x_k}^{n_k}$$

From (21) it follows that the probability of obtaining this particular order of events is

$$p_1{}^{n_1} p_2{}^{n_2} \cdots p_k{}^{n_k}$$

Now every arrangement of this set of x's has this same probability of occurring and satisfies the conditions of the problem; consequently it is necessary to count the number of such arrangements. But this is merely the number of permutations of n things of which n_1 are alike, n_2 are alike, etc., which by (22) is

$$\frac{n!}{n_1! n_2! \cdots n_k}$$

It therefore follows from (19) that the probability of obtaining n_1 x_1's, n_2 x_2's, etc., is

$$(39) \qquad \frac{n!}{n_1! n_2! \cdots n_k!} p_1{}^{n_1} p_2{}^{n_2} \cdots p_k{}^{n_k}$$

where $\sum_1^k n_i = n$. This expression is called the *multinomial* distribution function.

The name arises from the fact that (39) represents the general term in the expansion of the multinomial

$$(40) \qquad (p_1 + p_2 + \cdots + p_k)^n$$

just as the binomial distribution function represents the general term in the expansion of $(q + p)^n$. In order to verify this relationship, it is merely necessary to expand the multinomial step by step as a binomial.

Thus, when (40) is written in the form $(p_1 + q_1)^n$ and expanded, it will be observed that the only term involving $p_1{}^{n_1}$ is the term

$$\frac{n!}{n_1!(n - n_1)!}\, p_1{}^{n_1} q_1{}^{n-n_1}$$

Then if $q_1{}^{n-n_1} = (p_2 + q_2)^{n-n_1}$ is expanded, it will be observed that the only term involving $p_2{}^{n_2}$ is the term

$$\frac{(n - n_1)!}{n_2!(n - n_1 - n_2)!}\, p_2{}^{n_2} q_2{}^{n-n_1-n_2}$$

If this procedure is continued and the resulting terms are combined, the expression (39) will be obtained.

As an illustration of the multinomial distribution, consider the following problem. The diameters of 10 sample parts were measured with a precise measuring instrument. Of these 10 measurements, 3 ended with a zero, 2 ended with a 5, and 5 ended with some other integer. What is the probability (a) of obtaining a set of end digits like this if the integers from 0 to 9 are equally likely to occur as end digits in measurements of this kind, (b) of obtaining the expected set consisting of 1 zero, 1 five, and 8 other integers?

(a) Here $p_1 = \frac{1}{10}$, $p_2 = \frac{1}{10}$, $p_3 = \frac{8}{10}$, $n_1 = 3$, $n_2 = 2$, $n_3 = 5$; consequently by (39) the desired probability is

$$\frac{10!}{3!2!5!}\left(\frac{1}{10}\right)^3\left(\frac{1}{10}\right)^2\left(\frac{8}{10}\right)^5 = 0.0083$$

(b) Here $p_1 = \frac{1}{10}$, $p_2 = \frac{1}{10}$, $p_3 = \frac{8}{10}$, $n_1 = 1$, $n_2 = 1$, $n_3 = 8$; consequently the desired probability is

$$\frac{10!}{1!1!8!}\left(\frac{1}{10}\right)^1\left(\frac{1}{10}\right)^1\left(\frac{8}{10}\right)^8 = 0.1510$$

The practical interpretation of probabilities like these will be considered in later chapters; however, there appears to be evidence in these two probabilities that the individual taking the measurements was careless in the use of the instrument.

THEORETICAL DISTRIBUTIONS FOR TESTING HYPOTHESES

The theoretical distributions that have been studied in this chapter may serve as the basis for testing certain types of statistical hypotheses, which in turn may be used to solve certain types of problems. The second of the three problems considered in the section on applications of the binomial distribution illustrates one problem of this kind. In that problem the decision as to whether the new operator was to be judged satisfactory was made to depend upon the binomial distribution and a probability calculated on the assumption that $p = 0.05$ held for the new operator.

1. Nature of Statistical Hypotheses

A *statistical hypothesis* is usually an assumption about a population parameter. For example, in testing the "honesty" of a coin, the hypothesis might be the assumption that $p = \frac{1}{2}$ for the binomial population involved. For the problem concerning the machine operator, the hypothesis might be the assumption that $p = 0.05$. It is not customary to incorporate any assumption concerning the form of the population distribution function in the hypothesis. The form of this function is assumed known from other considerations. For example, in coin tossing, it is clear that the binomial distribution would be expected to hold. For the machine operator, however, one could not be certain without a satisfactory check that the successive parts turned out by the operator behave like independent trials of an event for which the probability of success is constant. The control-chart technique was introduced as a method for checking such assumptions.

2. Tests of Statistical Hypotheses

A *test* of a statistical hypothesis is a procedure for deciding whether to accept or reject the hypothesis. For example, in the problem of the machine operator, the procedure consisted in calculating the probability that a normal operator would turn out 30 or more defective parts and then making a decision on the basis of this probability. When such a probability has been calculated and it turns out to be very small, two explanations are possible. Either the hypothesis and its related assumptions are false, or else a rare event occurred. It is customary to choose the first of these two alternatives whenever the probability involved is less than a fixed value α called the *significance level* of the test. In this book the value of $\alpha = 0.05$ will ordinarily be selected. If the probability in question turns out to be less than α, the result is said to be *significant*. Thus, the hypothesis being tested will be rejected whenever a significant result is obtained. If an individual follows this rule of procedure with $\alpha = 0.05$, say, he will incorrectly reject true hypotheses only 5% of the time on the average. If a smaller error of this type is desired, a smaller value of α may be selected; however, if α is made very small there usually arises the danger that false hypotheses will then be accepted a large percentage of the time.

The principal difficulty in testing hypotheses is knowing what probability should be calculated for making a decision. In some problems, such as the one just discussed, a careful consideration of its practical implications will suggest what hypothesis to test and what probability to calculate in testing it. It does not follow, however, that a test which intuitively appears to be satisfactory is necessarily efficient or even correct. A logical approach to this whole problem of testing hypotheses will be discussed in Chapter XI. In the chapters preceding Chapter XI, numerous tests will be presented and applied, largely on an intuitive basis; however, a large percentage of these tests have been shown to be highly efficient from the point of view of Chapter XI.

REFERENCES

Additional material on the moment-generating function may be found in:

AITKEN, A. C., *Statistical Mathematics*, Oliver & Boyd.

KENNEY, J. F., *National Mathematics Magazine*, vol. xvii, no. 2, p. 51.

Most college algebra books contain the basic rules of probability and numerous exercises to develop facility in using those rules. If further information and exercises are desired, they may be found in:

KENDALL, M. G., *The Advanced Theory of Statistics*, Griffin and Company, vol. 1, pp. 166–172.

LEVY and ROTH, *Elements of Probability*, Clarendon Press.

USPENSKY, J. V., *Introduction to Mathematical Probability*, McGraw-Hill Company.

The two theorems concerning the relationship between moment-generating functions and distribution functions require advanced mathematical training for their complete understanding; however, a precise statement of these theorems and references to their proofs will be found in:

WILKS, S. S., *Mathematical Statistics*, Princeton University Press, p. 38.

A brief explanation of quality control methods which also contains useful references to more complete discussions may be found in:

DEMING, W. E., "Some Principles of the Shewhart Methods of Quality Control," *Mechanical Engineering*, March 1944, pp. 173–177.

A thorough discussion of the logic and principles of quality control methods will be found in the books by W. A. Shewhart which are referred to in this article.

The Poisson distribution has been used quite extensively in the study of telephone and other traffic problems, bacterial dilutions, accidents, and other rare events. The book

FRY, T. C., *Probability and Its Engineering Uses*, D. Van Nostrand Company, contains interesting engineering applications.   Further biological applications will be found in:

FISHER, R. A., *Statistical Methods for Research Workers*, Oliver & Boyd.

The Poisson approximation to the binomial is very useful when sums of binomial probabilities for which p is small and n is large are needed.   Complete tables of such sums are available in:

MOLINA, E. C., *Poisson's Exponential Binomial Limit*, D. Van Nostrand Company.

There are numerous other theoretical distributions, in addition to the four considered in this chapter, that may be used as mathematical models.   An extensive discussion of a general class of frequency distributions may be found in:

KENNEY, J. F., *Mathematics of Statistics*, Part Two, D. Van Nostrand Company, pp. 46–60.

EXERCISES

1. Given that $f(x) = 1$, $0 \leq x \leq 1$, find (a) μ_k' by integration, (b) $M_x(\theta)$, (c) μ_k' from $M_x(\theta)$.

2. Given that $f(x) = cx$, $0 \leq x \leq 1$, find (a) c, (b) μ_k' by integration, (c) $M_x(\theta)$, (d) μ_k' from $M_x(\theta)$.

3. Find the approximate value of the integral $\int_0^\infty e^{-\frac{x^2}{2}}\, dx$ by using $\frac{1}{2}$-unit intervals and Simpson's rule for numerical integration, and integrating from 0 to 3.

4. Find μ_k for the normal distribution by using the integral definition and repeated integrations by parts.

5. Fit a normal curve to the histogram for the data of problem 4, Chapter II.

6. What is the probability of rolling a total of less than 7 with 2 dice?

7. Compare the chances of rolling a 4 with one die and rolling a total of 8 with 2 dice.

8. A, B, and C in order toss a coin.   The first one to throw a head wins.   What are their respective chances of winning?   Note that the game may continue indefinitely.

9. Fourteen quarters and 1 five-dollar gold piece are in one purse, and 15 quarters are in another.   Ten coins are taken from the first and placed in the second, and then 10 coins are taken from the second and placed in the first.   Which purse would you choose, and how much better off would you be?

10. Eight dice are rolled.   Calling a 5 or 6 a success, find the probability of getting (a) 3 successes, (b) at most 3 successes.

11. How many throws with 2 dice will be required in order that the probability of getting a double 6 at least once will have the value $\frac{1}{2}$, approximately?

12. Find m and σ for the binomial distribution by using the definition of moments and the fact that $\Sigma x^2 P(x) = \Sigma x(x - 1)P(x) + \Sigma x P(x)$.

13. A coin is tossed 12 times.   Find the probability, both exactly and by the normal curve approximation, of getting (a) 4 successes, (b) at most 4 successes.

14. A die is tossed 12 times.   Counting a 5 or 6 as a success, what is the probability, both exactly and approximately, of getting (a) 4 successes, (b) at most 4 successes?

15. A die is tossed 90 times. Find the probability of getting 15 aces (*a*) using the formula and tables of factorials, (*b*) using the normal curve approximation.

16. Experience shows that 20% of a certain kind of seed germinates. If 50 out of 400 seeds germinated, would an explanation be needed?

17. A coin is tossed 400 times. Would 215 heads be a reasonable result?

18. About 9% of the population is between 20 and 24. A city of 12,000 has 1,300 in this age group. Test for reasonableness, and comment.

19. A manufacturer has found from experience that 3% of his product is rejected because of flaws. A new lot of 800 units comes up for inspection. (*a*) How many units would reasonably be expected to be rejected? (*b*) What is the approximate probability that less than 30 units will be rejected?

20. A life-insurance company has 1,000 policies averaging $2,000 on lives at age 25. From a mortality table it is found that, of 89,032 alive at 25, 88,314 are alive at 26. Find upper and lower values for the amount which the company would reasonably be expected to pay out during the year on these policies.

21. If people did not change their views on a candidate for a period of a week just before and including the election, approximately how large a sample would you need to take at the beginning of that week in order to be able to predict, with a probability of 0.95, the true percentage of votes to be cast for the candidate with an error of less than 1% if the true percentage is 50%? What further assumption are you making concerning expressing opinions and voting?

22. Roll a die 6 times. Call a 1 or 2 a success. Record the number of successes for each of 30 such experiments. (*a*) Find the approximate probability of obtaining a total number of successes further removed from expectation than this. (*b*) Apply binomial distribution theory to find the expected frequencies of successes for $p = \frac{1}{3}$ and $n = 6$.

23. The following data are for the number of seeds germinating out of 10 on damp filter paper for 80 sets of seeds. Fit a binomial distribution to these data.

x	0	1	2	3	4	5	6	7	8	9	10
f	6	20	28	12	8	6	0	0	0	0	0

24. In the manufacturing of parts the following data were obtained for the daily percentage defective for a production averaging 1,000 parts a day. Construct a control chart, and indicate times when production was out of control.

2.2,	2.3,	2.1,	1.7,	3.8,	2.5,	2.0,	1.6,	1.4,	2.6,
1.5,	2.8,	2.9,	2.6,	2.5,	2.6,	3.2,	4.6,	3.3,	3.0,
3.1,	4.3,	1.8,	2.6,	2.1,	2.2,	1.8,	2.4,	2.4,	1.6,
1.7,	1.6,	2.8,	3.2,	1.8,	2.6,	3.6,	4.2.		

25. For $n = 12$ and $p = \frac{1}{4}$, plot on the same piece of graph paper the (*a*) binomial histogram, (*b*) Poisson histogram, (*c*) fitted normal curve by ordinates. Note the extent to which (*b*) and (*c*) approximate the binomial.

26. Find m, σ, α_3, and α_4 for the Poisson distribution by using the values for the binomial distribution and allowing n to become infinite with m fixed. On the basis of these results, when would you expect the Poisson distribution to be nearly normal?

27. Fit a Poisson function to the following data on the number of deaths from the kick of a horse per army corps per year for 10 Prussian Army Corps for 20 years.

x	0	1	2	3	4
f	109	65	22	3	1

28. One cubic centimeter of a liquid suspected of containing a high density of bacteria is diluted until the density is $\frac{1}{10}$ of its previous value. Ten test tubes of a nutrient material are inoculated with this dilution. (*a*) If the original density was 30 bacteria per cubic centimeter, what is the probability that all 10 of the test tubes will show growth, that is, contain at least 1 bacterium each? (*b*) What is the probability that exactly 7 test tubes will show growth?

29. What is the probability in 12 rolls of a die that each side will come up twice? Find some other possible result, if any, which has a better chance of occurring.

$$m = np = \frac{65 + 44 + 9 + 4}{200} = \frac{122}{200} = 0.61$$

$$P(0) = \frac{e^{-0.61} (.61)^0}{0!} = 0.543$$

$$200 \times 0.543 = 108.6$$

CHAPTER IV

LARGE-SAMPLE THEORY OF ONE VARIABLE

FREQUENCY DISTRIBUTIONS OF MORE THAN ONE VARIABLE

1. Properties

Let $x_1, x_2, \cdots, x_n$ be n variables whose joint distribution is of interest. For example, if four different types of tests were being studied, four variables might be the scores of individuals on those tests and it would be of interest to know how abilities in these four subjects were interrelated and distributed. As another example, it might be of interest to investigate the interrelationship and distribution of the three variables hardness, ductility, and malleability, if properties of metals were being studied. The generalization of a distribution function of one variable to one of several variables is made easier if one thinks in terms of two variables because then the geometrical interpretation is simple. Thus, a distribution function of two variables, x and y, would be denoted by $f(x, y)$ and would be represented by a surface in three dimensions, just as a distribution function of one variable, $f(x)$, was represented by a curve in two dimensions. Similarly, a distribution function of n variables would be denoted by $f(x_1, x_2, \cdots, x_n)$. It is defined by analogy with (1), Chapter III, as that function for which

$$(1) \quad \int_{\alpha_n}^{\beta_n} \cdots \int_{\alpha_1}^{\beta_1} f(x_1, x_2, \cdots, x_n) \, dx_1 \, dx_2 \cdots dx_n$$

$$= P[\alpha_i < x_i < \beta_i] \qquad (i = 1, 2, \cdots, n)$$

where the expression on the right denotes the probability that all n inequalities will be satisfied and where $\alpha_i < \beta_i$ are any two values of the variable x_i. For two variables, (1) is easily interpreted geometrically. It shows that the probability that a point in the x, y plane will be in a given region is equal to the volume under the surface $z = f(x, y)$ which lies above this region.

For convenience, the letter f will always denote the distribution function of the indicated variables. Thus, $f(x_i)$ denotes the distribution function of the variable x_i and may differ considerably for different values of i. This notation differs from ordinary functional notation in which $f(y)$ would imply the value of $f(x)$ when x is replaced by y. Here $f(y)$ means the distribution function of y and has no connection with $f(x)$. No confusion will arise in future work because of this notation, and much explanation will be saved because of it.

2. Independent Variables

Consider the situation when the variables x_i are unrelated in a probability sense. For example, suppose that one has two variables representing respectively the length and pulse rate of male infants. One would not expect to find these two variables related in the sense that knowledge of the value of one of them would be of assistance in predicting the value of the other. Concerning the four tests mentioned in the preceding section, one would expect a relationship to exist between test scores, unless these tests were on quite different subjects. If these tests were designed to measure, say, arithmetical ability, manual dexterity, keenness of vision, and musical appreciation, then once more one would not be surprised if the scores on these four tests were unrelated. To say that variables like these are independent in a probability sense implies, for example, that the probability that an individual will make a score between 70 and 80 in arithmetical ability is independent of what score he made in the other three tests. For continuous variables, such a property would require a definition that does for intervals what (21), Chapter III, does for discrete variables. Such a definition is the following.

(2) *If $f(x_1, x_2, \cdots, x_n) = f(x_1)f(x_2) \cdots f(x_n)$, the variables x_i are said to be independently distributed.*

The desired feature in this definition will be apparent if property (1) is applied to (2). Here

$$P[\alpha_i < x_i < \beta_i]$$

$$= \int_{\alpha_n}^{\beta_n} \cdots \int_{\alpha_1}^{\beta_1} f(x_1)f(x_2) \cdots f(x_n) \, dx_1 \, dx_2 \cdots dx_n$$

$$= \int_{\alpha_1}^{\beta_1} f(x_1) \, dx_1 \int_{\alpha_2}^{\beta_2} f(x_2) \, dx_2 \cdots \int_{\alpha_n}^{\beta_n} f(x_n) \, dx_n$$

$$= P[\alpha_1 < x_1 < \beta_1]P[\alpha_2 < x_2 < \beta_2] \cdots P[\alpha_n < x_n < \beta_n]$$

This result states that the probability that the variables x_i will lie in any given region is equal to the product of the probabilities of the individual variables lying in the intervals that determine the region.

This property is the analogue for continuous variables of the definition of independent discrete variables given by (21), Chapter III.

3. Moments

By extending definitions (7) and (8), Chapter III, for a single variable, the definitions for the kth moment and the moment-generating function of a function, $g(x_1, x_2, \cdots, x_n)$, of several variables become

$$(3) \quad \mu_{k:g}' = \int_{a_n}^{b_n} \cdots \int_{a_1}^{b_1} g^k(x_1, x_2, \cdots, x_n) f(x_1, x_2, \cdots, x_n)$$
$$dx_1 \, dx_2 \cdots dx_n$$

and

$$(4) \quad M_g(\theta) = \int_{a_n}^{b_n} \cdots \int_{a_1}^{b_1} e^{\theta g(x_1, x_2, \cdots, x_n)} f(x_1, x_2, \cdots, x_n) \, dx_1 \, dx_2 \cdots dx_n$$

4. Sum of Independent Variables

A very useful formula for later theory arises when the variables x_i are independent and when $g(x_1, x_2, \cdots, x_n)$ is the special linear function

$$g(x_1, x_2, \cdots, x_n) = x_1 + x_2 + \cdots + x_n$$

From definitions (2) and (4), it follows that

$$M_{x_1 + \cdots + x_n}(\theta)$$
$$= \int_{a_n}^{b_n} \cdots \int_{a_1}^{b_1} e^{\theta[x_1 + x_2 + \cdots + x_n]} f(x_1) f(x_2) \cdots f(x_n) \, dx_1 \, dx_2 \cdots dx_n$$
$$= \int_{a_1}^{b_1} e^{\theta x_1} f(x_1) \, dx_1 \int_{a_2}^{b_2} e^{\theta x_2} f(x_2) \, dx_2 \cdots \int_{a_n}^{b_n} e^{\theta x_n} f(x_n) \, dx_n$$

But each of the integrals on the right is the moment-generating function of the indicated variable; consequently

$$(5) \quad M_{x_1 + \cdots + x_n}(\theta) = M_{x_1}(\theta) M_{x_2}(\theta) \cdots M_{x_n}(\theta)$$

This formula states that the moment-generating function of the sum of a set of independent variables is equal to the product of their individual moment-generating functions.

RANDOM SAMPLING

The idea of random sampling was considered briefly in section 1, Chapter III. There it was treated largely from a practical point of view. From a theoretical point of view, random sampling should possess properties that correspond to some of the useful features of what is considered practical random sampling. For example, suppose that tree diameters are being sampled randomly. From a practical point of view, random sampling implies among other things that the relative frequency of tree diameters found in any given interval should approach the relative frequency in that interval for the entire forest. Thus, a sampling method that consistently selected too high a percentage of average-size trees would not be considered random. This does not mean that non-representative samples will not be obtained, but rather that the method should be representative in nature. Furthermore, if these successive samples are marked off into sets of, say, 20 each, then the first measurement of each set will form a set of tree diameters that should behave like a random sample. Of course the same should hold for the second measurement, and so on, as well. Finally, these successive samples should be independent of one another. For example, if the first tree selected happened to be unusually large, that should have no effect on the size of the second tree selected. A consideration of these desirable features for practical random sampling leads to the following definition of random sampling for theoretical distribution functions.

Consider a single variable x with distribution function $f(x)$. Let $x_1, x_2, \cdots, x_n$ be a set of n values of x. This set will be called a sample of size n drawn from the population represented by $f(x)$. If repeated samples of n each are considered, x_i will be a variable which represents the ith value of x in each set. Now, the sampling will be said to be *random* if, in such repeated samples of n each, the x_i are independently distributed and each possesses the population distribution. Thus, because of (2) the sampling is random if

$$(6) \qquad f(x_1, x_2, \cdots, x_n) = f(x_1)f(x_2)\cdots f(x_n)$$

where all the f's on the right are the same function as $f(x)$.

DISTRIBUTION OF $\bar{x}$ FROM A NORMAL DISTRIBUTION

1. Theory

Let x be normally distributed with mean m and standard deviation σ, and let a random sample of size n be drawn from this normal population. Denote the sample mean by

$$\bar{x} = \frac{x_1 + x_2 + \cdots + x_n}{n}$$

In repeated samples, each x_i will be a variable; consequently in repeated samples $\bar{x}$ will be a variable also. If $\bar{x}$ is treated as a variable, and property (9), Chapter III, is used, its moment-generating function may be written as

$$M_{\bar{x}}(\theta) = M_{[x_1 + \cdots + x_n]/n}(\theta) = M_{x_1 + \cdots + x_n}\left(\frac{\theta}{n}\right)$$

Since the sampling is random, the variables x_i are independent and therefore property (5) may be applied to give

$$M_{\bar{x}}(\theta) = M_{x_1}\left(\frac{\theta}{n}\right) M_{x_2}\left(\frac{\theta}{n}\right) \cdots M_{x_n}\left(\frac{\theta}{n}\right)$$

But random sampling also implies that all the variables x_i have the same distribution function, and hence the same moment-generating function. Consequently, all the M's on the right are the same function, namely, the moment-generating function of the variable x. Thus,

$$(7) \qquad M_{\bar{x}}(\theta) = M_x{}^n\left(\frac{\theta}{n}\right)$$

But from (33), Chapter III, it follows that, for x normally distributed,

$$M_{x-m}(\theta) = e^{\frac{\sigma^2\theta^2}{2}}$$

By property (10), Chapter III, it follows that

$$(8) \qquad M_x(\theta) = e^{m\theta + \frac{\sigma^2\theta^2}{2}}$$

Consequently, from (7)

$$M_{\bar{x}}(\theta) = [e^{m\frac{\theta}{n} + \frac{\sigma^2}{2}\left(\frac{\theta}{n}\right)^2}]^n = e^{m\theta + \frac{\sigma^2}{n}\frac{\theta^2}{2}}$$

Since the expression on the right, when compared with (8), is seen to be the moment-generating function of a normal variable with mean m and standard deviation $\sigma/\sqrt{n}$, and since a moment-generating function uniquely defines a distribution function, this result proves the following theorem.

Theorem I. *If x is normally distributed with mean m and standard deviation σ and random samples of size n are drawn, then the sample mean, $\bar{x}$, will be normally distributed with mean m and standard deviation $\sigma/\sqrt{n}$.*

Theorem I shows how the precision of a sample mean for estimating the population mean increases as the sample size is increased. Since the standard deviation of $\bar{x}$ measures the variation of sample $\bar{x}$'s about m and hence may be treated as a measure of the precision of estimating

m by means of $\bar{x}$, it is clear from the theorem that it is necessary to take four times as large a sample if one desires to double the precision of an estimate at hand.

2. Applications

As an illustration of the application of the theorem, consider the following problem. The manufacturer of string has found from past experience that samples of a certain type of string have a mean breaking strength of 15.6 pounds and a standard deviation of 2.2 pounds. A time-saving change in the manufacturing process of this string is tried. A sample of 50 pieces is then taken, for which the mean breaking strength turns out to be 14.5 pounds and the standard deviation 2.1 pounds. On the basis of this sample can it be concluded that the new process has had a harmful effect on the strength of the string? Now experience indicates that the breaking strength of string is approximately normally distributed. Hence, it will be assumed that the breaking strength, x, is normally distributed with $m = 15.6$ and $\sigma = 2.2$. Now, following the procedure for testing hypotheses outlined in the preceding chapter, set up the hypothesis that the new process has not affected the breaking strength of the string. Then the sample may be treated as a random sample of size 50 from the specified normal population. Consequently, by Theorem I, $\bar{x}$ will be normally distributed with

$$m_{\bar{x}} = 15.6 \quad \text{and} \quad \sigma_{\bar{x}} = \frac{2.2}{\sqrt{50}} = 0.31$$

The $\bar{x}$ normal curve will therefore possess only about $\frac{1}{7}$ the spread of the x normal curve. The value of $\bar{x}$ for this one sample of 50 was 14.5; hence, the corresponding value of t is

$$t = \frac{\bar{x} - m_{\bar{x}}}{\sigma_{\bar{x}}} = \frac{14.5 - 15.6}{0.31} = -3.55$$

From Table II, the probability of obtaining a value of $t \leq -3.55$, and hence a value of $\bar{x} \leq 14.5$, is only about 0.0002. Since this probability is much smaller than the probability of 0.05 being used for judging significance, the value 14.5 is highly significant and accordingly the hypothesis will be rejected. It appears that the new process produces string of a slightly lower mean breaking strength.

For problems of the type just considered, it is rather common in applied statistics to call $\sigma/\sqrt{n}$ the standard error of the mean. The name *standard error* is also used in connection with statistics other than the mean, being always the same as the standard deviation of that statistic. The expression probable error is also fairly common in some circles. It is related to the standard error by means of the approximate formula P.E. = 0.6745S.E. For a normal variable x, the probability is $\frac{1}{2}$ that x will fall in the interval $m \pm$ P.E. Since it is more convenient to work with standard deviations than with probable errors, the use of the probable error is gradually being abandoned.

As another illustration, consider the following problem. An estimate of the new population mean in the preceding problem is desired which will be correct to $\frac{1}{2}$ pound. How large a sample is necessary to be reasonably certain that the resulting mean will not differ from the true mean by more than $\frac{1}{2}$ pound? Since the sample standard deviation turned out to be very close to the previous population standard deviation, it will be assumed that the new population standard deviation is also 2.2. Let m be the new population mean and as before assume that x is normally distributed. Then $\bar{x}$ will be normally distributed with mean m and standard deviation $2.2/\sqrt{n}$. The requirement of being reasonably certain will be understood to mean being certain with a probability of 0.95. Hence, in order to have sample values of $\bar{x}$ fall within $\frac{1}{2}$ pound of m 95% of the time, it is necessary that $\frac{1}{2}$ pound correspond to two standard deviations for the $\bar{x}$ distribution. Therefore, n must be such that

$$\frac{1}{2} = 2\sigma_{\bar{x}} = 2\frac{\sigma}{\sqrt{n}} = 2\frac{2.2}{\sqrt{n}} = \frac{4.4}{\sqrt{n}}$$

The solution of this equation is $n = 77$. Since a sample of size 50 is already available, only about 27 additional observations would be needed.

It is to be noted that the problem just solved specified only the magnitude of the deviation of the sample mean from the population mean in contrast to the preceding problem in which the question was whether the sample mean was too small to be attributed to sampling variation. It should also be noted that the population standard deviation was assumed known in both these problems. In most problems the population standard deviation is not known. Then the sample value of the standard deviation is often used in place of the unknown population value; however, this procedure introduces an error. The error is not serious for large samples; but for small samples a more refined procedure that does not require such approximations is necessary. Such methods will be considered in Chapter VIII.

DISTRIBUTION OF $\bar{x}$ FROM NON-NORMAL DISTRIBUTIONS

1. Theory

Since many variables of interest possess distributions that are not even approximately normal, it is important to know to what extent the theory developed on the basis of assuming normality holds for other distributions. Here it will be assumed that x is no longer normally distributed but merely possesses a distribution for which the moment-generating function exists. Then it will be shown that the distribution of $\bar{x}$ approaches a normal distribution as the size of the sample increases.

Consider the variable $t = (\bar{x} - m)\sqrt{n}/\sigma$ and its moment-generating function. If properties (9) and (10), Chapter III, and formula (7) are applied,

$$M_t(\theta) = M_{\bar{x}-m}\left(\frac{\sqrt{n}\theta}{\sigma}\right)$$

$$= e^{-\frac{m\sqrt{n}\theta}{\sigma}} M_{\bar{x}}\left(\frac{\sqrt{n}\theta}{\sigma}\right)$$

$$= e^{-\frac{m\sqrt{n}\theta}{\sigma}} M_x{}^n\left(\frac{\theta}{\sigma\sqrt{n}}\right)$$

Taking logarithms of both sides to the base e gives

$$\log M_t(\theta) = -\frac{m\sqrt{n}\theta}{\sigma} + n \log M\left(\frac{\theta}{\sigma\sqrt{n}}\right)$$

Replacing $M\left(\dfrac{\theta}{\sigma\sqrt{n}}\right)$ by its expanded form as given by (5), Chapter III, yields

$$\log M_t(\theta) = -\frac{m\sqrt{n}\theta}{\sigma} + n \log\left[1 + \mu_1{}'\frac{\theta}{\sigma\sqrt{n}} + \mu_2{}'\frac{\theta^2}{2\sigma^2 n} + \cdots\right]$$

If $|\theta|$ is chosen sufficiently small, the logarithm on the right may be treated as of the form $\log[1 + z]$; hence

$$\log M_t(\theta) = -\frac{m\sqrt{n}\theta}{\sigma} + n\left\{\left(\mu_1{}'\frac{\theta}{\sigma\sqrt{n}} + \mu_2{}'\frac{\theta^2}{2\sigma^2 n} + \cdots\right)\right.$$

$$\left. - \frac{1}{2}\left(\mu_1{}'\frac{\theta}{\sigma\sqrt{n}} + \mu_2{}'\frac{\theta^2}{2\sigma^2 n} + \cdots\right)^2 + \cdots\right\}$$

$$= \left(-\frac{m\sqrt{n}}{\sigma} + \mu_1{}'\frac{\sqrt{n}}{\sigma}\right)\theta + \frac{\mu_2{}' - \mu_1{}'^2}{\sigma^2}\frac{\theta^2}{2}$$

$$+ \text{ terms in } \theta^k, \quad k \geq 3$$

Since $m = \mu_1'$ and $\sigma^2 = \mu_2' - \mu_1'^2$,

$$(9) \qquad \log M_t(\theta) = \frac{\theta^2}{2} + \text{terms in } \theta^k, \quad k \geq 3$$

From an inspection of terms in θ^k, it will be seen that the only function of n which they contain is the factor $n^{-\frac{k}{2}+1}$. Since $k \geq 3$, all such terms will approach zero as n becomes infinite; consequently

$$\lim_{n \to \infty} \log M_t(\theta) = \frac{\theta^2}{2}$$

which implies that

$$\lim_{n \to \infty} M_t(\theta) = e^{\frac{\theta^2}{2}}$$

As in Theorem I, Chapter III, whose proof resembles this proof, these various expansions and limits require a knowledge of advanced calculus methods for their justification. Since the last limit is the moment-generating function of the standard normal distribution, the preceding arguments prove the following theorem.

Theorem II. *If x has a distribution with mean m and standard deviation σ for which the moment-generating function exists, then the variable $t = (\bar{x} - m)\sqrt{n}/\sigma$ has a distribution which approaches the standard normal distribution as n becomes infinite.*

From a practical point of view, this theorem is exceedingly important because it permits the use of normal curve methods on problems related to means of the type illustrated in the previous section even when the basic variable x has a distribution that differs considerably from normality. Of course the more the distribution differs from normality, the larger must n become to guarantee approximate normality for $\bar{x}$. Sampling experiments have shown that for $n > 50$ the form of $f(x)$ has little influence on the form of $f(\bar{x})$ for ordinary types of $f(x)$.

From (9) it will be observed that the expansion of $M_t(\theta)$ would contain no term in θ and that the coefficient of $\theta^2/2$ would be 1; consequently t is a standard variable. This shows that the formulas

$$m_{\bar{x}} = m$$

$$(10)$$

$$\sigma_{\bar{x}} = \frac{\sigma}{\sqrt{n}}$$

hold in general and hence do not depend upon any normality assumption.

2. Applications

The control-chart technique introduced in section 3, Chapter III, was designed to check on successive sample percentages to determine whether they behaved like random samples from a binomial distribution. A similar chart may be constructed for sample means. Because of Theorem II it is not essential that the basic variable be exactly normally distributed for such charts; consequently they are of wider applicability. Such a chart is shown in Fig. 1. It should be noted that the control band is a 3-standard-deviation band about the mean, and therefore for a normal variable the probability would be only 0.003 of a point falling outside this band. These particular control

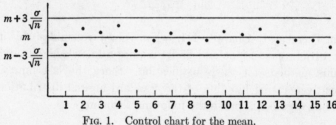

Fig. 1.   Control chart for the mean.

limits are chosen because industrial experience has found them to be especially useful. Since many industrial variables are not normally distributed, and since the sample means used in control charts are often based on only 4 or 5 measurements, one could hardly expect the probability of 0.003 to be very realistic. It will be observed from Fig. 1 that the process appears to be under control.

DISTRIBUTION OF THE DIFFERENCE OF TWO MEANS

1. Theory

A frequent problem in science is to determine whether real differences exist between two sets of similar data. One method of treating the problem statistically is to determine whether it is highly probable that real differences exist between the means of the populations from which the data were assumed taken.

Let $\bar{x}$ and $\bar{y}$ be the sample means of two sets of data based on random samples of sizes n_x and n_y respectively. These two means may be treated as the first pair of samples in repeated sampling; consequently $\bar{x}$ and $\bar{y}$ may be treated as variables for which one pair of values is available. Since the samples are random, $\bar{x}$ and $\bar{y}$ will be independently distributed. If x and y are normally distributed, or if n_x and n_y are sufficiently large, $\bar{x}$ and $\bar{y}$ will be normally distributed, or approximately so. It will be assumed therefore that $\bar{x}$ and $\bar{y}$ are normally distributed. Now consider the moment-generating function of the variable $\bar{x} - \bar{y}$. If property (5), property (9), Chapter III, formula (8), and formulas (10) are applied,

$$
\begin{aligned}
M_{\bar{x}-\bar{y}}(\theta) &= M_{\bar{x}}(\theta) M_{-\bar{y}}(\theta) \\
&= M_{\bar{x}}(\theta) M_{\bar{y}}(-\theta) \\
&= e^{m_{\bar{x}}\theta + \frac{\sigma_{\bar{x}}^2\theta^2}{2}} \cdot e^{-m_{\bar{y}}\theta + \frac{\sigma_{\bar{y}}^2\theta^2}{2}} \\
&= e^{(m_x - m_y)\theta + \left(\frac{\sigma_x^2}{n_x} + \frac{\sigma_y^2}{n_y}\right)\frac{\theta^2}{2}}
\end{aligned}
$$

Since this expression is the moment-generating function of a normal variable, this result proves the following theorem.

Theorem III. *If $\bar{x}$ and $\bar{y}$ are normally and independently distributed, then $\bar{x} - \bar{y}$ is normally distributed with mean $m_{\bar{x}-\bar{y}} = m_x - m_y$ and standard deviation $\sigma_{\bar{x}-\bar{y}} = \sqrt{\dfrac{\sigma_x^2}{n_x} + \dfrac{\sigma_y^2}{n_y}}$.*

2. Applications

Consider the following problem. A potential buyer of light bulbs bought 50 bulbs of each of two brands. Upon testing these bulbs, he found that brand A had a mean life of 1,282 hours with a standard deviation of 80 hours, whereas brand B had a mean life of 1,208 hours with a standard deviation of 94 hours. Do the two brands differ in quality? To answer this question, set up the hypothesis that the two samples came from normal populations with the same means. The samples are evidently independent; therefore by Theorem III, $\bar{x} - \bar{y}$ is normally distributed with

$$
m_{\bar{x}-\bar{y}} = 0 \quad \text{and} \quad \sigma_{\bar{x}-\bar{y}} = \sqrt{\frac{\sigma_x^2}{50} + \frac{\sigma_y^2}{50}}
$$

Since σ_x^2 and σ_y^2 are unknown, it is necessary to estimate them from their sample values. Such approximations introduce an error, but for samples as large as 50 this error is not serious. It can be shown that the error in $\sigma_{\bar{x}-\bar{y}}$ would probably not exceed 10% here. With these approximations,

$$
m_{\bar{x}-\bar{y}} = 0 \quad \text{and} \quad \sigma_{\bar{x}-\bar{y}} \doteq \sqrt{\frac{(80)^2}{50} + \frac{(94)^2}{50}} = 17.5
$$

If, as before, a significance level of 0.05 is chosen, then a value of $\bar{x} - \bar{y}$ exceeding 35 will be judged significant. Since $\bar{x} - \bar{y} = 74$ here, this difference is highly significant, and therefore the hypothesis of equal means is rejected. It seems quite certain that the two brands differ in quality as far as mean burning time is concerned. Although it was assumed that x and y were normally distributed, it would have sufficed to assume that $\bar{x}$ and $\bar{y}$ were normally distributed. Since the values of n_x and n_y are sufficiently large to make the latter assumption highly reasonable, the above significant difference cannot very well be attributed to a possible lack of normality for burning time.

After a test has indicated significant differences, it is usually of interest to determine how large a difference in population means may be reasonably assumed. This problem will be considered in Chapter VIII.

DISTRIBUTION OF THE DIFFERENCE OF TWO PERCENTAGES

1. Theory

If two sets of data drawn from binomial distributions are to be compared, it is necessary to work with percentages of successes rather than with the number of successes, unless the number of trials in each set is the same. For example, 40 heads in 100 tosses of a coin would not be compared with 30 heads in 50 tosses unless they were both placed on a percentage basis. Now from Theorem I, Chapter III, and (34), Chapter III, it follows that the percentage of successes, $p' = x/n$, may be assumed to be normally distributed with mean p and standard deviation $\sqrt{pq/n}$ provided that n is large.

Let p_1' and p_2' be two independent sample percentages based on n_1 and n_2 trials, respectively, from binomial distributions with probabilities p_1 and p_2, respectively. If p_1' and p_2' are treated as normal independent variables and if one proceeds as for $\bar{x} - \bar{y}$,

$$M_{p_1'-p_2'}(\theta) = M_{p_1'}(\theta) M_{p_2'}(\theta)$$

$$= e^{p_1\theta + \frac{p_1 q_1 \theta^2}{2n_1}} \cdot e^{-p_2\theta + \frac{p_2 q_2 \theta^2}{2n_2}}$$

$$= e^{(p_1 - p_2)\theta + \left(\frac{p_1 q_1}{n_1} + \frac{p_2 q_2}{n_2}\right)\frac{\theta^2}{2}}$$

This demonstrates the following theorem.

Theorem IV. *When the number of trials, n_1 and n_2, are sufficiently large, the difference of the sample percentages, $p_1' - p_2'$, will be approxi-*

mately normally distributed with $m_{p_1'-p_2'} = p_1 - p_2$ *and* $\sigma_{p_1'-p_2'} =$
$$\sqrt{\frac{p_1 q_1}{n_1} + \frac{p_2 q_2}{n_2}}.$$

As for the simple binomial distribution, the normal approximation will usually be satisfactory in applications if the $n_i p_i$ exceed 5.

2. Applications

As an illustration of Theorem IV, consider the following problem. A railroad company installed two sets of 50 red oak ties each. The

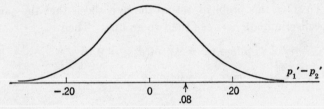

FIG. 2.   Distribution of $p_1' - p_2'$.

two sets were treated with creosote by two different processes. After a period of twenty years of service, it was found that 22 ties of the first set and 18 ties of the second set were still in good condition. Is one justified in claiming that there is no real difference between the preserving properties of the two processes? To answer this question, set up the hypothesis that the probability, p, of a tie surviving this period of service is the same for both processes. Then, from Theorem IV,

$$m_{p_1'-p_2'} = 0 \quad \text{and} \quad \sigma_{p_1'-p_2'} = \sqrt{\frac{pq}{50} + \frac{pq}{50}} = \frac{\sqrt{pq}}{5}$$

The value of p is unknown, and so its value must be estimated from sample values. Since the hypothesis treats the two samples as though they were drawn from populations with the same p, the samples may be combined into one sample of 100 for which there were 40 successes. Hence a good estimate of p here is 0.4. With this estimate,

$$m_{p_1'-p_2'} = 0 \quad \text{and} \quad \sigma_{p_1'-p_2'} \doteq 0.10$$

The situation here is described geometrically in Fig. 2. Since $p_1' - p_2' = 0.44 - 0.36 = 0.08$ lies well within a two-standard-deviation interval of the mean, there is no reason for doubting the truth of the hypothesis at the 0.05 significance level. The fact that the value of p must be estimated from sample values and that $p_1' - p_2'$ is only approximately normally distributed makes this test somewhat inaccurate unless both samples are large. Both samples are sufficiently large here to insure a fairly reliable test.

As a second illustration, consider this problem. A civil-service examination is given to a group of 200 candidates. On the basis of their total scores, the 200 candidates are divided into two groups, the upper 30% and the remaining 70%. Consider question one on this examination. Among the first group, 40 had the correct answer, whereas, among the second group, 80 had the correct answer. Is this first question any good for discriminating ability of the type examined here? To solve this problem, set up the hypothesis that the question does not discriminate between the two groups. Then

$$p_1' - p_2' = \frac{40}{60} - \frac{80}{140} = 0.10$$

$$m_{p_1' - p_2'} = 0$$

$$\sigma_{p_1' - p_2'} = \sqrt{\frac{pq}{60} + \frac{pq}{140}}$$

where p is the probability that an individual selected at random from the population from which this group of 200 is thought of as having been sampled will get the correct answer to this question. As an estimate of p, combine the two groups to give 120 successes in 200 trials, or a value of 0.6. With this approximation for p,

$$\sigma_{p_1' - p_2'} \doteq 0.076$$

Since the observed difference, $p_1' - p_2' = 0.10$, is less than the critical difference of 0.152, this result is not significant, and therefore there is no reason to doubt the truth of the hypothesis.

REFERENCES

An interesting discussion of random sampling may be found in:

KENDALL, M. G., *The Advanced Theory of Statistics*, vol. 1, Griffin and Company, pp. 186–196.

YULE and KENDALL, *An Introduction to the Theory of Statistics*, Griffin and Company, pp. 336–346.

A proof of Theorem II that requires more mathematical maturity may be found in:

WILKS, S. S., *Mathematical Statistics*, Princeton University Press, p. 82.

A discussion of the rapidity with which the distribution of $\bar{x}$ approaches normality will be found in:

KENNEY, J., *Mathematics of Statistics*, Part Two, D. Van Nostrand Company, pp. 111–113.

The formula $\sigma_{\bar{x}} = \sigma/\sqrt{n}$ is but one of many standard-error formulas that can be derived for solving certain large-sample problems. For example, problem 23 in Chapter VIII is concerned with proving that $\sigma_{s^2} = \sqrt{2(n-1)}/n^2\sigma^2$ provided that x is normally distributed. Since it can be shown that the sample variance of a normal variable possesses an approximate normal distribution for large samples, this standard-error formula could be used to solve certain large-sample variance problems similar to the mean problems of this chapter. However, more precise methods are usually available for such problems. Chapter VIII is concerned with such preferred methods. The technique of deriving standard error formulas is carefully explained and illustrated in:

YULE and KENDALL, *op. cit.*, pp. 380–411.

EXERCISES

1. Suggest how to sample randomly from (*a*) trees in a forest, (*b*) string being manufactured, (*c*) a carload of wheat, (*d*) households to obtain information about sizes of families, (*e*) the public concerning political views.

2. Past experience indicates that wire rods purchased from a company have a mean breaking strength of 400 pounds and a standard deviation of 15 pounds. (*a*) If one rod is selected at random from a lot, between what two values would you reasonably expect its breaking strength to lie? What assumptions are you making here? (*b*) If 25 rods are selected, between what two values would you reasonably expect their mean to lie? Are the same assumptions necessary here as in (*a*)? (*c*) How many rods would you select so that you would be certain with a probability of 0.95 that your resulting mean would not be in error by more than 2 pounds?

3. Use Tippett's numbers to draw samples of 10 from the discrete population

x	0	1	2	3	4
p	0.30	0.25	0.20	0.15	0.10

Draw 20 (or more) sets of 10 each, and calculate $\bar{x}$ for each set. Graph the histogram for these 20 (or more) $\bar{x}$'s, and note the approach to normality. Calculate the mean and standard deviation of these 20 $\bar{x}$'s, and compare with the values to be expected from theory.

4. The same type of test was given to two classes. The first class of 20 students averaged 123 points with a standard deviation of 32 points; the second class of 32 averaged 138 points with a standard deviation of 24 points. Was the second class superior?

5. The following data give the number of years after marriage in which divorce occurs, if it occurs. Is one justified in claiming that divorce occurs earlier than it used to?

	1887–1906	1929
Number of divorces	22,500	2,650
Mean time in years	10.37	9.83
Standard deviation	8.39	8.26

6. Two different samplers, A and B, were sent into the same forest to select trees at random. The diameters of trees were measured with the following results

	A	B
Number measured	100	100
Mean diameter in inches	19.2	20.3
Standard deviation	3.2	2.6

(*a*) Does the smaller standard deviation for B imply that he is more accurate than A? (*b*) What conclusions can be drawn concerning the relative accuracy of A and B? (*c*) If you knew that the true mean was 19.7, could you draw any further conclusions?

7. In a poll taken among college students, 46 out of 200 fraternity men favored a certain proposition while 51 out of 300 non-fraternity men favored it. Was there a real difference of opinion on this proposition?

8. A manufacturer of house dresses sent out advertising by mail. He sent samples of material to each of two groups of 1,000 women but for one group he enclosed a white return envelope and for the other group he enclosed a blue envelope; 10% and 13% respectively responded. Would the blue envelope help sales?

9. A civil-service examination was given to 200 people. On the basis of their total scores they were divided into the upper 30%, the middle 40%, and the lower 30%. On a certain question, 39 of the upper group got the correct answer while

29 of the lower group got the correct answer. Is this question likely to be useful for discriminating ability of this type?

10. (a) Construct a control chart for $\bar{x}$ for the following data on the blowing time of fuses, samples of 5 being taken every hour. (b) If these are the first data taken on this product, would you say that the process seemed to be under control and hence that the mean and standard deviation from these data could be used for future control? (c) If it is known that previous control existed with a mean and standard deviation about equal to these sample values, would these data justify some action on the part of the engineer in charge at any time? Each set of 5 has been arranged in order of magnitude.

42	42	19	36	42	51	60	18	15	69	64	61
65	45	24	54	51	74	60	20	30	109	91	78
75	68	80	69	57	75	72	27	39	113	93	94
78	72	81	77	59	78	95	42	62	118	109	109
87	90	81	84	78	132	138	60	84	153	112	136

11. What would you expect the control chart of a given operator to look like during an ordinary day's work of 8 hours if he turns out about the same number of parts each hour and samples are taken every hour?

12. With a 10-cm. line some distance away, draw 25 freehand lines, attempting to make them 10 cm. long. Cover all lines drawn to avoid being influenced by them. Assemble data for the class, and construct a control chart for $\bar{x}$ based on sets of 5. Each student supplies five $\bar{x}$'s.

13. If $f(x) = e^{-x}$, $x \geq 0$, find the moment-generating function of $\bar{x}$.

14. If $f(x) = ce^{-x}x^k$, $x \geq 0$, $k > 0$, find the moment-generating function of $\bar{x}$. Compare with that of x, and draw conclusions.

CHAPTER V

FREQUENCY DISTRIBUTIONS OF TWO VARIABLES

LINEAR REGRESSION

Thus far, data of a single variable only have been studied. A large percentage of the problems in statistical work, however, involve two or more variables. In some problems the variables are studied simultaneously to see how they are interrelated; in others there is one particular variable of interest and the remaining variables are studied for their possible aid in throwing light on this particular one. In such problems the investigator is often interested in using any relationships that he finds for making estimates or predictions of the basic variable in situations similar to the one at hand. With two variables, the basic variable will be denoted by y, and the related variable by means of which it is hoped to obtain information concerning y will be denoted by x. Then the problem is to determine the relationship between y and x in some form convenient for estimating y from x.

The investigation of the relationship between two variables usually begins with an attempt to discover the approximate form of the relationship by graphing the data as points in the plane. Such a graph is called a *scatter diagram*. By means of it one can quickly discern whether there is any pronounced relationship and, if so, whether the relationship may be treated as approximately linear, that is, whether the points tend to follow a straight line.

Consider the situation when the variables appear to be linearly related. In particular, consider the first two columns of Table 1, which give the vocabulary test and I.Q. scores of 20 fifth-grade students, and Fig. 1, which is the scatter diagram for these data. There appears to be a rather strong tendency here for I.Q.'s to increase with increasing vocabulary scores. Moreover, the trend appears to be approximately linear. Since it is of interest to estimate a student's I.Q. by means of his vocabulary score, the variables have been selected as indicated. Hence, the problem is to determine the best-fitting straight line for such estimating purposes.

There are numerous methods for fitting curves to a set of points, but the most generally satisfactory method is the following one, known as the *method of least squares*. Since the desired curve is to be used for estimating purposes, it is reasonable to require that the curve be such that it makes the errors of estimation small. If the value of the variable to be estimated is denoted by y and the corresponding curve value by y', then the error of estimate is given by $y - y'$. Since the errors may be positive or negative and might add up to a small value for a poorly fitted curve, it would not do to require merely that the sum of the errors should be as small as possible. This difficulty could be

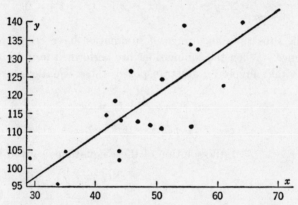

FIG. 1. Scatter diagram for I.Q. and vocabulary scores.

avoided by requiring that the sum of the absolute values of the errors should be as small as possible. However, sums of absolute values are not convenient to work with mathematically; consequently the difficulty is avoided by requiring that the sum of the squares of the errors should be a minimum.

Consider the application of this principle to the fitting of a straight line to a set of n points. Now the equation of any non-vertical line may be written in the form

$$(1) \qquad y' = a + m(x - \bar{x})$$

where m is its slope and $a - m\bar{x}$ is its y intercept. Then the problem is to determine the parameters a and m so that the sum of the squares of the errors of estimation will be a minimum. If the coordinates of the ith point are denoted by (x_i, y_i), this sum of squares will be $\sum_{1}^{n}(y_i - y_i')^2$. When y_i' is replaced by its value as given by (1), it becomes clear that this sum is a function of a and m only. If this function is denoted by $G(a, m)$,

$$G(a, m) = \sum_{1}^{n} [y_i - a - m(x_i - \bar{x})]^2$$

If this function is to have a minimum value, it is necessary that its partial derivatives vanish there; hence

$$\frac{\partial G}{\partial a} = \Sigma 2[y - a - m(x - \bar{x})][-1] = 0$$

$$\frac{\partial G}{\partial m} = \Sigma 2[y - a - m(x - \bar{x})][-(x - \bar{x})] = 0$$

where the subscripts and range of summation have been omitted for convenience. When the summations are performed term by term and the sums that involve y are transposed, these equations assume the form

(2)
$$an + m\Sigma(x - \bar{x}) = \Sigma y$$
$$a\Sigma(x - \bar{x}) + m\Sigma(x - \bar{x})^2 = \Sigma(x - \bar{x})y$$

Since $\Sigma(x - \bar{x}) = 0$, the solution of these equations is given by

$$a = \bar{y} \quad \text{and} \quad m = \frac{\Sigma(x - \bar{x})y}{\Sigma(x - \bar{x})^2}$$

As a result, the least-squares line may be written

(3)
$$y' - \bar{y} = m(x - \bar{x})$$

where

$$m = \frac{\Sigma(x - \bar{x})y}{\Sigma(x - \bar{x})^2}$$

This line is often called the *regression line* of y on x. It should be noted that this line passes through the mean point $(\bar{x}, \bar{y})$.

For computational purposes, it is convenient to change the form of m slightly in the following manner:

$$m = \frac{\Sigma xy - \bar{x}\Sigma y}{\Sigma x^2 - 2\bar{x}\Sigma x + \Sigma \bar{x}^2}$$

$$= \frac{\Sigma xy - n\bar{x}\bar{y}}{\Sigma x^2 - n\bar{x}^2}$$

Table 1 illustrates the computational procedure for the data mentioned previously. If a calculating machine is available, only the sums of the last two columns should be recorded for those columns. As a result of these computations, the equation of the regression line was found to be

$$y' - 116.4 = 1.132(x - 46.5)$$

The graph of this line is shown on the scatter diagram of Fig. 1.

TABLE 1

x	y	xy	x^2
30	94	2,820	900
33	96	3,168	1,089
29	103	2,987	841
44	103	4,532	1,936
35	105	3,675	1,225
44	105	4,620	1,936
51	112	5,712	2,601
48	113	5,424	2,304
56	113	6,328	3,136
43	114	4,902	1,849
47	114	5,358	2,209
41	115	4,715	1,681
42	118	4,956	1,764
61	124	7,564	3,721
51	126	6,426	2,601
46	126	5,796	2,116
56	134	7,504	3,136
55	135	7,425	3,025
54	139	7,506	2,916
64	140	8,960	4,096
930	2,329	110,378	45,082

LINEAR CORRELATION

1. Correlation Coefficient

After a regression line has been determined, it is of interest to know how useful the line is for estimating purposes. One might believe that a measure of a line's usefulness would be given by the standard deviation of the errors of estimation, with a small value corresponding to accurate estimates and hence to a useful line. However, consider the situations illustrated in Figs. 2 and 3. The standard deviation of the errors of estimation is about the same in these two illustrations, and yet the second line is of no value in helping one to estimate y from a knowledge of x.

If no attempt is made to fit a regression line to a set of data, the best estimate in the sense of least squares that one could make for y corresponding to any x would be $\bar{y}$. This is seen by minimizing $\Sigma(y - a)^2$ as a function of a. Thus,

$$\frac{d}{da} \Sigma(y - a)^2 = 2\Sigma(y - a)(-1) = 0$$

hence, solving for a gives

$$a = \frac{\Sigma y}{n} = \bar{y}$$

Now, as a measure of the usefulness of a line for estimating purposes, it seems natural to consider the ratio of the sum of the squares of the

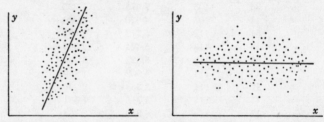

FIGS. 2 and 3.   Scatter diagrams for different degrees of correlation.

errors of estimation based on the regression line and the sum of the squares of the errors when no attempt is made to fit a regression line. In view of the preceding paragraph, such a measure would be written

$$\frac{\Sigma(y - y')^2}{\Sigma(y - \bar{y})^2}$$

The numerator of this ratio is Σe^2, whereas the denominator is ns_y^2. From (3) it follows that

$$\bar{e} = \frac{\Sigma e}{n} = \frac{\Sigma(y - y')}{n} = \frac{1}{n} \Sigma[(y - \bar{y}) - m(x - \bar{x})] = 0$$

Consequently,

$$\Sigma e^2 = \Sigma(e - \bar{e})^2 = ns_e^2$$

As a result, the above ratio may be written in the form

$$(4) \qquad \frac{\Sigma(y - y')^2}{\Sigma(y - \bar{y})^2} = \frac{s_e^2}{s_y^2}$$

For the situation illustrated in Fig. 3, this ratio would be approximately 1, while for the situation of Fig. 2, it would be a rather small fraction

Since it is conventional to have zero correspond to a useless line and to have 1 correspond to a line that estimates perfectly, a preferable form for this measure of usefulness is obtained by subtracting this ratio from 1. Then

$$(5) \qquad r^2 = 1 - \frac{s_e^2}{s_y^2}$$

defines the desired measure. The quantity r is called the *correlation coefficient*. Thus, the correlation coefficient is a statistic that measures the usefulness of a regression line for estimating purposes. It will have a value close to zero for a line incapable of prediction and close to ± 1 for a line capable of nearly perfect prediction. The positive square root is taken for r if the regression line slopes upward, and the negative root if it slopes downward. This convention merely tells one whether y increases or decreases as x increases. It is the magnitude of r that is important.

Interpretation. The correlation coefficient is usually spoken of as a measure of the strength of the relationship between two variables. However, it measures the strength of the relationship only when that relationship is linear. This statement is qualitative, just as is the above statement about r measuring the usefulness of the regression line for estimating purposes. In other words, no scale of measurement is provided to enable one to compare two sets of data for their relative strength of relationship. Thus, a correlation coefficient of 0.6 does not imply twice as strong a relationship as a correlation coefficient of 0.3, nor does it imply that the first regression line is four times as useful as the second line. However, a quantitative way of looking at a correlation coefficient can be obtained in the following manner.

Since the square of the standard deviation arises so often, it has been given a name and is called the variance. Consider, then, the following method of dividing the variance of y into two parts.

$$s_y^2 = \frac{1}{n} \Sigma(y - \bar{y})^2 = \frac{1}{n} \Sigma(y - y' + y' - \bar{y})^2$$

$$= \frac{1}{n}\{\Sigma(y - y')^2 + 2\Sigma(y - y')(y' - \bar{y}) + \Sigma(y' - \bar{y})^2\}$$

The value of y' is given by (3). After both sides of (3) are summed it will be observed that the mean of the estimated values, $\bar{y}'$, is equal to $\bar{y}$. With these two substitutions,

$$s_y^2 = \frac{1}{n}\{\Sigma(y-y')^2 + 2\Sigma[y-\bar{y}-m(x-\bar{x})]m(x-\bar{x}) + \Sigma(y'-\bar{y}')^2\}$$

$$= \frac{\Sigma(y-y')^2}{n} + 2m\frac{\Sigma(x-\bar{x})(y-\bar{y})}{n} - 2m^2\frac{\Sigma(x-\bar{x})^2}{n} + \frac{\Sigma(y'-\bar{y}')^2}{n}$$

From the definition of m in (3), it is easily seen that

$$\Sigma(x-\bar{x})(y-\bar{y}) = \Sigma(x-\bar{x})y = m\Sigma(x-\bar{x})^2$$

and hence that the second and third terms on the right cancel each other. From previous work leading to (4) it was shown that the first sum on the right is s_e^2; therefore

$$s_y^2 = s_e^2 + s_{y'}^2$$

This result shows that the variance of y can be written as the sum of the variances of the errors and of the estimated values. Dividing both sides by s_y^2 yields

(6) $$\frac{s_e^2}{s_y^2} + \frac{s_{y'}^2}{s_y^2} = 1$$

If the first fraction is transposed to the right side, it will be clear from (5) that

(7) $$r^2 = \frac{s_{y'}^2}{s_y^2}$$

This formula states that r^2 is equal to the percentage of s_y^2 that is contributed by the estimated values. Thus, a correlation coefficient may be interpreted quantitatively by stating that the square of a correlation coefficient is equal to the percentage of the variance of y that has been accounted for by the relationship with x. For example, if the correlation coefficient between the height and diameter of trees of a given species were 0.80, then 64% of the variation in tree height could be explained by the relationship of height to diameter. The remaining 36% of s_y^2 would be due to other factors. It is customary to speak of this remaining part of s_y^2 as the *error variance* since it is the variance of the errors of estimation. It should be noted that because of (6) the interpretation in terms of percentages must be confined to variances. If the interpretation were attempted for r and standard deviations, the percentages would not total 100%. This interpretation in terms of r^2 rather than of r has the tendency to curb unwarranted belief in the strength of relationship between two variables which would arise if r were treated as the quantitative measure of the relationship, because r^2 is considerably smaller than r, except for r close to 1.

Computation for unclassified data. The definition of r given by (5) is not convenient for computing r because it requires the computation of the errors of estimation. A form convenient for computation may be obtained in the following manner.

Since $\bar{y}' = \bar{y}$, (7) may be written

$$r^2 = \frac{\Sigma(y' - \bar{y}')^2}{ns_y^2} = \frac{\Sigma(y' - \bar{y})^2}{ns_y^2}$$

Expressing this in terms of m from (3) gives

$$(8) \qquad r^2 = \frac{m^2\Sigma(x - \bar{x})^2}{ns_y^2} = m^2\frac{s_x^2}{s_y^2}$$

Inserting the value of m and taking the positive square root results in

$$r = \frac{s_x}{s_y}\frac{\Sigma(x - \bar{x})y}{\Sigma(x - \bar{x})^2} = \frac{s_x}{s_y}\frac{\Sigma(x - \bar{x})(y - \bar{y})}{\Sigma(x - \bar{x})^2}$$

Hence,

$$(9) \qquad r = \frac{\Sigma(x - \bar{x})(y - \bar{y})}{ns_x s_y}$$

The positive root was taken here so that the sign of r would agree with the sign convention made following (5). The expression (9) is often given as the definition of r. The chief objection to (9) as the definition of r is that it is quite artificial and does not explain the dependence of correlation on linear regression.

If the value of m given by (8) is inserted in (3), the equation of the line of regression can be written in the commonly used form

$$(10) \qquad y' - \bar{y} = r\frac{s_y}{s_x}(x - \bar{x})$$

Form (9) is still not the most convenient for computational purposes. A better form for such purposes is obtained by multiplying out factors and inserting values for s_x and s_y as follows:

$$(11) \qquad r = \frac{\Sigma xy - n\bar{x}\bar{y}}{\sqrt{[\Sigma x^2 - n\bar{x}^2][\Sigma y^2 - n\bar{y}^2]}}$$

$$= \frac{n\Sigma xy - \Sigma x\Sigma y}{\sqrt{[n\Sigma x^2 - (\Sigma x)^2][n\Sigma y^2 - (\Sigma y)^2]}}$$

This form requires the sums of x, y, x^2, y^2, and xy. If x and y are positive and are not more than two- or possibly three-digit numbers each, all these sums can be computed in a single set of operations with a ten-bank calculating machine that has a split and locking upper dial by punching x and y on opposite sides of the keyboard. If the machine does not possess the split upper dial, the sums of x and y, say, must be computed in a second set of operations. If x and y contain more digits than those specified above, these sums should be computed by whatever means seems efficient. For the data of Table 1, which are plotted in Fig. 1, the only additional computations needed here are those for Σy^2. Computations give $r = 0.81$; hence about 66% of the variance in I.Q. scores can be attributed to the relationship with vocabulary scores. It appears that I.Q.'s can be estimated fairly well by means of vocabulary scores.

Computation for classified data. Data so numerous that the preceding computations would become unduly lengthy are conveniently classified with respect to both variables. When data have been classified, the short method of computation used for finding moments may be employed with advantage for computing r. Let

$$x_i = c_x u_i + x_0$$

and

$$y_i = c_y v_i + y_0$$

where c_x and c_y are class intervals, and u and v are the new integral variables. Then

$$x_i - \bar{x} = c_x(u_i - \bar{u})$$

and

$$y_i - \bar{y} = c_y(v_i - \bar{v})$$

Substituting in (9) and simplifying, it will be found that

$$r = \frac{\Sigma(u - \bar{u})(v - \bar{v})}{n s_u s_v}$$

where it is understood that the summation extends over all values, whether distinct or not. If only distinct values of $(u - \bar{u})(v - \bar{v})$ were implied, it would be necessary to multiply by the frequency for each such value. This shows that the correlation coefficient of the variables u and v is equal to that for x and y. The technique of computing r by means of the new variables is illustrated in Table 2. These classified data represent the relationship between the percentage of trend values for high-grade bond yields, x, and stock sales, y, at the New York Stock Exchange.

TABLE 2

x \ y	94.5	96.5	98.5	100.5	102.5	104.5	106.5	108.5	110.5	f_y	v	vf_y	v^2f_y	uv
29.5			4	3		4	1		1	13	−3	−39	117	−36
59.5	1	3	6	18	6	9	2	3	1	49	−2	−98	196	−64
89.5	7	3	16	16	4	4	1		1	52	−1	−52	52	23
119.5	5	9	10	9	2		1	2		38	0			
149.5	3	5	8	1		1				18	1	18	18	−25
179.5	4	2	3	1						10	2	20	40	−38
209.5	4	4	1							9	3	27	81	−60
239.5	1	1								2	4	8	32	−20
f_x	25	27	47	49	12	18	5	5	3	191		−116	536	−220
u	−3	−2	−1	0	1	2	3	4	5					
uf_x	−75	−54	−47		12	36	15	20	15	−78				
u^2f_x	225	108	47		12	72	45	80	75	664				
vu	−54	−32	26		−16	−66	−24	−24	−30	−220				

If x and y are replaced in formula (11) by u and v,

$$r = \frac{(191)(-220) - (-116)(-78)}{\sqrt{[(191)(536) - (-116)^2][(191)(664) - (-78)^2]}} = -0.49$$

The only new feature of these computations is the method of computing the products of u and v in the last row and column. This sum is computed two ways to give a check. In computing the entries in the uv column, for example, it is convenient to start with the first row and compute the uv terms for it first. Since all uv terms in this row have the same value of v, namely −3, it is merely necessary to compute the sum of the u values in this row and then multiply by the common v. Thus, the third cell contains a frequency of 4 corresponding to $u = -1$; hence −4 is mentally recorded. Next, the frequency of 3 corresponds to $u = 0$; hence it contributes nothing to the sum. Next, the frequency of 4 corresponds to $u = 2$; hence 8 is mentally added to the previous sum of −4 to give 4. Then the frequency of 1 corresponding to $u = 3$ brings the sum to 7, and finally the frequency of 1 corresponding to $u = 5$ brings the total to 12. This value is then multiplied by the common v value of -3 to give -36, which is then recorded. This procedure is followed for each row and column, all computations being performed mentally when the frequencies are small.

Cause and effect. The interpretation of a correlation coefficient, either qualitatively as a measure of the strength of relationship of two variables or quantitatively in terms of r^2 as giving the percentage of the variance of y as accounted for by the relationship, is a purely mathematical interpretation and is completely devoid of any cause or effect implications. The fact that two variables tend to increase or decrease together does not imply that one has any direct or indirect effect on the other. Both of them may be influenced by other variables in such a manner as to give rise to a strong mathematical relationship. For example, over a period of years the correlation coefficient between teachers' salaries and the consumption of liquor turned out to be 0.90. During this period of time there was a steady rise in wages and salaries of all types and a general upward trend of good times. Under such conditions, teachers' salaries would also increase. Moreover, the general upward trend in wages and buying power would be reflected in increased purchases of liquor. Thus, this high correlation merely reflects the common effect of the upward trend on the two variables. Correlation coefficients must be handled with care if they are to give sensible information concerning relationships between pairs of variables. Success with correlation coefficients requires familiarity with the field of application as well as with their mathematical properties.

Reliability. In any given problem involving linear correlation, the value of r may be thought of as the first sample value of a sequence of possible sample values that would be obtained if repeated sets of similar data were obtained. Such sets of data are then thought of as samples of size n drawn at random from some population. This population in turn is thought of as being represented by a distribution function of two variables, x and y, which contains a parameter, ρ, to serve as a measure of the relationship between x and y. Then the value of r may be used to estimate the population parameter ρ, just as a sample mean, $\bar{x}$, is used to estimate the population mean, m.

If the distribution function of x and y is assumed to be of a certain common type that will be studied in the next chapter, such repeated sample values of r will follow a known distribution function. The form and derivation of this distribution function are too complicated to be considered in this book. Fortunately, there exists a simple change of variable which transforms this complicated distribution function into an approximately normal distribution. The normal approximation may then be used to determine the precision of r as an estimate of ρ in much the same way that the normal distribution of $\bar{x}$ was used to determine the precision of $\bar{x}$ as an estimate of m. This change of variable,

$$(12) \qquad z = \frac{1}{2} \log_e \frac{1 + r}{1 - r}$$

is such that z will be approximately normally distributed with mean

$$m_z = \frac{1}{2} \log_e \frac{1 + \rho}{1 - \rho}$$

and standard deviation

$$\sigma_z = \frac{1}{\sqrt{n - 3}}$$

As an illustration, consider the following problem. Is a correlation of $r = 0.20$ between the face index and the cephalic index of 50 members of a certain race significant? Set up the hypothesis that $\rho = 0$. Then the variable z will be approximately normally distributed with $m_z = 0$ and $\sigma_z = 1/\sqrt{47} = 0.15$. If a significance level of 0.05 is taken and if the two tails of this normal distribution are used as a critical region, a sample value of r will be significant if it has a value of z such that $|z| > 0.30$. Here,

$$z = \frac{1}{2} \log_e \frac{1.2}{0.8} = 0.20$$

Since this value does not exceed the critical value, the value of $r = 0.20$ is not significant. A value as large as this would be obtained fairly often in random samples from a population in which the two variables were uncorrelated.

CURVILINEAR REGRESSION

1. Polynomial Regression

If a scatter diagram indicates that a straight line will not fit a set of points satisfactorily because of the non-linearity of the relationship, it may be possible to find some simple curve that will yield a satisfactory fit. Unless there are theoretical reasons for expecting a curve of a certain type to represent the relationship, polynomials are usually selected because of their simplicity and flexibility. The proper degree to use can often be determined by an inspection of the scatter diagram. After the degree has been determined, the best-fitting polynomial of that degree may then be fitted by the method of least squares.

It will suffice to derive the least-squares equations for a polynomial of the third degree because the methods are the same for higher degrees. Let

(13)
$$y' = a + bx + cx^2 + dx^3$$

represent such a polynomial. Then the sum of the squares of the errors of estimation, $\sum_1^n [y_i - y_i']^2$, will be a function of the four parameters a, b, c, and d only. If this function is denoted by $G(a, b, c, d)$, then

(14)
$$G(a, b, c, d) = \Sigma[y - a - bx - cx^2 - dx^3]^2$$

In order that this function shall have a minimum value, it is necessary that

$$\frac{\partial G}{\partial a} = \frac{\partial G}{\partial b} = \frac{\partial G}{\partial c} = \frac{\partial G}{\partial d} = 0$$

there.   Differentiation of (14) produces the equations

$$\Sigma 2[y - a - bx - cx^2 - dx^3][-1] = 0$$

$$\Sigma 2[y - a - bx - cx^2 - dx^3][-x] = 0$$

$$\Sigma 2[y - a - bx - cx^2 - dx^3][-x^2] = 0$$

$$\Sigma 2[y - a - bx - cx^2 - dx^3][-x^3] = 0$$

If the quantities in brackets are multiplied out and the individual terms summed, these equations will reduce to the form

$$an + b\Sigma x + c\Sigma x^{2} + d\Sigma x^3 = \Sigma y$$

$$a\Sigma x + b\Sigma x^2 + c\Sigma x^3 + d\Sigma x^4 = \Sigma xy$$

$$a\Sigma x^2 + b\Sigma x^3 + c\Sigma x^4 + d\Sigma x^5 = \Sigma x^2 y$$

$$a\Sigma x^3 + b\Sigma x^4 + c\Sigma x^5 + d\Sigma x^6 = \Sigma x^3 y$$

These equations are called the *normal equations* of least squares. Their solution when substituted in (13) yields the desired polynomial of best fit.

2. Functional Linear Regression

There are numerous non-linear relationships in science in which the explicit form of the relationship is given from theoretical considerations.   In such situations the fundamental problem is to find estimates of the parameters that are needed to determine the equation of the curve representing the relationship. For example, the equation

$$pv^\gamma = \text{constant}$$

represents the relation between the pressure and volume of an ideal gas undergoing adiabatic change. Here γ is a parameter whose value depends upon the particular gas and for which an estimate may be obtained experimentally.

The problem of fitting non-polynomial curves to a set of points is not nearly as simple as that of fitting polynomials. It will be discovered that the technique of least squares in such problems often gives rise to normal equations that can be solved only by tedious numerical methods. Sometimes it is possible to reduce the equation of the curve to a simpler form by considering functions of the variables as new variables. As an illustration, the equation $y = ae^{bx}$, which arises for example in the study of simple growth phenomena, can be reduced to linear form by taking logarithms of both sides. Then

$$\log_e y = \log_e a + bx$$

This equation may be written in the form

$$Y = A + bx$$

In this form it would be possible to fit a straight line to the set of points plotted in the x, $\log_e y$ plane, or to the set of points x, y plotted on semi-log paper. This least-squares line, of course, is not equivalent to the least-squares exponential curve fitted to the original set of points; however, it usually differs very little from it.

This same technique could be applied to a curve of the type $y = ax^b$, which arises, for example, in certain engineering problems.

Techniques of this type fail on a curve of the form $y = c + ae^{bx}$, which arises in the study of more complex growth phenomena and certain chemical reactions. In such situations it is often possible to determine satisfactory values of the parameters by passing the curve through a sufficient number of carefully selected points of the set to obtain as many equations to be satisfied as there are parameters.

The various methods that have been discussed briefly in this section for determining curvilinear regression equations are justified by convenience rather than by strong theoretical considerations.

CURVILINEAR CORRELATION

Since r is defined in terms of the least-squares line, it is clear that r will serve as a satisfactory measure of relationship only when the general trend of the scatter diagram is approximately linear. If the relationship between x and y is strong but curvilinear, it may happen that r will be small numerically and thus give a false impression of the true relationship. For example, if x and y possessed a semicircular type of relationship as indicated in Fig. 4, the least-squares line would be approximately horizontal and hence r would be very small, in spite of the strong relationship. It is therefore necessary to define a measure of relationship that will hold for non-linear relationships. The obvious approach is to use the definition of r given by (5) with the understanding that s_e^2 is to be the variance of the errors of estimation based on the least-squares polynomial rather than on the least-squares line. This generalized version of r is called the *correlation index*. It is interpreted in much the same manner as the correlation coefficient, although its computation is quite different.

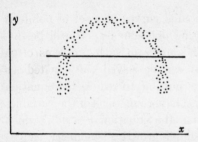

Fig. 4. Hypothetical distribution with strong non-linear relationship but weak linear correlation.

REFERENCES

An interesting interpretation of r in terms of common elements, as well as a consideration of other measures of correlation, may be found in:

PETERS and VAN VOORHIS, *Statistical Procedures and Their Mathematical Bases*, McGraw-Hill Book Company, pp. 101–109, 118–123.

The derivation of the distribution function of r is very complicated; however, the student with sufficient mathematical background may find it in:

WILKS, S. S., *Mathematical Statistics*, Princeton University Press, pp. 116–120.
KENDALL, M. G., *The Advanced Theory of Statistics*, Griffin and Company, vol. 1, pp. 339–342.

The transformation used to approximately normalize the distribution of r was originated by R. A. Fisher. A discussion of this transformation and its adequacy will be found in:

FISHER, R. A., *Statistical Methods for Research Workers*, 8th ed., Oliver & Boyd, pp. 190–195.
KENDALL, *op. cit.*, pp. 345–346.

If a high-degree polynomial is to be used to fit a set of points, the solution of the normal equations involves much computational labor. For such problems it is advisable to follow an efficient computational procedure such as the Doolittle technique. This procedure is outlined in:

CROXTON and COWDEN, *Applied General Statistics*, Prentice-Hall, pp. 716–720.

If a polynomial is being fitted to time data in which there corresponds one value of y to each value of t, and if the values of t are equally spaced, the normal equations can be simplified a great deal by choosing $x = t - \bar{t}$, because then $\Sigma x^k = 0$ for k odd. The normal equations will then be found to split into two simpler sets of equations.

If the degree of the polynomial to be used is uncertain and it is fairly likely that higher-degree terms will be added after the first fitting attempt, a better procedure exists in the form of orthogonal polynomials. These polynomials possess the desirable property of leaving unchanged the coefficients of the previously fitted polynomial when higher degree terms are added. If orthogonal polynomials were not used in such a situation, the entire set of coefficients would have to be recomputed. The technique of orthogonal polynomials is explained in:

FISHER, *op. cit.*, pp. 140–146.

Further material on empirical curve fitting may be found in:

RICHARDSON, C. H., *An Introduction to Statistical Analysis*, Harcourt, Brace and Company, pp. 306–361.

KENNEY, J. F., *Mathematics of Statistics*, Part One, D. Van Nostrand Company, pp. 130–158.

A measure of correlation closely related to the correlation index is the correlation ratio. It is often used for measuring non-linear correlation because it does not require the fitting of a curve to obtain errors of estimation but bases the errors upon the means of columns after the data have been classified. A brief discussion of this measure may be found in the preceding reference on pages 198–204.

EXERCISES

1. The following data are for the amount of water applied in inches and the yield of alfalfa in tons per acre. (*a*) Find the equation of the line of regression. (*b*) Calculate r.

Water (x)	12	18	24	30	36	42	48	60
Yield (y)	5.27	5.68	6.25	7.21	8.20	8.71	8.42	8.24

2. The following data are for tensile strength (100 lb./in.²) and hardness (Rockwell E) of die-cast aluminum. (*a*) Calculate r. (*b*) Calculate the standard error of estimate using this value of r. (*c*) From (*b*), using the mean tensile strength, determine an interval of percentage errors within which about 50% of such percentage errors will fall.

Tensile strength	293	349	368	301	340	308	354	313	322	334
Hardness	53	70	84	55	78	64	71	53	82	67

Tensile strength	377	247	348	298	287	292	345	380	257	258
Hardness	70	56	86	60	72	51	88	95	51	75

Tensile strength	265	281	246	258	237	286	324	282	340
Hardness	54	78	52	69	54	64	83	56	70

3. The following data are for intelligence-test scores, grade point averages, and reading rates of students. Calculate r between I.T. scores and G.P.A. by classifying the data with respect to both variables.

I.T.	295	152	214	171	131	178	225	141	116	173
G.P.A.	2.4	0.6	0.2	0.0	1.0	0.6	1.0	0.4	0.0	2.6
R.R.	41	18	45	29	28	38	25	26	22	37

I.T.	230	174	177	210	236	198	217	143	186	233
G.P.A.	2.6	1.8	0.0	0.4	1.8	0.8	1.0	0.2	2.8	1.4
R.R.	39	24	32	26	29	34	38	40	27	44

I.T.	136	183	223	106	134	211	151	231	135	146
G.P.A.	0.2	0.4	1.4	0.0	0.8	0.8	0.4	2.2	1.4	1.2
R.R.	32	26	50	24	48	18	20	26	26	19

I.T.	227	204	223	142	176	238	268	163	195	184
G.P.A.	1.4	1.4	1.4	0.8	0.8	2.6	2.6	0.2	0.0	0.8
R.R.	35	26	18	22	23	27	40	33	38	32

I.T.	192	121	316	234	146	261	175	233	261	242
G.P.A.	0.8	0.6	2.6	1.2	0.6	2.6	1.2	1.6	2.4	1.4
R.R.	22	34	42	41	18	35	30	34	25	49

4. Would you consider students' high-school marks highly useful for predicting college marks if the correlation coefficient between them was 0.40?

5. For the following data on the yield of wheat in bushels per acre and the number of pounds of nitrogen applied per acre (*a*) calculate r, (*b*) fit a polynomial of the second degree, (*c*) calculate the index of correlation, (*d*) compare these two measures of correlation.

Nitrogen

Yield	0–20	20–40	40–60	60–80	80–100	100–120	120–140	140–160	160–180
32–36				6	15	10	4	6	2
28–32			1	18	20	9	5	1	
24–28		1	15	20	3				
20–24		2	12						
16–20		10	2						
12–16		8							
8–12	4	4							
4–8	10								
0–4	6								

6. What explanation would you give if told that r between fertilizer added and profit made in raising vegetables on a certain experimental farm was only 0.30?

7. Test the hypothesis that the population correlation in problem 2 is equal to 0.6.

8. How large a correlation coefficient is needed for a sample of size 25 before one is justified in claiming that the variables are related?

9. Prove that $s_{x-y}^2 = s_x^2 + s_y^2 - 2r\, s_x s_y$.

10. Find s^2 for the first n positive integers by using the formula for the sum of the squares of these integers.

11. If x and y are the ranks of an individual, prove that $r_r = 1 - \dfrac{6\Sigma(x-y)^2}{n(n^2-1)}$, where r_r is the correlation of the ranks for n individuals, by utilizing the results of problems 9 and 10.

12. By means of the formula of problem 11, find the correlation of ranks for the data of Table 1.

13. Prove that the regression line fitted to the means of columns when weighted with column frequencies is the same as the ordinary regression line for least squares.

14. Consider the following coin-tossing experiment. Toss 3 pennies and 2 dimes. Let x be the total number of heads showing. Pick up the 3 pennies and toss them again. Let y be the total number of heads now showing. Perform the experiment 25 times, and calculate r. Calculate the theoretical value of r by finding the expected frequencies in various cells from probability considerations. This latter result, when generalized, shows how a correlation coefficient may be interpreted in terms of common elements.

15. The following data give the velocity of the Mississippi River in feet per second corresponding to various depths expressed in terms of the ratio, D, of the measured depth to the depth of the river. (a) Fit a parabola $V = a + bD + cD^2$ to the data, choosing a convenient origin. (b) Find V when $D = 0.9$ (observed $V = 2.976$). (c) When would you consider extrapolation as used in (b) a valid procedure?

D	0	0.1	0.2	0.3	0.4	0.5	0.6	0.7	0.8
V	3.195	3.230	3.253	3.261	3.252	3.228	3.181	3.127	3.059

16. The following data are for a growing plant. (a) Plot the data on ordinary, semi-log, and log-log paper. (b) Fit a simple exponential.

Day	0	1	2	3	4	5	6	7	8
Height (inches)	0.75	1.20	1.75	2.50	3.45	4.70	6.20	8.25	11.50

17. The pressure of a gas and its volume are related by an equation of the form $pv^a = b$. In a certain experiment the following values were obtained. Determine a and b by least squares on the logarithmic equation.

p (kg./cm.^{2})	0.5	1.0	1.5	2.0	2.5	3.0
v (liters)	1.62	1.00	0.75	0.62	0.52	0.46

18. Derive the least-squares equations for fitting a modified exponential, $y = c + ae^{bt}$, to a set of n points, and indicate why these equations would be difficult to solve.

CHAPTER VI

THEORETICAL FREQUENCY DISTRIBUTIONS OF TWO VARIABLES

ADDITIONAL PROPERTIES OF DISTRIBUTIONS OF TWO VARIABLES

1. Discrete Probability

Consider the multiplication rule of probability for discrete variables given by (20), Chapter III, written in the form

$$(1) \qquad P(x, y) = P(x)P_x(y)$$

Here x will be treated as a discrete variable which takes on different values corresponding to the different results of the trials of an event. For example, if a die is being rolled, x will assume an integral value from 1 to 6; or, if a coin is being tossed, x will assume a value of 0 or 1, 0 corresponding to a tail, say, and 1 corresponding to a head. The variable y will be treated similarly with respect to a second event. Hence, to every possible result of two events there will correspond a point in the x, y plane to which will be attached a probability $P(x, y)$.

Since $P_x(y)$ gives the probability distribution of y for a fixed value of x, the sum of $P_x(y)$ over all possible values of y for this fixed value of x must be 1; consequently if both sides of (1) are summed over these values of y,

$$(2) \qquad \sum_y P(x, y) = P(x)$$

In a similar manner it follows that

$$\sum_x P(x, y) = P(y)$$

These formulas show that, if one has the joint probability distribution for two variables and desires the probability distribution of one of them, it is merely necessary to sum the joint probability function over all values of the other. $P(x)$ and $P(y)$ are called the *marginal* distribution functions of $P(x, y)$.

If formula (1) is written in the form

$$(3) \qquad P_x(y) = \frac{P(x, y)}{P(x)}$$

it shows that if one has the joint probability distribution for two variables and desires the conditional probability distribution for one of them when the other is held fixed, it is merely necessary to divide this joint probability function by the marginal distribution function of the fixed variable. $P_y(x)$ is obtained and interpreted in a similar manner. The two functions $P_x(y)$ and $P_y(x)$ are often called the x and y *array* distribution functions of $P(x, y)$.

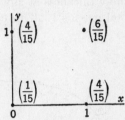

For the purpose of illustrating these ideas, suppose that a bag contains 4 white and 2 black balls and that 2 balls are drawn from the bag. Let x and y represent the results of the two drawings, 0 corresponding to a black ball (failure) and 1 corresponding to a white ball (success). Then every possible result will be represented by one of the four points indicated in Fig. 1. From the contents of the bag and formula (1) it follows directly that

Fig. 1. Discrete probability distribution.

$$P(0, 0) = P(0)P_0(0) = \tfrac{2}{6} \cdot \tfrac{1}{5} = \tfrac{1}{15}$$

$$P(0, 1) = P(0)P_0(1) = \tfrac{2}{6} \cdot \tfrac{4}{5} = \tfrac{4}{15}$$

$$P(1, 0) = P(1)P_1(0) = \tfrac{4}{6} \cdot \tfrac{2}{5} = \tfrac{4}{15}$$

$$P(1, 1) = P(1)P_1(1) = \tfrac{4}{6} \cdot \tfrac{3}{5} = \tfrac{6}{15}$$

If, instead, it is assumed that only the final values of the $P(x, y)$ just calculated are known, the x marginal distribution, for example, could be obtained by applying (2). Here

$$P(0) = P(0, 0) + P(0, 1) = \tfrac{1}{15} + \tfrac{4}{15} = \tfrac{1}{3}$$

$$P(1) = P(1, 0) + P(1, 1) = \tfrac{4}{15} + \tfrac{6}{15} = \tfrac{2}{3}$$

Finally, with these same assumptions, the x array distribution for $x = 1$, for example, could be obtained by applying (3). Here

$$P_1(0) = \frac{P(1, 0)}{P(1)} = \tfrac{2}{5}$$

$$P_1(1) = \frac{P(1, 1)}{P(1)} = \tfrac{3}{5}$$

2. Probability Density

For a continuous distribution function of two variables, $f(x, y)$, it is often convenient to think of $f(x, y)$ as representing a probability density distribution in the x, y plane, just as $P(x, y)$ is often thought of as giving the masses for a discrete set of points. Figure 2, without the curve, illustrates this manner of interpretation for two continuous variables, just as Fig. 1 does for two discrete variables. In this connection, it is helpful to conceive of the x, y plane as being a metal sheet whose thickness at any point x, y is proportional to $f(x, y)$ and whose total mass is 1. This corresponds to the situation for one variable in which the x axis is thought of as a wire whose thickness at any point x is proportional to $f(x)$ and whose total mass is 1.

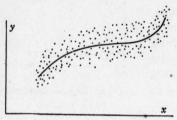

FIG. 2. Probability density distribution and curve of regression.

On other occasions it is convenient to think of $f(x, y)$ as representing a surface in three dimensions with properties analogous to those of a distribution curve for one variable. From this point of view, because of (1), Chapter IV, it follows that the probability that a point x, y will lie in a given rectangle in the x, y plane is equal to the volume under the surface $z = f(x, y)$ which lies above this rectangle. The total volume under this surface and above the x, y plane is, of course, 1.

From the density point of view, the probability that a point will lie in a given rectangle is equal to the mass of this rectangle. Both these physical interpretations of probability clearly hold for regions other than rectangles in the x, y plane.

3. Marginal Distributions

For the purpose of obtaining a formula for a continuous variable corresponding to (2), consider

$$P[\alpha < x < \beta] = P\begin{bmatrix} \alpha < x < \beta \\ a_2 < y < b_2 \end{bmatrix}$$

$$= \int_\alpha^\beta \int_{a_2}^{b_2} f(x, y) \, dy \, dx$$

$$= \int_\alpha^\beta g(x) \, dx$$

where as usual a_2, b_2 indicates the total range of y values and where

(4) $$g(x) = \int_{a_2}^{b_2} f(x, y) \, dy$$

Now, if x is considered independently of y, then by definition

$$P[\alpha < x < \beta] = \int_\alpha^\beta f(x)\,dx$$

If these two expressions for P are equated,

(5) $$\int_\alpha^\beta g(x)\,dx = \int_\alpha^\beta f(x)\,dx$$

Since this equality is to hold for all intervals (α, β), α may be held fixed and β allowed to vary, in which event these integrals may be treated as functions of β. By a well-known calculus formula, if

$$F(\beta) = \int_\alpha^\beta f(x)\,dx$$

then

$$\frac{dF(\beta)}{d\beta} = f(\beta)$$

If (5) is differentiated with respect to β, this formula may be applied to give

$$g(\beta) = f(\beta)$$

Since this is an identity in β, it follows from (4) that

(6) $$\int_{a_2}^{b_2} f(x, y)\,dy = f(x)$$

This formula corresponds to (2) for the discrete case. In a similar manner, the integration of $f(x, y)$ with respect to x over its range (a_1, b_1) would yield $f(y)$. The functions $f(x)$ and $f(y)$ are called the *marginal* distribution functions of $f(x, y)$. From the density point of view, $f(x)$ represents the probability density distribution on the x axis after the entire mass in the x, y plane has been projected onto the x axis.

4. Array Distributions

By analogy with (3), consider the function defined by

(7) $$f_x(y) = \frac{f(x, y)}{f(x)}$$

If x is held fixed but is such that $f(x) > 0$, (7) defines a non-negative function of y for which, because of (6),

$$\int_{a_2}^{b_2} f_x(y)\, dy = \int_{a_2}^{b_2} \frac{f(x, y)}{f(x)}\, dy = \frac{1}{f(x)} \int_{a_2}^{b_2} f(x, y)\, dy = 1$$

Thus, $f_x(y)$ has properties that enable it to serve as a distribution function of y. It is often called the *conditional* distribution function of y because it gives the probability distribution of y for a fixed value of x, just as $P_x(y)$ in (3) does for a discrete variable. It is also called the *x array* distribution function of $f(x, y)$. The function $f_y(x)$ is defined and named in an analogous manner.

From a density point of view, $f_x(y)$ may be thought of as giving the probability density distribution along the vertical line corresponding to the fixed value of x, the total mass of this line being 1. The density function $f(x, y)$ as it stands could not be used as a probability density function along such a line because by (6) it would not give a total probability of 1 unless $f(x)$ were equal to 1. The factor $1/f(x)$ insures that the total mass of the line will be 1.

5. Curve of Regression

Consider the mean value of the array distribution function $f_x(y)$. If this mean value is denoted by $\bar{y}_x$, then by definition and (7)

$$(8) \qquad \bar{y}_x = \int_{a_2}^{b_2} y f_x(y)\, dy$$

$$= \int_{a_2}^{b_2} y \frac{f(x, y)}{f(x)}\, dy$$

Now $\bar{y}_x$ is evidently a function of x; hence it defines a curve in the x, y plane which is called the *curve of regression* of y on x. Thus, the curve of regression of y on x is the locus of the mean points of the x array distributions. The situation is illustrated in Fig. 2.

6. Product Moments

Product moments about the origin and about the mean for two variables are defined by

$$(9) \qquad \mu_{pq}' = \int_{a_2}^{b_2} \int_{a_1}^{b_1} x^p y^q f(x, y)\, dx\, dy$$

and

$$(10) \qquad \mu_{pq} = \int_{a_2}^{b_2} \int_{a_1}^{b_1} (x - m_x)^p (y - m_y)^q f(x, y)\, dx\, dy$$

The product moment μ_{11}, called the *covariance*, is of particular interest because the theoretical correlation coefficient, ρ, is defined in terms of it by means of

$$(11) \qquad \rho = \frac{\mu_{11}}{\sigma_x \sigma_y}$$

From (9) and (10), with the aid of (6), it follows that

$$\mu_{00}' = 1, \quad \mu_{10}' = m_x, \quad \mu_{01}' = m_y, \quad \mu_{20} = \sigma_x{}^2, \quad \mu_{02} = \sigma_y{}^2$$

From (10) it will be observed that μ_{11} is the theoretical counterpart of $\Sigma(x - \bar{x})(y - \bar{y})/n$ in the numerator of (9), Chapter V, and therefore that ρ is the theoretical counterpart of r.

NORMAL DISTRIBUTION FUNCTION OF TWO VARIABLES

1. Definition

The definition here arises from a generalization of that for one variable. However, rather than start with a quadratic exponential function of a certain type and then determine the parameters of this function in terms of familiar statistical quantities as was done with one variable, here the results of such determinations will be used. Hence, a normal distribution function of two variables will be defined by

$$(12) \quad f(x, y) = \frac{e^{-\frac{1}{2(1-\rho^2)}\left[\left(\frac{x-m_x}{\sigma_x}\right)^2 - 2\rho\left(\frac{x-m_x}{\sigma_x}\right)\left(\frac{y-m_y}{\sigma_y}\right) + \left(\frac{y-m_y}{\sigma_y}\right)^2\right]}}{2\pi\sigma_x\sigma_y\sqrt{1 - \rho^2}}$$

It will be found that this function possesses the essential properties for a distribution function. Furthermore, it will be found that the parameters m_x, m_y, σ_x, σ_y, and ρ are consistent with their values as given by the product moment definitions in (11) and immediately following.

2. Marginal Distributions

If (6) is applied to (12), the x marginal distribution function will be given by

$$f(x) = \int_{-\infty}^{\infty} \frac{e^{-\frac{1}{2(1-\rho^2)}\left[\left(\frac{x-m_x}{\sigma_x}\right)^2 - 2\rho\left(\frac{x-m_x}{\sigma_x}\right)\left(\frac{y-m_y}{\sigma_y}\right) + \left(\frac{y-m_y}{\sigma_y}\right)^2\right]}}{2\pi\sigma_x\sigma_y\sqrt{1 - \rho^2}} \, dy$$

Let $u = (x - m_x)/\sigma_x$ and $v = (y - m_y)/\sigma_y$; then $dy = \sigma_y \, dv$ and

$$f(x) = \frac{1}{2\pi\sigma_x\sqrt{1 - \rho^2}} \int_{-\infty}^{\infty} e^{-\frac{1}{2(1-\rho^2)}[u^2 - 2\rho uv + v^2]} \, dv$$

Adding and subtracting $\rho^2 u^2$ to the exponent in order to complete the square in v gives

$$f(x) = \frac{1}{2\pi\sigma_x\sqrt{1-\rho^2}} \int_{-\infty}^{\infty} e^{-\frac{1}{2(1-\rho^2)}[v^2 - 2\rho uv + \rho^2 u^2 - \rho^2 u^2 + u^2]} \, dv$$

$$= \frac{e^{-\frac{u^2}{2}}}{2\pi\sigma_x\sqrt{1-\rho^2}} \int_{-\infty}^{\infty} e^{-\frac{1}{2(1-\rho^2)}[v-\rho u]^2} \, dv$$

If $z = \dfrac{v - \rho u}{\sqrt{1-\rho^2}}$, then $dv = \sqrt{1-\rho^2}\, dz$ and

$$f(x) = \frac{e^{-\frac{u^2}{2}}}{2\pi\sigma_x} \int_{-\infty}^{\infty} e^{-\frac{z^2}{2}} \, dz$$

Substituting back the value of u in terms of x and inserting the value of this familiar integral reduces $f(x)$ to

$$(13) \qquad f(x) = \frac{1}{\sqrt{2\pi}\sigma_x} e^{-\frac{1}{2}\left(\frac{x-m_x}{\sigma_x}\right)^2}$$

Since the corresponding result for y follows from symmetry, (13) shows that the marginal distributions of a joint normal distribution are normal. By means of (13), one may also show that several of the product moment definitions are consistent with the labeling of the parameters in (12). For example, it follows at once from (13) that the coefficient of the exponential in (12) is such as to produce unit volume under the surface $z = f(x, y)$.

For the particular case of uncorrelated variables, $\rho = 0$ and then (12) reduces to

$$f(x, y) = \frac{e^{-\frac{1}{2}\left(\frac{x-m_x}{\sigma_x}\right)^2}}{\sqrt{2\pi}\sigma_x} \cdot \frac{e^{-\frac{1}{2}\left(\frac{y-m_y}{\sigma_y}\right)^2}}{\sqrt{2\pi}\sigma_y} = f(x)f(y)$$

Because of definition (2), Chapter IV, this result shows that, if two normal variables are uncorrelated, they are independently distributed. From the discussion of curvilinear correlation in Chapter V, it should be clear that a lack of correlation does not guarantee a lack of relationship in general.

3. Array Distributions

A joint normal distribution possesses array distributions with unusually interesting properties. It will suffice to study the x array distribution function, $f_x(y)$. A direct application of definition (7) to (12) and (13) gives

$$f_x(y) = \frac{e^{-\frac{1}{2(1-\rho^2)}[u^2-2\rho uv+v^2]}}{2\pi\sigma_x\sigma_y\sqrt{1-\rho^2}} \div \frac{e^{-\frac{u^2}{2}}}{\sqrt{2\pi}\sigma_x}$$

$$= \frac{e^{-\frac{1}{2(1-\rho^2)}[v^2-2\rho uv+\rho^2 u^2]}}{\sqrt{2\pi}\sigma_y\sqrt{1-\rho^2}}$$

$$= \frac{e^{-\frac{1}{2}\left[\frac{v-\rho u}{\sqrt{1-\rho^2}}\right]^2}}{\sqrt{2\pi}\sigma_y\sqrt{1-\rho^2}}$$

If the values of u and v in terms of x and y are inserted and if the value of y is denoted by y_x to show its dependence on x, $f_x(y)$ reduces to

$$(14) \qquad f_x(y) = \frac{e^{-\frac{1}{2}\left[\frac{y_x-m_y-\rho\frac{\sigma_y}{\sigma_x}(x-m_x)}{\sigma_y\sqrt{1-\rho^2}}\right]^2}}{\sqrt{2\pi}\sigma_y\sqrt{1-\rho^2}}$$

Since x has a fixed value and y_x is the variable, (14) shows that y_x posseses a normal distribution with mean $m_y + \rho\dfrac{\sigma_y}{\sigma_x}(x-m_x)$ and standard deviation $\sigma_y\sqrt{1-\rho^2}$. Thus, the array distributions, as well as the marginal distributions, of a joint normal distribution are normal. Since by definition (8) a curve of regression is the locus of the means of array distributions, it follows from (14) that the curve of regression of y on x for x and y jointly normally distributed is the straight line

$$(15) \qquad \bar{y}_x = m_y + \rho\frac{\sigma_y}{\sigma_x}(x-m_x)$$

A comparison of this equation with

$$y' = \bar{y} + r\frac{s_y}{s_x}(x-\bar{x})$$

which is the least-squares line of regression for a set of points as given by (10), Chapter V, shows that for normal variables this least-squares line may be treated as a sample approximation to the population line of regression. Since it is not unusual to find variables that are approximately normally distributed, one might expect to find related pairs of such variables which possess an approximate joint normal distribution. For such variables one would expect to find approximate linear regression and to find that r would serve as a satisfactory measure of the usefulness of such regression lines for estimating purposes. These theoretical results help to make the use of linear regression and correlation coefficients seem more logical and also help to explain why so many sets of data of two variables can be treated satisfactorily by these simpler methods.

Another feature of (14) which is of practical importance is that all the x array distributions possess the same standard deviation $\sigma_y \sqrt{1 - \rho^2}$. This characteristic is sometimes denoted by the term *homoscedasticity*. Since $\sigma_y \sqrt{1 - \rho^2}$ is the theoretical standard deviation of the errors of estimation, which have been shown to be normally distributed, this property implies that the precision of the estimation of y from x is the same for all values of x. Thus, if one is interested in predicting only y's for a fixed x but has data for other values of x as well, he may compute his standard error of estimate based on all the data, namely $s_y \sqrt{1 - r^2}$, and use it as his standard error of estimate for the y's that interest him. It is clear that the value of $s_y \sqrt{1 - r^2}$ based on all the data would be much more reliable than the standard error of estimate computed directly from only those y's that are of particular interest.

4. Normal Surface

Instead of thinking in terms of probability density in the plane, consider now the geometry of (12), treating it as the equation of a surface in three dimensions. If (7) and the particular results (13) and (14) are applied, the equation of this surface may be written

$$(16) \qquad z = f(x) \frac{e^{-\frac{1}{2}\left[\frac{y - m_y - \rho\frac{\sigma_y}{\sigma_x}(x - m_x)}{\sigma_y\sqrt{1-\rho^2}}\right]^2}}{\sqrt{2\pi}\sigma_y\sqrt{1 - \rho^2}}$$

For the purpose of studying this surface, consider its intersections with planes perpendicular to the x axis. The equations of the intersecting curves are obtained by replacing x by the constant values corresponding to the cutting planes. From (16) it will be observed that these curves are normal curves with their means lying on the regression line (15), all having the same standard deviation $\sigma_y \sqrt{1 - \rho^2}$, and varying in maximum height according to the factor $f(x)$. The tallest such normal curve will be the one lying in the cutting plane $x = m_x$, since this value makes $f(x)$ a maximum. By symmetry, planes perpendicular to the y axis will intersect the surface in normal curves with corresponding properties.

Further information is obtained by considering the intersection of the surface by planes perpendicular to the z axis. In this connection it is more convenient to use the original form (12) with $f(x, y)$ replaced by z. If z assumes different constant values, the quantity in brackets will assume corresponding values that can be calculated from the

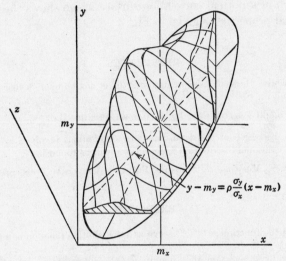

$$y - m_y = \rho \frac{\sigma_y}{\sigma_x} (x - m_x)$$

FIG. 3. Normal correlation surface.

constant values assigned to z. Hence the equations of such intersecting curves may be written in the form

$$\left(\frac{x - m_x}{\sigma_x}\right)^2 - 2\rho \left(\frac{x - m_x}{\sigma_x}\right)\left(\frac{y - m_y}{\sigma_y}\right) + \left(\frac{y - m_y}{\sigma_y}\right)^2 = k$$

where k corresponds to the selected value of z. Since this is a quadratic function in x and y, these curves of intersection must be conic sections. Furthermore, since the type of conic section depends only on the quadratic terms, the discriminant for testing conic sections may be applied directly to give

$$B^2 - 4AC = \left(\frac{2\rho}{\sigma_x \sigma_y}\right)^2 - 4 \frac{1}{\sigma_x^2} \frac{1}{\sigma_y^2}$$

$$= \frac{4[\rho^2 - 1]}{\sigma_x^2 \sigma_y^2} \leq 0$$

This result shows that the intersecting curves are ellipses, except in the trivial case of $\rho = \pm 1$. Allowing k to assume different values will merely change the sizes of these ellipses; consequently these ellipses have the same centers and the same orientation of principal axes. It will be found upon rotating axes properly to eliminate the xy term that the principal axis of these ellipses is not parallel to a line of regression as might be supposed. The line of regression turns out to be parallel to a diameter of the ellipses.

A sketch of a normal correlation surface which shows these various geometrical properties is given in Fig. 3.

REFERENCES

If the calculus theorem used in deriving (6) is not familiar, a discussion of it may be found in:

SHERWOOD and TAYLOR, *Calculus*, section 69, Prentice-Hall.

A careful discussion of the definitions and assumptions involved in arriving at (7) as the conditional distribution function of y will be found in:

WILKS, S. S., *Mathematical Statistics*, Princeton University Press, pp. 15–17.

EXERCISES

1. Could the function $ce^{-(x+y)}$ serve as a distribution function of x and y over some region?

2. Verify by integration that definition (12) is consistent with the moment properties given by (11) and immediately following.

3. Given $f(x, y) = 1 \begin{Bmatrix} 0 \le x \le 1 \\ 0 \le y \le 1 \end{Bmatrix}$, find (a) μ_{k0}', (b) μ_{pq}', (c) ρ, (d) $\bar{y}_x$.

4. Given $f(x, y) = \dfrac{2}{a^2} \begin{Bmatrix} 0 \le x \le a \\ 0 \le y \le x \end{Bmatrix}$, find (a) μ_{pq}', (b) ρ, (c) $\bar{y}_x$.

5. Prove or disprove that all vertical plane sections of a normal correlation surface are normal curves.

6. If x and y are uncorrelated and normally distributed, find the mean and variance of xy.

7. Prove that the line of regression for a normal distribution is a diameter of the ellipses of constant probability.

8. Assume that a bomber is making a bombing run in the direction along the positive y axis at a square target 200 feet by 200 feet whose center is at the origin and whose sides are parallel to the coordinate axes. Assume further that the x and y errors in repeated bombing runs are normally distributed about zero.

(a) If the x and y errors are also independently distributed with $\sigma = 400$ feet, find the probability that the target will be hit on the first run.

(b) Under the conditions of (a), find the probability of getting at least 1 hit in 10 runs.

(c) Under these same conditions, how many runs, that is how many planes, would be needed to make the probability at least 0.9 of getting at least 1 hit on the target?

(d) Show why it would be difficult to work (a) if the x and y errors were correlated, say, with $\rho = \frac{1}{5}$.

CHAPTER VII

FREQUENCY DISTRIBUTIONS OF MORE THAN TWO VARIABLES

MULTIPLE LINEAR REGRESSION

It happens quite often that the methods of Chapter V for estimating one variable by means of a related variable yield poor results, not because the relationship is far removed from the linear one assumed there but because there is no single variable sufficiently closely related to the variable being estimated to yield good results. However, it may happen that there are several variables which, when taken jointly, will serve as a satisfactory basis for estimating the desired variable. Since linear functions are so simple to manipulate and since experience shows that many sets of variables are approximately linearly related, it is reasonable to attempt to estimate the desired variable by means of a linear function of the remaining variables. For this purpose, let $X_1, X_2, \cdots, X_k$ represent the k variables available, and consider the problem of estimating variable X_1 by means of a linear function of the remaining variables. If the estimated value of X_1 is denoted by X_1', the relationship may be expressed as

$$(1) \qquad X_1' = c_0 + c_2 X_2 + c_3 X_3 + \cdots + c_k X_k$$

where the c's are to be determined by means of available data. Geometrically, the problem is one of fitting a plane to a set of points in k dimensions.

Suppose that a sample of size n is available for these k variables. For example, n different skilled workmen may have been rated by their foreman and been given $k - 1$ different tests designed to measure ability in that particular type of work. Then it would be of interest to see whether success in this type of work could be estimated well by means of a linear combination of the $k - 1$ test scores.

As in dealing with two variables, the unknown c's in (1) will be determined by the principle of least squares; consequently the c's will be chosen to minimize $\Sigma(X_1 - X_1')^2$, where the sum extends over the n sample values. It is more convenient, however, to work with variables measured from their sample means than with the variables themselves; hence first let

$$x_i = X_i - \overline{X}_i \qquad (i = 1, 2, \cdots, k)$$

If x_1' is defined by $x_1' = X_1' - \overline{X}_1$, then

(2) $$X_1 - X_1' = x_1 + \overline{X}_1 - (x_1' + \overline{X}_1) = x_1 - x_1'$$

If now the capital X's in (1) are expressed in terms of the small x's, that equation can be written

(3) $$x_1' = a_0 + a_2 x_2 + a_3 x_3 + \cdots + a_k x_k$$

in which the a's could be expressed in terms of the c's and $\overline{X}$'s if so desired. However, from (2) it is clear that minimizing $\Sigma(X_1 - X_1')^2$ is equivalent to minimizing $\Sigma(x_1 - x_1')^2$; consequently one can just as well determine the a's so as to minimize the latter sum, which because of (3) may be written

$$G(a_0, a_2, \cdots, a_k) = \Sigma[x_1 - a_0 - a_2 x_2 - \cdots - a_k x_k]^2$$

As in polynomial fitting, the normal equations of least squares are obtained by setting the k partial derivatives of G equal to zero. If, as was done following (14), Chapter V, these equations are multiplied by $\frac{1}{2}$, the summations performed term by term, and the first sum transposed to the right side, these equations assume the form

$$a_0 n + a_2 \Sigma x_2 + \cdots + a_k \Sigma x_k = \Sigma x_1$$

$$a_0 \Sigma x_2 + a_2 \Sigma x_2^2 + \cdots + a_k \Sigma x_2 x_k = \Sigma x_2 x_1$$

$$a_0 \Sigma x_k + a_2 \Sigma x_k x_2 + \cdots + a_k \Sigma x_k^2 = \Sigma x_k x_1$$

Since $\Sigma x_i = \Sigma(X_i - \overline{X}_i) = 0$, all terms in the first equation, except the first term, vanish. This implies that $a_0 = 0$, and thus the number of equations to be solved has been reduced by 1. The advantage of using variables measured from their sample means to simplify the notation and solution of the normal equations should be clear from this result. Now the coefficients in these equations can be expressed in terms of familiar statistical quantities, because by (9) Chapter V,

(4) $$\Sigma x_i x_j = \Sigma(X_i - \overline{X}_i)(X_j - \overline{X}_j) = n r_{ij} s_i s_j$$

where r_{ij} denotes the sample correlation coefficient between the variables X_i and X_j, and s_i is the sample standard deviation of X_i.

If such expressions are inserted for all sums, and common factors are canceled, the normal equations become

$$a_2 r_{22} s_2 + a_3 r_{23} s_3 + \cdots + a_k r_{2k} s_k = r_{21} s_1$$

$$a_2 r_{32} s_2 + a_3 r_{33} s_3 + \cdots + a_k r_{3k} s_k = r_{31} s_1$$

$$\cdot \qquad \cdot \qquad \qquad \cdot \qquad \cdot$$

$$a_2 r_{k2} s_2 + a_3 r_{k3} s_3 + \cdots + a_k r_{kk} s_k = r_{k1} s_1$$

The solution of these equations may be expressed in a convenient form by means of determinants, provided the determinant of the coefficients is not zero. Solving for a_i and factoring out all common factors from both numerator and denominator determinants gives

$$(5) \qquad a_i = \frac{s_1 \cdots s_{i-1} s_{i+1} \cdots s_k}{s_2 \cdots s_{i-1} s_i s_{i+1} \cdots s_k} \cdot \frac{\begin{vmatrix} r_{22} & r_{23} & \cdots & r_{21} & \cdots & r_{2k} \\ r_{32} & r_{33} & \cdots & r_{31} & \cdots & r_{3k} \\ \cdot & \cdot & & \cdot & & \cdot \\ \cdot & \cdot & & \cdot & & \cdot \\ \cdot & \cdot & & \cdot & & \cdot \\ r_{k2} & r_{k3} & \cdots & r_{k1} & \cdots & r_{kk} \end{vmatrix}}{\begin{vmatrix} r_{22} & r_{23} & \cdots & r_{2i} & \cdots & r_{2k} \\ r_{32} & r_{33} & \cdots & r_{3i} & \cdots & r_{3k} \\ \cdot & \cdot & & \cdot & & \cdot \\ \cdot & \cdot & & \cdot & & \cdot \\ \cdot & \cdot & & \cdot & & \cdot \\ r_{k2} & r_{k3} & \cdots & r_{ki} & \cdots & r_{kk} \end{vmatrix}}$$

It should be noted that these two determinants differ only in the elements occurring in the $i - 1$ column. For the purpose of evaluating these determinants, consider the following determinant:

$$(6) \qquad R = \begin{vmatrix} r_{11} & r_{12} & r_{13} & \cdots & r_{1k} \\ r_{21} & r_{22} & r_{23} & \cdots & r_{2k} \\ r_{31} & r_{32} & r_{33} & \cdots & r_{3k} \\ \cdot & \cdot & \cdot & & \cdot \\ \cdot & \cdot & \cdot & & \cdot \\ \cdot & \cdot & \cdot & & \cdot \\ r_{k1} & r_{k2} & r_{k3} & \cdots & r_{kk} \end{vmatrix}$$

It will be observed that the determinant in the denominator of (5) is the minor of r_{11} in R. It will also be observed that, if the column in the numerator determinant of (5) which is headed by r_{21} is shifted to the first column position, the resulting determinant will be the minor of r_{1i} in R. Since the interchange of two columns of a determinant changes the sign of the determinant, and $i - 2$ such interchanges are needed to bring this column into the first-column position, the value of the numerator determinant will be the minor of r_{1i} multiplied by $(-1)^{i-2}$. By using cofactors rather than minors, the question of the proper sign is answered at once. The cofactor of an element r_{ij} is defined as $(-1)^{i+j}$ times the minor of r_{ij} and is usually denoted by the corresponding capital letter R_{ij}. Since the numerator determinant of (5) is $(-1)^{i-2}$ times the minor of r_{1i}, which is equivalent to $-(-1)^{i+1}$ times the minor of r_{1i}, and since $R_{1i} = (-1)^{1+i}$ times the minor of r_{1i}, it follows that the value of this determinant is $-R_{1i}$. This result, together with the fact that the denominator determinant is equal to R_{11}, reduces (5) to

$$a_i = -\frac{s_1 R_{1i}}{s_i R_{11}}$$

If these values are substituted into (3), the equation of the *least-squares regression plane* becomes

$$(7) \qquad \frac{R_{11}}{s_1} x_1' + \frac{R_{12}}{s_2} x_2 + \frac{R_{13}}{s_3} x_3 + \cdots + \frac{R_{1k}}{s_k} x_k = 0$$

As an illustration of the application of this formula, consider the following information concerning the three variables X_1, the amount of hay in units of hundreds of pounds per acre, X_2, the spring rainfall in inches, and X_3, the accumulated temperature above $42°$ F. in spring.

$$\overline{X}_1 = 28.0, \quad s_1 = 4.4, \quad r_{12} = 0.80$$

$$\overline{X}_2 = 4.91, \quad s_2 = 1.10, \quad r_{13} = -0.40$$

$$\overline{X}_3 = 594, \quad s_3 = 85, \quad r_{23} = -0.56$$

Here

$$R = \begin{vmatrix} 1 & 0.80 & -0.40 \\ 0.80 & 1 & -0.56 \\ -0.40 & -0.56 & 1 \end{vmatrix}, \quad R_{11} = \begin{vmatrix} 1 & -0.56 \\ -0.56 & 1 \end{vmatrix} = 0.69$$

$$R_{12} = -\begin{vmatrix} 0.80 & -0.56 \\ -0.40 & 1 \end{vmatrix} = -0.58, \quad R_{13} = \begin{vmatrix} 0.80 & 1 \\ -0.40 & -0.56 \end{vmatrix} = -0.05$$

If these values and the values of the s's are inserted in (7), the equation of the desired regression plane becomes

$$0.16x_1' - 0.53x_2 - 0.0006x_3 = 0$$

If this equation is expressed in terms of the original variables, it reduces to

$$X_1' = 3.3X_2 + 0.004X_3 + 9.5$$

This equation indicates that, if X_3 is held fixed, the amount of hay increases about 330 pounds per acre with each inch increase in spring rainfall. On the other hand, if spring rainfall is held fixed, the accumulated spring temperature would have to increase about 3 standard deviations, which is 255 units, in order to increase the amount of hay by 100 pounds per acre. Thus, it appears that the spring temperature is relatively of little importance compared with spring rainfall. Such conclusions, of course, are only approximately true. They depend upon the variables' being approximately linearly related, and they express only average relationships.

The relative importance of the independent variables in a regression equation can be ascertained by comparing the coefficients of those variables after the equation has been written with all variables expressed in standard units. Since it is merely necessary to write each standard deviation in (7) under the corresponding x to express the variables in standard units, the relative importance of a variable X_i for estimating X_1 is determined by R_{1i}. In this problem $R_{12} = -0.58$ and $R_{13} = -0.05$; hence rainfall is much more important than temperature for hay production under these conditions.

As in polynomial fitting, if the number of variables is large, the solution of the normal equations may be expedited by the Doolittle technique.

STANDARD ERROR OF ESTIMATE

After a regression equation has been obtained, it is important to know how useful the equation is for estimating purposes. With two variables, it was found that the correlation coefficient gave a measure of the usefulness of the regression line for estimating y from x. For more than two variables, it is possible to generalize the definition of the correlation coefficient to give such a measure. Toward this end, consider the variance of the errors of estimation.

Because the x's are measured from their means, it follows from (7) that

$$\bar{e} = \frac{1}{n} \Sigma(x_1 - x_1') = \frac{1}{n} \{\Sigma x_1 - \Sigma x_1'\} = 0$$

consequently

$$s_e{}^2 = \frac{1}{n} \Sigma(e - \bar{e})^2 = \frac{1}{n} \Sigma e^2 = \frac{1}{n} \Sigma(x_1 - x_1')^2$$

If the value of x_1' given by (7) is inserted and common terms are factored out, this variance becomes

$$s_e^2 = \frac{s_1^2}{nR_{11}^2} \Sigma \left[R_{11} \frac{x_1}{s_1} + R_{12} \frac{x_2}{s_2} + \cdots + R_{1k} \frac{x_k}{s_k} \right]^2$$

The right side will simplify readily if the squaring is performed by multiplying the quantity in brackets in turn by each member inside and then performing all summations on the x's with the common factor $1/n$ inserted. If such sums are expressed in terms of correlation coefficients by means of (4), s_e^2 can be expressed as

$$s_e^2 = \frac{s_1^2}{R_{11}^2} \{ R_{11}[r_{11}R_{11} + r_{12}R_{12} + \cdots + r_{1k}R_{1k}] + $$

$$R_{12}[r_{21}R_{11} + r_{22}R_{12} + \cdots + r_{2k}R_{1k}] + $$

$$\cdot \qquad \cdot \qquad \cdot \qquad \cdot$$

$$\cdot \qquad \cdot \qquad \cdot \qquad \cdot$$

$$\cdot \qquad \cdot \qquad \cdot \qquad \cdot$$

$$R_{1k}[r_{k1}R_{11} + r_{k2}R_{12} + \cdots + r_{kk}R_{1k}] \}$$

From (6) it will be observed that the first pair of brackets above contains the expansion of R by means of minors of elements of the first row. The second pair of brackets contains the sum of products of the elements of the second row of R by the cofactors of the elements of the first row. But this is the expansion of the determinant obtained by replacing the first row of R by the second row of R. Since the value of a determinant with two rows alike is zero, the value of the quantity inside the second pair of brackets is zero. In the same manner it can be shown that the remaining quantities in brackets vanish; hence s_e^2 reduces to

(8) $$s_e^2 = s_1^2 \frac{R}{R_{11}}$$

Although this formula is useful for measuring the precision of (7) for estimating X_1, it was derived here primarily for application in the next section.

MULTIPLE CORRELATION COEFFICIENT

The *multiple correlation coefficient* is defined by analogy with the definition of the ordinary correlation coefficient for two variables given by (5), Chapter V. To distinguish it from the ordinary correlation coefficient, it is denoted by $r_{1\cdot23\cdots k}$. By definition

$$r_{1\cdot23\cdots k}^2 = 1 - \frac{s_e^2}{s_1^2}$$

The same reasoning that was followed for two variables may be applied here to show that $r_{1\cdot23\ldots k}$ may serve as a measure of the usefulness of the regression plane for estimating purposes. Although there are k possible regression planes and hence k multiple correlation coefficients, ordinarily there is but one variable which it is desired to estimate; consequently $r_{1\cdot23\ldots k}$ is usually the only multiple correlation coefficient of interest. If $r_{1\cdot23\ldots k}$ is close to 1, the n points corresponding to the sample of n must lie near the regression plane and therefore the k variables are likely to be approximately linearly related, thereby justifying the use of a linear function. However, if $r_{1\cdot23\ldots k}$ is close to 0, the relationship is either a weak linear one or a curvilinear relationship of unknown strength. For example, $r_{1\cdot23\ldots k}$ would be small if the n points were somewhat uniformly distributed inside a parallelepiped with sides parallel to the coordinate planes or if the points lay near the surface of a hemisphere with its base perpendicular to the X_1 axis.

The following formula for calculating $r_{1\cdot23\ldots k}$ as a function of ordinary correlation coefficients is obtained by inserting the value of s_e^2 given by (8) into the definition. Thus,

$$(9) \qquad r_{1\cdot23\ldots k} = \sqrt{1 - \frac{R}{R_{11}}}$$

It is customary to choose the positive root here. Incidentally, it can be shown that R and R_{ii} are non-negative and that $R \leq R_{ii}$; consequently an imaginary value for $r_{1\cdot23\ldots k}$ indicates an error in computations.

For the illustrative problem of the first section, calculations give

$$r_{1\cdot23} = \sqrt{1 - \frac{0.24}{0.69}} = 0.81$$

Since the regression plane cannot give a worse fit than the regression line in the X_1, X_2 plane, the multiple correlation coefficient must be at least as large as any simple correlation coefficient with the integer 1 as one of its subscripts. The fact that $r_{1\cdot23}$ is only slightly larger than r_{12} shows that the variable X_3 contributed practically nothing toward the usefulness of this regression plane for estimating hay yield. One could have estimated about as well with the regression line of X_1 on X_2.

PARTIAL CORRELATION COEFFICIENT

When several variables are interrelated, the simple correlation coefficients between pairs of such variables may give misleading information. For example, for the illustrative exercise of the first section, the fact that $r_{13} = -0.40$ would seem to indicate that, the warmer the weather was in the spring, the less was the yield of hay. However, this fairly large negative correlation is due to the fact that rainy weather is usually cool weather and that hay yield increases with rainfall. Thus, the true relationship between temperature and hay production is masked by the effect of rainfall on these variables. In order to study the true relationship between two such variables, it is necessary to hold all other closely related variables fixed. The correlation coefficient between two variables when the remaining variables under consideration are held fixed is known as the partial correlation coefficient. In practice, this correlation coefficient will usually vary with the particular values assigned to the remaining variables; consequently it is customary to define the partial correlation coefficient somewhat differently. Furthermore, if one had a sample of size 100 or less, the amount of data available for calculating a correlation coefficient for particular small ranges of values of the remaining variables would be so small as to yield a coefficient of questionable validity.

To obtain a formula that may serve as the definition of the partial correlation coefficient, consider the following idealized situation for three variables. Instead of having but n points in three dimensions, let the three-dimensional space with the X_1 axis vertical be filled with a probability density distribution analogous to the procedure with two dimensions in the section on probability density in Chapter VI. Then consider the density distribution in the vertical plane whose equation is $X_3 = k$. From the discussion concerning (8), Chapter VI, there exists a regression curve of X_1 on X_2 in this plane which is the locus of the mean points of vertical array distributions. If $X_3 = k$ is permitted to vary continuously, this regression curve which is a function of X_3 will generate a regression surface of X_1 on X_2 and X_3 in the three-dimensional space. In a similar manner, there exists a regression curve of X_2 on X_1 in the plane $X_3 = k$ which is the locus of the mean points of horizontal array distributions. As the variable $X_3 = k$ assumes continuously changing values, this regression curve generates a second regression surface, now of X_2 on X_1 and X_3. From the preceding geometry it follows that, if the equations of the two regression surfaces are known, the equations of the two regression curves in the $X_3 = k$ plane could be obtained by merely replacing X_3 by k in the surface equations. The derivation of the formula for partial correlations rests upon this relation between regression curves and regression surfaces. The geometry of the relationship is illustrated in Fig. 1 for linear regression.

For a finite number, n, of points in three dimensions, such an idealized situation can be only approximated. It is possible to approximate a regression surface by its sample least-squares value provided that the form of the surface is known. For example, if the regression surface of X_1 on X_2 and X_3 is known to be a plane, equation (7) may serve as an approximation to the population regression equation. It is also

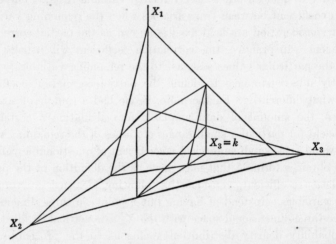

FIG. 1. Theoretical regression surface and regression lines for linear regression.

possible, but highly unsatisfactory because of the scarcity of such points, to approximate the regression curve of X_1 on X_2 in the $X_3 = k$ plane by using the sample points lying in or very near this plane. To circumvent the difficulty, the relation between regression curves and regression surfaces which was discussed in the preceding paragraph will be utilized to obtain an approximation to the desired regression curve in the $X_3 = k$ plane from its corresponding regression surface.

Now it will be assumed that the population regression surfaces of X_1 on X_2 and X_3, and of X_2 on X_1 and X_3, are planes. It can be shown that they are, for example, if the three variables are normally distributed. As a result of the assumption, the regression curves of X_1 on X_2 and of X_2 on X_1 lying in the $X_3 = k$ plane will be straight lines. Now by means of (7) the equations of the least-squares approximations to these two regression planes will be

$$(10) \qquad x_1' = -\frac{R_{12}s_1}{R_{11}s_2}\, x_2 - \frac{R_{13}s_1}{R_{11}s_3}\, x_3$$

and

$$x_2' = -\frac{R_{21}s_2}{R_{22}s_1}\, x_1 - \frac{R_{23}s_2}{R_{22}s_3}\, x_3$$

Since $x_3 = X_3 - \overline{X}_3$, if x_3 in these equations is replaced by its value $x_3 = k - \overline{X}_3$, the equations will become the equations of the two lines lying in the $X_3 = k$ plane which may serve as approximations to the corresponding population regression lines in that plane. By means of the resulting equations it will be possible to obtain the desired correlation between X_1 and X_2 in the $X_3 = k$ plane. The procedure for using the two regression line equations in a plane for obtaining the correlation coefficient in that plane will therefore be considered next.

From (10), Chapter V, and symmetry, it follows that the equations of the two regression lines in the x, y plane may be written in the form

$$y' = r\,\frac{s_y}{s_x}\,x = m_1 x$$

and

$$x' = r\,\frac{s_x}{s_y}\,y = m_2 y$$

It will be observed that r can be computed from these equations by means of the formula

$$(11) \qquad r = \pm\sqrt{m_1 m_2}$$

where the sign of the radical is chosen to be the same as that of the slope coefficients, m_1 and m_2.

A direct application of (11) to the regression-line equations given by (10) with $x_3 = k - \overline{X}_3$ yields

$$r = \pm\sqrt{\left(-\frac{R_{12}s_1}{R_{11}s_2}\right)\left(-\frac{R_{21}s_2}{R_{22}s_1}\right)}$$

$$(12) \qquad = \pm\frac{R_{12}}{\sqrt{R_{11}R_{22}}}$$

Since it is conventional to choose the sign of r to be the same as the sign of m_1 and m_2, the negative sign should be chosen here because $m_1 > 0$ when $R_{12} < 0$ and $m_1 < 0$ when $R_{12} > 0$. It is clear that this formula does not depend upon what particular value of x_3 is inserted in equations (10); consequently formula (12) possesses the desirable feature of measuring the correlation between X_1 and X_2 for a fixed value of X_3, regardless of what fixed value is used.

This derivation does not depend on the number of variables involved provided that the corresponding assumptions of linear regressions are made for the additional variables. In the equations (10) one would merely set the additional variables occurring on the right equal to their assigned fixed values. Thus, (12) may be generalized for the case of k variables to give the correlation coefficient between X_1 and X_2 with all other variables held fixed. This correlation coefficient is called the *partial correlation coefficient* and is denoted by $r_{12 \cdot 34 \cdots k}$; hence

$$(13) \qquad r_{12 \cdot 34 \cdots k} = - \frac{R_{12}}{\sqrt{R_{11} R_{22}}}$$

Although the assumptions made here may seem rather strong, the geometry of the situation indicates that the formula represents a compromise or averaging of the actual situation. Experience also indicates that the formula is highly useful for measuring what it claims to measure.

As an illustration of the use of (13), consider once more the data following (7). Calculations give

$$r_{12 \cdot 3} = - \frac{-0.58}{\sqrt{(0.69)(0.84)}} = 0.76$$

$$r_{13 \cdot 2} = - \frac{-0.05}{\sqrt{(0.69)(0.36)}} = 0.10$$

$$r_{23 \cdot 1} = - \frac{0.24}{\sqrt{(0.84)(0.36)}} = -0.44$$

The most interesting of these values is that for $r_{13 \cdot 2} = 0.10$. A comparison of this value with $r_{13} = -0.40$ shows that the latter value is highly deceptive. Without a knowledge of partial correlations, one might be tempted to claim that cold weather is beneficial to hay yield. The partial correlation of $r_{13 \cdot 2} = 0.10$ shows that the converse seems to be true. If temperature and rainfall were independent rather than negatively correlated, this seeming paradox would not have occurred. In making statements about the relationship between two variables, it is important to make clear whether it is one that permits the influence of other closely related variables or whether it is one in which the influence of certain of those related variables has been eliminated.

LINEAR DISCRIMINANT FUNCTIONS

A problem that arises quite often in science is to discriminate between two groups of individuals or objects on the basis of several properties of those individuals or objects. For example, a botanist might wish to classify a set of plants, some of which belong to one species and the rest to a second species, into their proper species by means of three or four measurements taken on each plant. If the two species were fairly similar with respect to all these measurements, it might not be possible to classify the plants correctly by means of any one measurement because of a fairly large amount of overlap in the distributions of this measurement for the two species; however, it might be possible to find a linear combination of these various measurements whose distributions for the two species would possess very little overlap. This linear combination could then be used to yield a type of index number by means of which plants of those two species could be differentiated with a high percentage of success. The procedure for discriminating would consist in finding a critical value of the index such that any plant whose index value fell below the critical value would be classified as belonging to one species, otherwise to the other species.

The principal difference between a *linear discriminant function* and an ordinary linear regression function arises from the nature of the dependent variable. A linear regression function uses values of the dependent variable to determine a linear function that will estimate the values of the dependent variable, whereas the discriminant function possesses no such values or variable but uses instead a two-way classification of the data to determine the linear function.

Consider a set of k variables, $x_1, x_2, \cdots, x_k$, by means of which it is desired to discriminate between two groups of individuals. Let

$$(14) \qquad z = \lambda_1 x_1 + \lambda_2 x_2 + \cdots + \lambda_k x_k$$

represent a linear combination of these variables. The problem then is to determine the λ's by means of some criterion that will enable z to serve as an index for differentiating between members of the two groups. For the purpose of simplifying the geometrical discussion of the problem, consider two variables with n_1 and n_2 individuals, respectively, in the two groups. The equation

$$z = \lambda_1 x_1 + \lambda_2 x_2$$

then represents a plane in three dimensions passing through the origin and having direction numbers λ_1, λ_2, and -1. If the two sets of points corresponding to the values of x_1 and x_2 for the two groups of individuals can be separated by means of a plane through the origin as in Fig. 2, it is clear that the values of z corresponding to the two groups will assume increasingly divergent negative and positive values as the separating plane approaches perpendicularity to the x_1, x_2 plane. At the same time, however, the variation in the values of z within a group becomes increasingly large for both groups; consequently the increase in the separation of the values of z for the two groups occurs at the

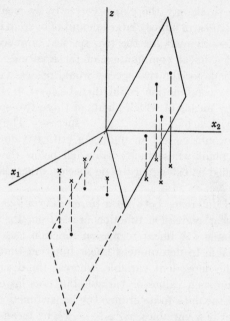

FIG. 2.   Example of a discriminating plane.

expense of an increase in the separation of the values of z within each group. This situation corresponds to that in which the means of two distributions are separating but for which the standard deviations are increasing to such an extent that greater discrimination between the two distributions does not necessarily result. It would be desirable, therefore, to choose the plane that separates the values of z for the two groups as widely as possible relative to the variation of the values of z within the two groups. As a measure of the separation of the two groups, it is convenient to use $(\bar{z}_1 - \bar{z}_2)^2$, where $\bar{z}_1$ and $\bar{z}_2$ are the means of the two groups. As a measure of the variation of the values of z

within the two groups, it is convenient to use $\sum\limits_{i=1}^{2} \sum\limits_{j=1}^{n_i} (z_{ij} - \bar{z}_i)^2$.
Then the desired plane will be that plane for which the λ's are determined to maximize the function

$$(15) \qquad G = \frac{(\bar{z}_1 - \bar{z}_2)^2}{\sum\limits_{i=1}^{2} \sum\limits_{j=1}^{n_i} (z_{ij} - \bar{z}_i)^2}$$

Although the arguments leading to (15) were elucidated by means of two variables and three-dimensional geometry, they hold equally well for k variables; consequently the solution of the problem will be carried out for the general case.

Let x_{pij} represent the value of x_p for the jth individual in the ith group, and let $\bar{x}_{pi}$ represent the mean value of x_p for the n_i individuals in that group. Then from (14) it follows that

$$(16) \qquad \bar{z}_1 - \bar{z}_2 = \lambda_1(\bar{x}_{11} - \bar{x}_{12}) + \cdots + \lambda_k(\bar{x}_{k1} - \bar{x}_{k2}),$$

and

$$(17) \qquad z_{ij} - \bar{z}_i = \lambda_1(x_{1ij} - \bar{x}_{1i}) + \cdots + \lambda_k(x_{kij} - \bar{x}_{ki})$$

If $d_p = \bar{x}_{p1} - \bar{x}_{p2}$, it follows from (16) that

$$(\bar{z}_1 - \bar{z}_2)^2 = (\lambda_1 d_1 + \cdots + \lambda_k d_k)^2$$

$$= \sum_{p=1}^{k} \sum_{q=1}^{k} \lambda_p \lambda_q d_p d_q$$

If $S_{pq} = \sum\limits_{i=1}^{2} \sum\limits_{j=1}^{n_i} (x_{pij} - \bar{x}_{pi})(x_{qij} - \bar{x}_{qi})$, it follows from (17) that

$$\sum_{i=1}^{2} \sum_{j=1}^{n_i} (z_{ij} - \bar{z}_i)^2 = \sum_{i=1}^{2} \sum_{j=1}^{n_i} [\lambda_1(x_{1ij} - \bar{x}_{1i}) + \cdots + \lambda_k(x_{kij} - \bar{x}_{ki})]^2$$

$$= \sum_{i=1}^{2} \sum_{j=1}^{n_i} \sum_{p=1}^{k} \sum_{q=1}^{k} \lambda_p \lambda_q (x_{pij} - \bar{x}_{pi})(x_{qij} - \bar{x}_{qi})$$

$$= \sum_{p=1}^{k} \sum_{q=1}^{k} \lambda_p \lambda_q \sum_{i=1}^{2} \sum_{j=1}^{n_i} (x_{pij} - \bar{x}_{pi})(x_{qij} - \bar{x}_{qi})$$

$$= \sum_{p=1}^{k} \sum_{q=1}^{k} \lambda_p \lambda_q S_{pq}$$

When these values are inserted in (15), it reduces to

$$(18) \qquad G = \frac{\sum\limits_{p=1}^{k} \sum\limits_{q=1}^{k} \lambda_p \lambda_q d_p d_q}{\sum\limits_{p=1}^{k} \sum\limits_{q=1}^{k} \lambda_p \lambda_q S_{pq}} = \frac{A}{B}$$

Since the λ's are to be determined to make G a maximum, it is necessary that $\dfrac{\partial G}{\partial \lambda_r} = 0$ for $r = 1, \cdots, k$. This requirement may be expressed in the form

$$\frac{\partial G}{\partial \lambda_r} = \frac{B \dfrac{\partial A}{\partial \lambda_r} - A \dfrac{\partial B}{\partial \lambda_r}}{B^2} = 0 \quad (r = 1, \cdots, k)$$

which is equivalent to

$$(19) \qquad \frac{\partial B}{\partial \lambda_r} = \frac{1}{G} \frac{\partial A}{\partial \lambda_r} \quad (r = 1, \cdots, k)$$

For ease of differentiating, it is convenient to write out B in the form

$$B = \lambda_1 \lambda_1 S_{11} + \cdots + \lambda_1 \lambda_r S_{1r} + \cdots + \lambda_1 \lambda_k S_{1k} +$$

$$\lambda_r \lambda_1 S_{r1} + \cdots + \lambda_r \lambda_r S_{rr} + \cdots + \lambda_r \lambda_k S_{rk} +$$

$$\lambda_k \lambda_1 S_{k1} + \cdots + \lambda_k \lambda_r S_{kr} + \cdots + \lambda_k \lambda_k S_{kk}$$

It will be observed that λ_r occurs as a common factor of both the rth row and the rth column. Since $S_{ij} = S_{ji}$, it therefore follows that

$$\frac{\partial B}{\partial \lambda_r} = 2[\lambda_1 S_{r1} + \cdots + \lambda_k S_{rk}]$$

Similarly,

$$\frac{\partial A}{\partial \lambda_r} = 2[\lambda_1 d_r d_1 + \cdots + \lambda_k d_r d_k]$$

$$= 2[\lambda_1 d_1 + \cdots + \lambda_k d_k] d_r$$

If these expressions are inserted in (19), it will reduce to

$$(20) \qquad \lambda_1 S_{r1} + \lambda_2 S_{r2} + \cdots + \lambda_k S_{rk} = cd_r \quad (r = 1, \cdots, k)$$

where $c = [\lambda_1 d_1 + \cdots + \lambda_k d_k]/G$ is independent of r.

Since

$$(21) \qquad S_{pq} = \sum_{i=1}^{2} \sum_{j=1}^{n_i} (x_{pij} - \bar{x}_{pi})(x_{qij} - \bar{x}_{qi})$$

and

$$(22) \qquad d_p = \bar{x}_{p1} - \bar{x}_{p2}$$

are numerical quantities in any given problem, the necessary conditions (20) constitute a set of k linear equations in the λ's. The solution of these equations determines the λ's except for the unknown factor c. From (14) it is clear that such a factor can be ignored because the two sets of z's would merely differ by this constant factor and thus would be equivalent as far as discriminating between the two groups is concerned. As a matter of fact, it is usually convenient to choose $c = 1$, solve the equations, and then reduce (14) to the form in which one of the λ's, say λ_1, is unity.

As an illustration of the use of this function, consider the data of Table 1 on the mean numbers of teeth found on the proximal (x_1) and distal (x_2) combs of two races of insects. The problem here is to discriminate between members of the two races by means of the two indicated variables.

TABLE 1

Race A	x_1	6.36	5.92	5.92	6.44	6.40	6.56	6.64	6.68	6.72	6.76	6.72
	x_2	5.24	5.12	5.36	5.64	5.16	5.56	5.36	4.96	5.48	5.60	5.08
Race B	x_1	6.00	5.60	5.64	5.76	5.96	5.72	5.64	5.44	5.04	4.56	5.48	5.76
	x_2	4.88	4.64	4.96	4.80	5.08	5.04	4.96	4.88	4.44	4.04	4.20	4.80

Computations give $S_{11} = 2.68$, $S_{12} = 1.29$, $S_{22} = 1.75$, $d_1 = 0.915$, $d_2 = 0.597$; consequently if c is chosen equal to 1, equations (20) become

$$2.68\lambda_1 + 1.29\lambda_2 = 0.915$$

$$1.29\lambda_1 + 1.75\lambda_2 = 0.597$$

The solution of these equations is $\lambda_1 = 0.274$ and $\lambda_2 = 0.139$. If these values are used, the linear discriminant function (14) becomes

$$z = 0.274x_1 + 0.139x_2$$

For the purpose of computing values of z, it is more convenient to choose c so that either λ_1 or λ_2 equals 1. If c is chosen to make λ_1 equal 1, this discriminant function reduces to

$$z = x_1 + 0.507x_2$$

The values of z corresponding to the various members of the two races given in Table 1 are as follows:

Race A	9.02	8.52	8.64	9.30	9.02	9.38	9.36	9.19	9.50	9.60	9.30	
Race B	8.47	7.95	8.15	8.19	8.54	8.28	8.15	7.91	7.29	6.61	7.61	8.19

It will be noted that the two races are segregated by means of z except for the slight overlap found in the second entry for Race A and the fifth entry for Race B.

REFERENCES

The properties of determinants used in deriving the multiple regression formulas in this chapter may be found in most college algebra books, or preferably in some book on the theory of equations.

If the multiple correlation coefficient shows that multiple linear regression methods are not very useful for estimating the desired variable, it may be profitable to consider non-linear regression methods. One approach to such methods is to introduce functions of the independent variables as new variables. Another approach is to introduce additional terms in the form of higher powers of the variables. A third approach is to attempt to discover the relationship between the variables by graphical methods. An extensive discussion of such methods will be found in:

EZEKIEL, M., *Methods of Correlation Analysis*, 2nd edition, John Wiley & Sons.

The definition of a normal distribution function of several variables and the derivation of its more interesting properties follow as generalizations of the definition and derivations given in Chapter VI for two variables. Material on this generalization may be found in:

WILKS, S. S., *Mathematical Statistics*, Princeton University Press, pp. 63–68.

The discriminant function technique has been generalized so that it can be applied to discriminate between more than two groups of individuals. An elementary discussion and application of this generalization may be found in:

DAY, B. B., and M. M. SANDOMIRE, "Use of the Discriminant Function for More Than Two Groups," *Journal of the American Statistical Association*, vol. 37 (1942), pp. 461–472.

The discriminant function can also be adapted to the problem of testing whether two groups differ significantly with respect to certain variables. It may happen that an insufficient amount of data will prevent the difference of the means of the individual variables of the two groups from being significant but will suffice to show a significant difference in the means of the discriminant function. An exposition of this use may be found in:

FISHER, R. A., *Statistical Methods for Research Workers*, 8th edition, Oliver & Boyd, pp. 279–289.

EXERCISES

1. The following values represent sample values for 450 college students in which the three variables represent honor points, general intelligence scores, and hours of study. (*a*) Find the regression equation for estimating honor points. (*b*) By means of the multiple correlation coefficient, determine whether this regression equation would enable one to predict grade point averages with a fair degree of success. (*c*) Find all three partial correlations, and interpret them in the light of the corresponding simple correlations.

$$\bar{X}_1 = 18.5, \quad \bar{X}_2 = 100.6, \quad \bar{X}_3 = 24$$

$$s_1 = 11.2, \quad s_2 = 15.8, \quad s_3 = 6.0$$

$$r_{12} = 0.60, \quad r_{13} = 0.32, \quad r_{23} = -0.35$$

2. The following correlation coefficients are for the variables: average grade the first semester at college, arithmetic test score, average grade in high-school work, and student interest breadth. Find and interpret those quantities which would be of particular interest.

$$\begin{Vmatrix} 1 & 0.465 & 0.546 & 0.365 \\ & 1 & 0.401 & 0.197 \\ & & 1 & 0.345 \\ & & & 1 \end{Vmatrix}$$

3. Show that $r_{12\cdot3} = \dfrac{r_{12} - r_{13}r_{23}}{\sqrt{(1 - r_{13}^2)(1 - r_{23}^2)}}$.

4. Using problem 3, find limits for the possible values of r_{23} in each case if r_{12} and r_{13} have the following pairs of values:

$$r_{12} = 0, \quad +1, \quad +1, \quad +0.5, \quad +0.5$$

$$r_{13} = 0, \quad +1, \quad -1, \quad +0.5, \quad -0.5$$

5. If the relation $aX_1 + bX_2 + cX_3 = 0$ holds for all values of X_1, X_2, and X_3, what are the values of the partial correlations?

6. Is there anything in the derivation of the formulas of this chapter which would not permit the variables to be $X_1 = y$, $X_2 = t$, $X_3 = t^2$, etc., and hence to yield formulas for polynomial curve fitting?

7. Show that the simple correlation coefficient between X_1 and X_1' is the multiple correlation coefficient. Use the same type of technique as that employed in deriving the formula for s_e^2.

8. For the case of three variables, show that the simple correlation coefficient between the deviations $X_1 - X_1'$ and $X_2 - X_2'$, in which the prime indicates the regression value on the variable X_3, is the partial correlation coefficient $r_{12\cdot3}$.

9. Classify the first 16 individuals in problem 3, Chapter V, into one of two groups on the basis of having a G.P.A. less than or greater than 0.9. (*a*) Using the remaining variables, find the equation of the discriminant function for segregating individuals into the proper G.P.A. group. (*b*) Calculate the values of z for the selected individuals, and note whether the discriminant function discriminates noticeably better than either variable alone.

10. For the case of three variables show that $R_{11} \geq R \geq 0$.

CHAPTER VIII

SMALL-SAMPLE DISTRIBUTIONS

EXPECTED VALUES

By the *expected value* of a function of a statistical variable is meant its mean value. The expression arose from its connection with the amount of money one could expect to win at a game of chance. If the expected value is denoted by E, then by (7), Chapter III, the expected value of a function $g(x)$ is

$$E[g(x)] = \int_a^b g(x)f(x)\,dx$$

where $f(x)$ is the distribution function of x. For a discrete variable this integral would be replaced by a sum. It is clear from a direct application of this definition that

(1) $$E[cg(x)] = cE[g(x)]$$

where c is a constant, and that

(2) $$E[g_1(x) + g_2(x)] = E[g_1(x)] + E[g_2(x)]$$

where $g_1(x)$ and $g_2(x)$ are any two functions of x possessing expected values.

1. Unbiased Estimate of σ^2 Based on One Sample Variance

Consider the expected value of a sample variance based upon a sample of size n. From properties (1) and (2) and the definition of σ^2, it follows that

$$E[s^2] = E\left[\frac{1}{n}\Sigma(x - \bar{x})^2\right]$$

$$= E\left[\frac{1}{n}\Sigma\left\{(x - m) - (\bar{x} - m)\right\}^2\right]$$

$$= \frac{1}{n}\Sigma E[(x - m)^2] - E[(\bar{x} - m)^2]$$

$$= \frac{1}{n}\Sigma\sigma^2 - \sigma_{\bar{x}}^2$$

$$= \sigma^2 - \frac{\sigma^2}{n}$$

(3) $$= \frac{n-1}{n}\sigma^2$$

This shows that if repeated samples of size n are taken and if the resulting sample variances are averaged, the average will not approach the true variance in value but will be consistently too small by the factor of $(n-1)/n$. For small samples this factor becomes important; consequently one must be careful how he combines samples in making an estimate of the true variance. In order to overcome this defect of s^2 as an estimate of σ^2, it is merely necessary to multiply s^2 by $n/(n-1)$ and use the resulting quantity as the estimate of σ^2. Then

$$E\left[\frac{n}{n-1}s^2\right] = \frac{n}{n-1}E[s^2] = \sigma^2$$

When the expected value of a statistic is equal to the population parameter of which it is intended as an estimate, the statistic is called an *unbiased* estimate of the parameter. It is clear that s^2 is biased, whereas $\frac{n}{n-1}s^2$ is unbiased. In this chapter an unbiased estimate will be indicated by placing a circumflex over the parameter of which it is an unbiased estimate. Therefore,

(4) $$\hat{\sigma}^2 = \frac{n}{n-1}s^2 = \frac{\Sigma(x-\bar{x})^2}{n-1}$$

Thus, it appears that one can avoid the bias in estimating variances by dividing the sum of squares of deviations by $n-1$ rather than by n as was the practice with large samples. It is because of this property that some authors define the sample variance, s^2, to be $\Sigma(x-\bar{x})^2/(n-1)$. It should be remarked that $\hat{\sigma}^2$ is not the same as $(\hat{\sigma})^2$, which denotes the square of an unbiased estimate of σ.

2. Unbiased Estimate of σ^2 Based on Several Sample Variances

It often happens that several sample variances are available for estimating the population variance. In order to obtain an average value from these sample values that will make allowance for differences in precision due to differences in sample sizes, a weighted average of some kind is necessary. Furthermore, it is important with small samples to select a weighting that is free of bias. Although various weightings can be designed which lack bias, the simplest scheme would seem to be to weight each variance with the size of the sample on which it is based and then multiply by a factor that will make the result unbiased. If k sample variances are available, such a choice leads to

$$(5) \qquad \hat{\sigma}^2 = \frac{n_1 s_1{}^2 + n_2 s_2{}^2 + \cdots + n_k s_k{}^2}{n_1 + n_2 + \cdots + n_k - k}$$

From (3) it follows that $E[n_i s_i{}^2] = (n_i - 1)\sigma^2$; consequently, if properties (1) and (2) are applied to (5), it will be found that $E[\hat{\sigma}^2] = \sigma^2$ and therefore that this estimate is unbiased as indicated.

Formula (5) is particularly useful when several sets of data are available for which the variability can be assumed to be constant but for which the means vary more than could be reasonably attributed to chance. If such sets of data were combined into one set and the variance of this entire set used as an estimate of the population variance, the result would be to overestimate the value of σ^2. However, if one calculates the variance of each set and combines as in (5), the result will be unbiased.

CONFIDENCE LIMITS

The problems that were considered in the chapter on large-sample theory were largely of the hypothesis-testing type. For example, a sample mean was tested to see whether it might reasonably have come from a population with a specified mean, or the difference between two sample means was tested to see whether these means might reasonably have come from two populations with the same means. However, a problem that arises just as frequently is the estimating of a population parameter, such as the mean or variance. Not only an estimate is desired, but also limits within which one can have confidence that the population parameter lies. For the purpose of studying this type of problem, consider a numerical illustration.

Suppose that a random sample of size 100 has been taken from a population that is known to be normal and whose variance is known to be 16. Suppose further that the mean of this sample is 30. Then the problem is to estimate the population mean, m, by means of an interval of values of x. Since $\sigma^2 = 16$, $\sigma_{\bar{x}} = \sigma/\sqrt{n} = 0.4$. Although the value of m is unknown, it is known from large-sample theory that, for repeated samples of the type being considered, $\bar{x}$ will be normally distributed about this value of m with a standard deviation of 0.4;

consequently the fixed interval $m \pm 0.8$ will contain 95% of such sample means on the average. Since m is unknown, one would be tempted to replace m by $\bar{x}$, whose value is known to be 30 for this first sample of 100, and then make the same probability statement as before. However, it is clear that $\bar{x}$ will change from one sampling experiment to the next and that conceivably the first value of $\bar{x}$, namely 30, might

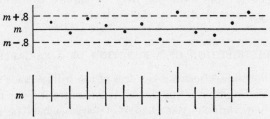

Fig. 1.   Illustration of confidence interval methods.

be a very poor one for estimating m, so that such probability statements not only would be false but might give highly incorrect results. Correct probability statements can be made here in the following manner. If the interval $\bar{x} \pm 0.8$ is treated as a variable interval, changing with each sample of 100, then, in repeated sampling, 95% of such intervals on the average will contain m. This follows from the fact that, if 95% of sample means lie within 0.8 of m, in 95% of such samples m must lie within 0.8 of the corresponding $\bar{x}$. The situation is represented geometrically in Fig. 1. Each point represents an $\bar{x}$ based on a sample of 100. The upper diagram corresponds to the case in which m is assumed known and a probability statement is made concerning $\bar{x}$'s. The lower diagram corresponds to the case in which m is unknown and the variable intervals $\bar{x} \pm 0.8$ are plotted. If a point lies inside the 95% band of the upper diagram, its interval in the lower diagram must cover m.

Now in practice only one such $\bar{x}$ is available, so that only the first point and its corresponding interval of 30 ± 0.8 is available. On the basis of this one experiment, the claim will be made that the interval 30 ± 0.8 contains the population mean m. If for each such experiment one made the same claim for the interval corresponding to that experiment, then, in repeated experiments, 95% of such claims would be true on the average. It is in this sense that correct probability statements may be made concerning population parameters. The interval 30 ± 0.8 is called a 95% *confidence interval* for m. If one uses confidence intervals as above on all estimation problems that arise, on the average 95% of such confidence intervals will contain the parameters claimed for them. Confidence intervals enable one to obtain a useful type of information about population parameters without the necessity of treating such parameters as statistical variables. It should be clearly understood that one is merely betting on the correctness of the rule of procedure when applying the confidence-interval technique to a given experiment. It will be observed in the following sections of this chapter that this technique may be applied to various familiar population parameters such as the variance and the regression slope.

DISTRIBUTION OF A FUNCTION OF A VARIABLE

In the following sections a great deal of use will be made of a change of variable in distribution functions. If x denotes the original variable and y the new variable, this change of variable may be represented by $x = g(y)$. Since probabilities are given by integrals, the procedure for making a change of variable for distribution functions is precisely that for integrals. Thus, in making this change of variable in the following integral, it is merely necessary to evaluate $dx = g'(y)\,dy$ and obtain

$$(6) \qquad \int_{x_1}^{x_2} f(x)\,dx = \int_{y_1}^{y_2} f(x)g'(y)\,dy$$

where the value of x on the right is replaced by $x = g(y)$ and the values of y_1 and y_2 are the values of y corresponding to x_1 and x_2 for x. Now it is necessary to restrict the function $g(y)$ to be monotonic, that is, to be a function that either never decreases or never increases; otherwise $f(x)g'(y)$ would change signs and therefore could not serve as a distribution function. It is assumed here that $g(y)$ has a continuous derivative. If $g(y)$ were not monotonic, there would also be the difficulty of having more than one value of y correspond to some values of x.

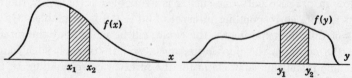

FIG. 2.   Illustration of a change of variable for a distribution function.

The geometry of a typical change of variable is indicated in Fig. 2, in which the first graph is that of $f(x)$ and the second graph is that of $f(x)g'(y)$. The two shaded areas correspond to the left and right integrals in (6). In these graphs $g(y)$ is monotonic increasing because increasing values of x are made to correspond to increasing values of y. Since the integral on the left side of (6) yields the $P[x_1 < x < x_2]$, the integral on the right side must do likewise. Because of the monotonic property of $g(y)$, which insures in this case that y increases with x, the probability that y will lie in a given interval must equal the probability that x will lie in its corresponding interval. The monotonic property sets up a correspondence between intervals on the x and y axes of Fig. 2 such that y will lie in an interval (y_1, y_2) if and only if x lies in its corresponding interval (x_1, x_2). Thus, for all intervals (x_1, x_2),

$$P[x_1 < x < x_2] = P[y_1 < y < y_2]$$

The integral on the right side of (6) must therefore yield the $P[y_1 < y < y_2]$, and its integrand must be the distribution function of y. If $g(y)$ had been monotonic decreasing, it would have been necessary to take the negative value of the integrand before it could have been treated as a distribution function. In either case the formula

$$(7) \qquad\qquad f(y) = f(x) \mid g'(y) \mid$$

with x replaced by $g(y)$, yields the desired distribution function of y. Although the f notation being used here was explained in Chapter III, it may be worth repeating that $f(x)$ and $f(y)$ denote the respective distribution functions of x and y and that these functions will be different unless $g(y) = y$. Although (7) may appear to be new, it represents in formula fashion the new integrand which the student of elementary

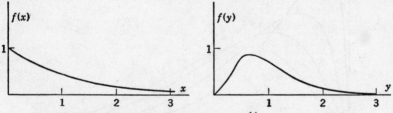

FIG. 3.   Distribution functions of x and $y = x^{\frac{1}{2}}$ for $f(x) = e^{-x}$, $x \geq 0$.

integral calculus obtains automatically when performing an integration by means of a substitution to a new variable.

As an illustration, consider the problem of finding the distribution function of y if $x = y^2$ and $f(x) = e^{-x}$, $x \geq 0$. Since $g(y) = y^2$, $g'(y) = 2y$, and therefore by (7)

$$f(y) = 2ye^{-y^2}$$

The relationship between these two distribution functions is shown geometrically in Fig. 3. It should be noted that only positive values of y are considered here; otherwise there would be two values of y to each value of x and $g(y)$ would not be monotonic.

THE χ^2 DISTRIBUTION

1. Moment-Generating Function of χ^2

One of the most widely used continuous distribution functions in statistical work is the χ^2 function. This function received its name in connection with early work by K. Pearson on the problem of measuring the goodness of fit of frequency curves. Its application to such problems will be treated in Chapter X. The χ^2 function arises in this chapter in connection with the problem of finding the distribution function of s^2. This function is defined in terms of the variable χ^2 by

$$(8) \qquad f(\chi^2) = \frac{1}{2^{\frac{\nu}{2}}\Gamma\left(\frac{\nu}{2}\right)} (\chi^2)^{\frac{\nu-2}{2}} e^{-\frac{\chi^2}{2}}$$

in which the parameter ν is called the number of degrees of freedom and Γ represents the gamma function defined in the section on moments in Chapter III. A sketch of (8) for several values of ν is given in Fig. 4.

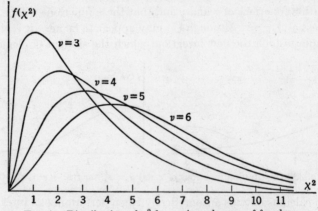

Fig. 4.   Distribution of χ^2 for various degrees of freedom.

The moment-generating function of χ^2 will be needed in the next three sections; therefore its derivation will be considered next. For convenience of notation let $v = \chi^2$; then the moment-generating function of v will be given by

$$M_v(\theta) = \int_0^\infty e^{\theta v} f(v)\, dv$$

$$= \frac{1}{2^{\frac{\nu}{2}}\Gamma\left(\frac{\nu}{2}\right)} \int_0^\infty e^{\theta v} \cdot v^{\frac{\nu-2}{2}} e^{-\frac{v}{2}} \, dv$$

$$= \frac{1}{2^{\frac{\nu}{2}}\Gamma\left(\frac{\nu}{2}\right)} \int_0^\infty e^{-\frac{v}{2}(1-2\theta)} v^{\frac{\nu}{2}-1} \, dv$$

Let $y = \frac{v}{2}(1 - 2\theta)$; then $dv = \dfrac{2}{1 - 2\theta} \, dy$ and

$$M_v(\theta) = \frac{1}{2^{\frac{\nu}{2}}\Gamma\left(\frac{\nu}{2}\right)} \int_0^\infty e^{-y} \left(\frac{2y}{1-2\theta}\right)^{\frac{\nu}{2}-1} \frac{2}{1-2\theta} \, dy$$

$$= \frac{(1-2\theta)^{-\frac{\nu}{2}}}{\Gamma\left(\frac{\nu}{2}\right)} \int_0^\infty e^{-y} y^{\frac{\nu}{2}-1} \, dy$$

Since the integral on the right is that for $\Gamma\left(\dfrac{\nu}{2}\right)$, the moment-generating function of χ^2 for ν degrees of freedom is given by

$$(9) \qquad M_{\chi^2}(\theta) = (1 - 2\theta)^{-\frac{\nu}{2}}$$

2. Distribution of a Sum of Squares

Let x be normally distributed with zero mean and unit variance. Suppose that a random sample of size n has been drawn from this population. These sample values will be denoted by $x_1, x_2, \cdots, x_n$. The object of this section is to find the distribution function of w, where

$$(10) \qquad w = \sum_{i=1}^n x_i^2$$

The derivation of $f(w)$ will be accomplished by means of its moment-generating function.

Since the sampling is random, the x_i are independent and possess the same distribution function; hence

$$M_w(\theta) = M_{x_1^2 + \cdots + x_n^2}(\theta)$$

$$= M_{x_1^2}(\theta) M_{x_2^2}(\theta) \cdots M_{x_n^2}(\theta)$$

$$(11) \qquad = M_{x^2}^n(\theta)$$

Now x is a standard normal variable; therefore

$$M_{x^2}(\theta) = \frac{1}{\sqrt{2\pi}} \int_{-\infty}^{\infty} e^{\theta x^2} \cdot e^{-\frac{x^2}{2}} \, dx$$

$$= \frac{1}{\sqrt{2\pi}} \int_{-\infty}^{\infty} e^{-\frac{x^2}{2}(1-2\theta)} \, dx$$

Let $y = x\sqrt{1 - 2\theta}$; this integral reduces to

$$M_{x^2}(\theta) = (1 - 2\theta)^{-\frac{1}{2}} \frac{1}{\sqrt{2\pi}} \int_{-\infty}^{\infty} e^{-\frac{y^2}{2}} \, dy$$

$$= (1 - 2\theta)^{-\frac{1}{2}}$$

From this result and (11) it therefore follows that

(12) $$M_w(\theta) = (1 - 2\theta)^{-\frac{n}{2}}$$

A comparison of this result with formula (9) will show that w has the moment-generating function of χ^2 with n degrees of freedom. Since a distribution function is uniquely determined by its moment-generating function, the preceding derivation proves the following theorem.

Theorem I. *If x is normally distributed with zero mean and unit variance, the sum of the squares of n random sample values of x has a χ^2 distribution with n degrees of freedom.*

3. Distribution of s^2

The theorem that was just demonstrated is the basis for deriving the distribution functions of many useful statistical variables. In particular, it can be used to derive the distribution function of s^2 when the basic variable is normally distributed. To this end, let x be normally distributed with mean m and variance σ^2, and let $\bar{x}$ and s^2 be the sample values of these parameters based upon a random sample of size n.

Now it can be shown, but only with considerable difficulty, that $\bar{x}$ and s^2 are independently distributed when the basic variable is normally distributed. This fact will be assumed here. Consider

$$s^2 = \frac{1}{n} \Sigma(x - \bar{x})^2$$

$$= \frac{1}{n} \Sigma[(x - m) - (\bar{x} - m)]^2$$

$$= \frac{1}{n} \Sigma(x - m)^2 - (\bar{x} - m)^2$$

Because of the convenience of working with standard units, this relationship will be multiplied through by n/σ^2 and then written in the form

$$\frac{ns^2}{\sigma^2} + \left(\frac{\bar{x} - m}{\sigma/\sqrt{n}}\right)^2 = \Sigma\left(\frac{x - m}{\sigma}\right)^2$$

or symbolically as

$$J + K = L$$

If the moment-generating function of both sides is taken,

(13) $$M_{J+K}(\theta) = M_L(\theta)$$

Because of the previously mentioned independence of $\bar{x}$ and s^2, it follows that J and K are independently distributed. Although this seems clear from the meaning of independence, it can easily be demonstrated by showing that the distribution function of J and K is the product of its marginal distribution functions, under the assumption that the distribution function of $\bar{x}$ and s^2 is the product of its marginal distribution functions. Because of this independence, the function on the left side of (13) can be factored; therefore

$$M_J(\theta)M_K(\theta) = M_L(\theta)$$

Since L is the sum of squares of n sample values of a normal variable with zero mean and unit variance, it has the properties of w in (10); consequently it has the same moment-generating function as w. Therefore,

$$M_J(\theta)M_K(\theta) = M_w(\theta)$$

Since s^2 is the variable of interest here, this equation will be written in the form

$$M_J(\theta) = \frac{M_w(\theta)}{M_K(\theta)}$$

Both the functions on the right can be evaluated by means of (12). Since $\dfrac{\bar{x} - m}{\sigma/\sqrt{n}}$ is a normal variable with zero mean and unit variance, its square can be treated as a special case of w in (10) for which $n = 1$. It therefore follows from (12) that

$$M_{\frac{ns^2}{\sigma^2}}(\theta) = \frac{(1 - 2\theta)^{-\frac{n}{2}}}{(1 - 2\theta)^{-\frac{1}{2}}} = (1 - 2\theta)^{-\frac{n-1}{2}}$$

Since a distribution function is uniquely determined by its moment-generating function, this result together with (9) proves the following theorem.

Theorem II. *If x is normally distributed with variance σ^2 and s^2 is the sample variance based on a random sample of size n, then ns^2/σ^2 has a χ^2 distribution with $n-1$ degrees of freedom.*

Two applications of this important theorem will be considered immediately after the next section.

4. Additive Nature of χ^2

Situations may arise in which an experimenter has several sets of data that he would like to combine into one experimental result or conclusion. Such a situation was indicated in section 2 with regard to the combining of several sample variances into one good estimate of σ^2. If the statistics that are to be added possess independent χ^2 distributions, the distribution of the sum can be found as follows.

Let χ_1^2 and χ_2^2 possess independent χ^2 distributions with ν_1 and ν_2 degrees of freedom, respectively. Consider the variable $z = \chi_1^2 + \chi_2^2$. From moment-generating functions and (9), it follows that

$$M_z(\theta) = M_{\chi_1^2}(\theta) M_{\chi_2^2}(\theta)$$

$$= (1 - 2\theta)^{-\frac{\nu_1}{2}} (1 - 2\theta)^{-\frac{\nu_2}{2}}$$

$$= (1 - 2\theta)^{-\frac{\nu_1 + \nu_2}{2}}$$

This result demonstrates the following theorem.

Theorem III. *If χ_1^2 and χ_2^2 possess independent χ^2 distributions with ν_1 and ν_2 degrees of freedom, respectively, then $\chi_1^2 + \chi_2^2$ will possess a χ^2 distribution with $\nu_1 + \nu_2$ degrees of freedom.*

APPLICATIONS OF THE χ^2 DISTRIBUTION

1. Confidence Limits for σ^2

Let x be normally distributed with variance σ^2, and let s^2 be the sample variance based on a random sample of size n. Then 95% confidence limits for σ^2 may be obtained in the following manner.

From Table III for $n-1$ degrees of freedom find two values of χ^2, namely χ_1^2 and χ_2^2, such that the probability is 0.975 that $\chi^2 > \chi_1^2$ and such that the probability is 0.025 that $\chi^2 > \chi_2^2$. Then it follows from Theorem II that the probability is 0.95 that

$$\chi_1^2 < \frac{ns^2}{\sigma^2} < \chi_2^2$$

or that

(14)
$$\frac{ns^2}{\chi_2^2} < \sigma^2 < \frac{ns^2}{\chi_1^2}$$

These two numbers constitute 95% confidence limits for σ^2. From the discussion in the section on confidence limits, it follows that on the average 95% of the inequalities of this type that are computed will be true inequalities. This method, of course, is not restricted to 95% limits.

As an application, consider the data of problem 10, Chapter IV. Suppose that an estimate of the variance is desired on the basis of the first 5 sets of data. If these 25 observations are combined, it will be found that

$$ns^2 = \Sigma(x - \bar{x})^2 = 9,715$$

A direct application of (14) and Table III will show that 96% confidence limits for σ^2 are given by

$$\frac{9,715}{40.27} < \sigma^2 < \frac{9,715}{11.99}$$

which is equivalent to

$$241 < \sigma^2 < 809$$

It is clear that σ^2 cannot be estimated with much accuracy for such a small sample and such variable data.

As a second illustration, consider the problem of finding confidence limits for σ^2 when several sets of data are available for which the means differ considerably but for which the variances are expected to be homogeneous. The data of the first illustration might have been of this type if some change had been made in the manufacturing process that would have raised the mean quality of the product without affecting the variability of the quality. The problem here is closely related to the problem considered in section 2. As in that problem, the variance of the combined data would be seriously in error if the means differed considerably. The proper approach in such a situation will be illustrated on the sets of data just considered, even though these sets of data may legitimately be combined as in the first illustration. If each set of 5 measurements is treated separately, it will be found that

$$n_1 s_1^2 = 1,185, \quad n_4 s_4^2 = 1,478$$

$$n_2 s_2^2 = 1,599, \quad n_5 s_5^2 = 705$$

$$n_3 s_3^2 = 4,214, \quad \Sigma n_i s_i^2 = 9,181$$

If it is assumed that each set has the same population variance, σ^2, even though they may have different means here, then the $n_i s_i^2/\sigma^2$ will have independent χ^2 distributions with 4 degrees of freedom each. From Theorem III it follows that $\Sigma n_i s_i^2/\sigma^2$ will have a χ^2 distribution with 20 degrees of freedom. Therefore, by (14) and Table III, 96% confidence limits will be given by

$$\frac{9,181}{35.02} < \sigma^2 < \frac{9,181}{9.237}$$

or

$$262 < \sigma^2 < 994$$

It will be noted that these confidence limits do not differ appreciably from those found by the first method. In both these illustrations it is assumed that the basic variables are normally distributed.

STUDENT'S t DISTRIBUTION

Consider the data of Table 1 on the additional hours of sleep gained by 10 patients in an experiment with a certain drug. The problem is to determine whether these data justify the claim that this drug does produce additional sleep.

TABLE 1

Patient	1	2	3	4	5	6	7	8	9	10
Hours gained	0.7	−1.1	−0.2	1.2	0.1	3.4	3.7	0.8	1.8	2.0

Assume that the hours of additional sleep is a normally distributed variable, and set up the hypothesis that the population mean is zero. Furthermore, assume that these 10 patients may be treated as a random sample of size 10 from this population.

If this problem were treated in the traditional large-sample manner of Chapter IV, the experimenter would use the data of Table 1 to obtain

$$\bar{x} = 1.24 \quad \text{and} \quad s = 1.45$$

Then he would calculate

$$\tau = \frac{\bar{x} - m}{\sigma_{\bar{x}}} = \frac{\bar{x} - 0}{\sigma/\sqrt{n}} \doteq \frac{1.24\sqrt{10}}{1.45} = 2.70$$

small < 30

From Table II the probability of obtaining a value of $\tau > 2.70$ is 0.0035; consequently the hypothesis that $m = 0$ would be rejected here even at the 1% significance level. If possible psychological factors were under control here, it appears that the drug does increase sleep.

This large-sample method is subject to one serious objection. For a sample as small as this, the sample standard deviation, s, will not be an accurate estimate of σ; consequently a serious error may be introduced in the value of τ in replacing σ by its sample value. In most applied problems the true standard deviation is unknown. In order to overcome this defect in the test, it is necessary to consider a new variable which involves the sample standard deviation rather than the population standard deviation. Such a consideration will lead to what is known as Student's t distribution.

To this end, let u be normally distributed with zero mean and unit variance, let v^2 have a χ^2 distribution with ν degrees of freedom, and let u and v be independently distributed. Furthermore, let c denote any and all constants whose specific values are of no interest. This last notational device eliminates the necessity for writing out the explicit form of numerous constants in the following derivations.

In the derivation of the t distribution it is necessary to obtain the distribution function of the variable v. Since $v^2 = \chi^2$, the distribution function of $v \geq 0$ can be obtained from that of χ^2 by considering the change of variable from χ^2 to v through the relation $\chi^2 = v^2$ and applying formula (7). Here χ^2 corresponds to x, v corresponds to y, and $g(v) = v^2$; consequently

$$f(v) = f(\chi^2)2v$$

If the value of $f(\chi^2)$ from (8) is inserted and χ^2 is replaced by v^2, the distribution function of v reduces to

$$f(v) = cv^{\nu-1}e^{-\frac{v^2}{2}}$$

Since u and v are independently distributed and u is a standard normal variable,

$$f(u, v) = f(u)f(v)$$

$$= ce^{-\frac{u^2}{2}}cv^{\nu-1}e^{-\frac{v^2}{2}}$$

$$= cv^{\nu-1}e^{-\frac{1}{2}(u^2+v^2)}$$

Now let $t = u\sqrt{\nu}/v$ represent a change of variable from u to t with v held fixed. Such a purocedre is equivalent to making a change of variable in the first of the two integrations of a double integral. Since $du = \dfrac{v}{\sqrt{\nu}}\, dt$ here, it follows from (7) that

$$f(t, v) = f(u, v)\, \frac{v}{\sqrt{\nu}}$$

$$= cv^{\nu} e^{-\frac{1}{2}\left(\frac{t^2 v^2}{\nu} + v^2\right)}$$

$$= cv^{\nu} e^{-\frac{v^2}{2}\left(1 + \frac{t^2}{\nu}\right)}$$

The purpose of the present section is to find the distribution function of t. It will be recalled from (6), Chapter VI, that this can be accomplished by integrating out the variable v from the joint distribution function of t and v; hence

$$f(t) = c \int_0^{\infty} v^{\nu} e^{-\frac{v^2}{2}\left(1 + \frac{t^2}{\nu}\right)} dv$$

Let $y = \dfrac{v^2}{2}\left(1 + \dfrac{t^2}{\nu}\right)$; then $dv = \dfrac{dy}{\sqrt{2y}\sqrt{1 + \dfrac{t^2}{\nu}}}$ and

$$f(t) = c \int_0^{\infty} \left(\frac{y}{1 + \dfrac{t^2}{\nu}}\right)^{\frac{\nu}{2}} e^{-y} \frac{dy}{\sqrt{y}\sqrt{1 + \dfrac{t^2}{\nu}}}$$

$$= c\left(1 + \frac{t^2}{\nu}\right)^{-\frac{\nu+1}{2}} \int_0^{\infty} y^{\frac{\nu-1}{2}} e^{-y}\, dy$$

$$= c\left(1 + \frac{t^2}{\nu}\right)^{-\frac{\nu+1}{2}}$$

since the last integral is merely a constant as far as the variable t is concerned. The preceding derivation proves the following theorem.

Theorem IV. *If u is normally distributed with zero mean and unit variance and v^2 has a χ^2 distribution with ν degrees of freedom, and if u and v are independently distributed, then the variable*

$$t = \frac{u\sqrt{\nu}}{v}$$

has Student's t distribution with v degrees of freedom given by

$$f(t) = c\left(1 + \frac{t^2}{\nu}\right)^{-\frac{\nu+1}{2}}$$

Now consider once more the problem that was introduced at the beginning of this section in order to see how this theorem can remedy the defect in the large-sample method of solution. Since x is normally distributed with zero mean, the variable

$$u = \frac{\bar{x}}{\sigma_{\bar{x}}} = \frac{\bar{x}\sqrt{n}}{\sigma}$$

possesses the properties of u in Theorem IV. From Theorem II it follows that

$$v^2 = \frac{ns^2}{\sigma^2}$$

possesses the properties of v^2 in Theorem IV with $\nu = n - 1$. Since it is known that $\bar{x}$ and s^2 are independently distributed, Theorem IV may be applied to give

$$\frac{u\sqrt{\nu}}{\sqrt{\nu}} = t = \frac{\bar{x}\sqrt{n-1}}{s} = \frac{1.24\sqrt{9}}{1.45} = 2.57, \quad \nu = 9$$

From Table IV it will be found that the probability is approximately 0.017 of obtaining a value of $t > 2.57$. This result is also significant at the 5% significance level.

A comparison of this probability of $P = 0.017$ with that of $P = 0.0035$ obtained by the use of large-sample methods shows that the large-sample method is not accurate for a sample as small as 10. It will be found that the large-sample method gives probabilities that are consistently too small; consequently large-sample methods will claim significant results more often than is justified. The explanation for this bias on the part of large-sample methods is that the t distribution has a slightly larger dispersion than the standard normal distribution. The situation is shown graphically in Fig. 5, which gives the graphs of the standard normal distribution and Student's t distribution for 4 degrees of freedom.

The important feature of the t distribution is that it does not depend on any unknown population parameters and hence there is no necessity for replacing parameter values by questionable sample estimates as there is in the large-sample normal curve method.

The inaccuracy of the large-sample method could have been reduced somewhat by using the unbiased estimate of σ^2; however, for samples as small as 10 the error would still be considerable.

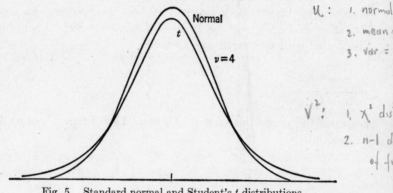

Fig. 5.   Standard normal and Student's t distributions.

APPLICATIONS OF THE t DISTRIBUTION

1. Confidence Limits for a Mean

Let x be normally distributed with mean m and variance σ^2. Let $\bar{x}$ and s^2 be their sample values based on a random sample of size n. Then

$$u = \frac{\bar{x} - m}{\sigma/\sqrt{n}}$$

and

$$v^2 = \frac{ns^2}{\sigma^2}$$

satisfy the requirements of u and v in Theorem IV; consequently

$$(15) \qquad t = \frac{(\bar{x} - m)\sqrt{n - 1}}{s}$$

has a t distribution with $n - 1$ degrees of freedom. If $t_{0.05}$ represents the value of t for $n - 1$ degrees of freedom such that the probability is 0.05 that $|t| > t_{0.05}$, then the probability is 0.95 that

$$\left| \frac{(\bar{x} - m)\sqrt{n - 1}}{s} \right| < t_{0.05}$$

or that

$$\bar{x} - t_{0.05} \frac{s}{\sqrt{n-1}} < m < \bar{x} + t_{0.05} \frac{s}{\sqrt{n-1}}$$

This inequality determines a 95% confidence interval for m. If some probability other than 0.95 is desired, it is merely necessary to replace $t_{0.05}$ by the corresponding value of t from Table IV.

2. Difference between Two Means

The t distribution may be used to eliminate the error in large-sample methods when testing the difference between two means in the same manner as for testing one mean. Let x and y be normally distributed with means m_x and m_y and with the same variance, σ^2. Let random samples of size n_x and n_y be taken from these two populations. Denote the sample means and variances by $\bar{x}$, $\bar{y}$, s_x^2, and s_y^2. Then

$$u = \frac{(\bar{x} - \bar{y}) - (m_x - m_y)}{\sigma_{\bar{x}-\bar{y}}}$$

$$= \frac{(\bar{x} - \bar{y}) - (m_x - m_y)}{\sigma\sqrt{\dfrac{1}{n_x} + \dfrac{1}{n_y}}}$$

will possess the required properties of u in Theorem IV. Furthermore,

$$v^2 = \frac{n_x s_x^2 + n_y s_y^2}{\sigma^2}$$

with $\nu = n_x + n_y - 2$ degrees of freedom, is easily seen to possess the properties of v^2 in Theorem IV. This follows from Theorem II and Theorem III because

$$\frac{n_x s_x^2}{\sigma^2} \quad \text{and} \quad \frac{n_y s_y^2}{\sigma^2}$$

possess independent χ^2 distributions with $n_x - 1$ and $n_y - 1$ degrees of freedom, respectively. Consequently,

$$(16) \quad t = \frac{(\bar{x} - \bar{y}) - (m_x - m_y)}{\sqrt{n_x s_x^2 + n_y s_y^2}} \sqrt{\frac{n_x n_y (n_x + n_y - 2)}{n_x + n_y}},$$

$$\nu = n_x + n_y - 2$$

will have Student's t distribution with $n_x + n_y - 2$ degrees of freedom. Then, to test the hypothesis that $m_x = m_y$, it is merely necessary to calculate the value of t and use Table IV to see whether the sample value of t numerically exceeds the critical value.

It will be noted that the value of t does not depend upon any population parameters as in the large-sample method explained just after Theorem III, Chapter IV. It will also be noted, however, that the t test is less general than the large-sample method because here it is necessary to assume equality of the variances, which was not true for the large-sample approach. In a later section the problem of testing for the equality of variances will be considered so that this assumption can be checked for its reasonableness. A method is available that does not require equality of the variances; however, its theory is too advanced to be considered here.

Formula (16) may also be used to determine confidence limits for $m_x - m_y$. If it has been shown that the hypothesis of $m_x = m_y$ is not reasonable, it is of interest to know how large or how small a difference is reasonable. For a given probability, confidence limits will give the minimum and maximum differences.

As a numerical illustration, consider the data of Table 2 on the yield of corn in bushels on 10 pairs of plots in which plot one of each pair received some phosphorus as a fertilizer.

TABLE 2

Plot 1	6.2	5.7	6.5	6.0	6.3	5.8	5.7	6.0	6.0	5.8
Plot 2	5.6	5.9	5.6	5.7	5.8	5.7	6.0	5.5	5.7	5.5

It will be assumed that all pairs of plots were treated alike except for the addition of phosphorus to half of them and that the yield of corn may be treated as a normal variable. If x and y correspond to plots 1 and 2, respectively, it will also be assumed that $\sigma_x = \sigma_y$. Now set up the hypothesis that $m_x = m_y$. Calculations here give

$$\bar{x} = 6.0, \quad n_x s_x^2 = 0.64$$

$$\bar{y} = 5.7, \quad n_y s_y^2 = 0.24$$

When (16) is applied,

$$t = \frac{0.3}{\sqrt{0.64 + 0.24}} \sqrt{\frac{100(18)}{20}} = 3.03, \quad \nu = 18$$

From Table IV the 1% critical value of $t = 2.55$, only the right tail being considered; consequently this result is highly significant, and the hypothesis of no increase in mean yield will be discarded. If the assumptions of normality and equality of variances are reasonable so that the experimenter can justifiably claim that this significant difference is due to a real difference in the population means, it becomes of interest to know how large a real difference is likely. Confidence limits for $m_x - m_y$ will give the desired information. The same calculations as above give

$$t = \frac{0.3 - (m_x - m_y)}{0.0989}$$

Then 95% confidence limits are given by

$$\left| \frac{0.3 - (m_x - m_y)}{0.0989} \right| < 2.101$$

which reduces to

$$0.092 < m_x - m_y < 0.508$$

From this result it is clear that, for a sample as small as 10, one cannot promise with any great degree of certainty more than about a 2% increase in yield due to the addition of the phosphorus.

3. Confidence Limits for a Regression Coefficient

The problem to be considered in this section is determining whether the difference between the slopes of a sample and a theoretical regression line might reasonably be due to sampling variation. Let X and Y denote the two variables, and let X_i and $Y_i (i = 1, 2, \cdots, n)$ denote their sample values for a random sample of size n. Then the corresponding small letter will be used to represent the variable measured from its mean. With this notation, the equation of the least-squares regression line as given by (3), Chapter V, is $y' = bx$, where

$$b = \frac{\sum_{1}^{n} x_i Y_i}{\sum_{1}^{n} x_i^2}$$

Now let repeated random samples of size n be selected such that precisely the same set of X values as the original set is obtained each time. This restriction means that the X_i are not treated as variables once the first sample of n has been taken. As a matter of fact, the original set of X's need not be selected at random. Then it will be assumed that the Y_i are normally distributed about a true regression line, whose equation will be written

$$Y' = \alpha + \beta X$$

with the same variance, σ^2, for all Y_i. It should be noted that $X_i(i = 1, \cdots, n)$ is fixed but that to each sample of n there corresponds one value of Y_i, so that Y_i is a statistical variable. The assumptions made here concerning the variables Y_i may seem rather stringent; however, it may be recalled that it was shown in Chapter VI that the properties assumed here are possessed if X and Y are jointly normally distributed.

For simplicity of notation, let

$$(17) \qquad\qquad w_i = \frac{x_i}{\Sigma x_i^2}$$

Then

$$b = \Sigma w_i Y_i$$

Since the x_i are fixed, they may be treated as constants; consequently b may be treated as a linear function of the Y_i. Now the Y_i are statistically independent and have the same variances; therefore it is readily shown that

$$\sigma_b^2 = \Sigma w_i^2 \sigma_{Y i}^2 = \sigma^2 \Sigma w_i^2$$

Substitute (17); then

$$\sigma_b^2 = \frac{\sigma^2}{\Sigma x_i^2}$$

By means of the methods employed in Chapter IV in the section devoted to the distribution of $\bar{x}$ from a normal distribution, it is easy to show that a linear combination of independent normal variables is normally distributed. Since the Y_i are independent normal variables and b is a linear combination of them,

$$u = \frac{b - \beta}{\sigma_b} = \frac{b - \beta}{\sigma} \sqrt{\Sigma x_i^2}$$

possesses the properties of u in Theorem IV. Furthermore, it can be shown with considerably more difficulty that the measure of variation

$$v^2 = \frac{\Sigma (Y_i - Y_i')^2}{\sigma^2}, \quad \nu = n - 2$$

where Y_i' represents the sample linear regression estimate of Y_i, possesses the properties of v^2 in Theorem IV with $n - 2$ degrees of freedom. This fact will be assumed here. Therefore, by Theorem IV,

$$(18) \qquad t = (b - \beta) \sqrt{\frac{(n - 2)\Sigma(X_i - \bar{X})^2}{\Sigma(Y_i - Y_i')^2}}, \quad \nu = n - 2$$

will have Student's t distribution with $n - 2$ degrees of freedom. Formula (18) can be used to test compatibility between a sample and a theoretical regression coefficient or to find confidence limits for β.

As an illustration of (18), consider the data of Table 3 on the relationship between the thickness of coatings of galvanized zinc by a standard stripping method, Y, and a magnetic method, X. If the

TABLE 3

Y	116	132	104	139	114	129	720	174	312	338	465
X	105	120	85	121	115	127	630	155	250	310	443

magnetic method were reliable, it would be preferred because it is a non-destructive test. If a least-squares line is fitted to this set of points, its equation will be found to be

$$Y = -1.79 + 1.12X$$

It will also be found that

$$\Sigma(X_i - \overline{X})^2 = 301{,}826$$

$$\Sigma(Y_i - Y_i')^2 = 2{,}766$$

Although the investigator here would undoubtedly be interested in obtaining a measure of the precision of the magnetic method as a substitute for the stripping method, that problem can be treated by the confidence-limits technique of the variance applied to the variance of the errors of estimate. The problem was introduced here to test whether the magnetic method was consistent over the range of thicknesses. It might happen, for example, that the magnetic method gives too small a reading for thin coatings and too large a reading for thick coatings. If the method were biased in this direction, the slope of the regression line would tend to be too large. In this problem, therefore, set up the hypothesis that $\beta = 1$. If it is assumed that the necessary conditions for applying (18) are satisfied, then

$$t = 0.12 \sqrt{\frac{9(301{,}826)}{2{,}766}} = 3.76, \quad \nu = 9$$

From Table IV the 5% critical value of t is 2.26; consequently this value is significant. It appears that there is a slight bias in the magnetic method. If the magnetic method were to be used, a larger experiment should be run in order to obtain an accurate estimate of the bias and correct for it.

THE F DISTRIBUTION

It will be recalled that it was necessary to assume that $\sigma_x = \sigma_y$ in order to apply the t distribution to testing the difference between two means. In order to justify the reasonableness of this assumption, it is necessary to derive a distribution function for testing the equality of two variances. It will be found that such a distribution function has many other uses as well. To this end, let u and v possess independent χ^2 distributions with ν_1 and ν_2 degrees of freedom, respectively. Then consider the problem of finding the distribution function of u/v.

Because of the independence of u and v, it follows from (8) that

$$f(u, v) = f(u)f(v)$$
$$= cu^{\frac{\nu_1-2}{2}} e^{-\frac{u}{2}} \cdot cv^{\frac{\nu_2-2}{2}} e^{-\frac{v}{2}}$$

where c denotes any and all constants of no immediate interest. Let

$$w = \frac{u}{v}$$

represent a change of variable from u to w with v held fixed. Since $u = vw$, it follows from (7) that

$$f(w, v) = f(u, v)v$$
$$= cu^{\frac{\nu_1-2}{2}} v^{\frac{\nu_2}{2}} e^{-\frac{u+v}{2}}$$
$$= cw^{\frac{\nu_1-2}{2}} v^{\frac{\nu_1+\nu_2-2}{2}} e^{-\frac{v}{2}(1+w)}$$

In order to obtain the distribution function of w, it is necessary to integrate out the variable v; hence

$$f(w) = \int_0^\infty f(w, v)\, dv$$
$$= cw^{\frac{\nu_1-2}{2}} \int_0^\infty v^{\frac{\nu_1+\nu_2-2}{2}} e^{-\frac{v}{2}(1+w)}\, dv$$

Let $y = \dfrac{v}{2}(1 + w)$; then $f(w)$ reduces to

$$f(w) = cw^{\frac{\nu_1-2}{2}} \int_0^\infty \left(\frac{2y}{1+w}\right)^{\frac{\nu_1+\nu_2-2}{2}} e^{-y} \frac{2}{1+w}\, dy$$

$$= \frac{cw^{\frac{\nu_1-2}{2}}}{(1+w)^{\frac{\nu_1+\nu_2}{2}}} \int_0^\infty y^{\frac{\nu_1+\nu_2-2}{2}} e^{-y}\, dy$$

(19)
$$= \frac{cw^{\frac{\nu_1-2}{2}}}{(1+w)^{\frac{\nu_1+\nu_2}{2}}}$$

For certain applications, it is more convenient to work with a slight variation of w than with w itself; therefore consider the variable

$$F = \frac{u/\nu_1}{v/\nu_2} = \frac{\nu_2}{\nu_1}\frac{u}{v} = \frac{\nu_2}{\nu_1}w$$

If this change of variable from w to F is made in (19), it follows that

$$f(F) = f(w)\frac{\nu_1}{\nu_2}$$

$$= \frac{cF^{\frac{\nu_1-2}{2}}}{(\nu_2 + \nu_1 F)^{\frac{\nu_1+\nu_2}{2}}}$$

These derivations prove the following theorem.

Theorem V. *If u and v possess independent χ^2 distributions with ν_1 and ν_2 degrees of freedom, respectively, then*

$$F = \frac{u/\nu_1}{v/\nu_2}$$

has the F distribution function with ν_1 and ν_2 degrees of freedom given by

$$f(F) = \frac{cF^{\frac{\nu_1-2}{2}}}{(\nu_2 + \nu_1 F)^{\frac{\nu_1+\nu_2}{2}}}$$

APPLICATIONS OF THE F DISTRIBUTION

1. Testing the Compatibility of Two Variances

Since the F distribution was derived partly in order to justify the assumption of the equality of variances which is needed in the t test when that test is applied to testing the difference between two means, consider the problem of testing the hypothesis that $\sigma_x = \sigma_y$ under the assumption that x and y are normally distributed. Let s_x^2 and s_y^2 be sample variances based upon random samples of size n_x and n_y, respectively, from these two populations. Then, since $n_x s_x^2 / \sigma_x^2$ and $n_y s_y^2 / \sigma_y^2$ possess independent χ^2 distributions,

$$\frac{u}{\nu_1} = \frac{n_x s_x^2}{(n_x - 1)\sigma_x^2}$$

and

$$\frac{v}{\nu_2} = \frac{n_y s_y^2}{(n_y - 1)\sigma_y^2}$$

satisfy the requirements for u/ν_1 and v/ν_2 in Theorem V. By hypothesis $\sigma_x = \sigma_y$; therefore by Theorem V

$$F = \frac{n_x s_x^2 / (n_x - 1)}{n_y s_y^2 / (n_y - 1)}$$

$$= \frac{\hat{\sigma}_x^2}{\hat{\sigma}_y^2}$$

possesses the F distribution with $n_x - 1$ and $n_y - 1$ degrees of freedom. This test, like the t test, possesses the desirable feature of being independent of population parameters.

As a numerical illustration, consider the problem that illustrated the application of the t distribution to the testing of the difference between two normal means. From Table 2 and immediately following,

$$\hat{\sigma}_x^2 = \frac{n_x s_x^2}{n_x - 1} = 0.071$$

and

$$\hat{\sigma}_y^2 = \frac{n_y s_y^2}{n_y - 1} = 0.027$$

Therefore $F = 2.63$ with $\nu_1 = \nu_2 = 9$ degrees of freedom. It is necessary to consult tables of critical values of the F distribution in order to decide whether this value of F is unreasonably large or small. Such values are to be found in Table V.

Since the F distribution depends on the two parameters ν_1 and ν_2, a three-way table would be needed to tabulate the value of F corresponding to different probabilities and values of ν_1 and ν_2. As a consequence, only the 5% and 1% right-tail-area points are tabulated corresponding to various values of ν_1 and ν_2. The technique of the use of Table V will be explained by means of the graph in Fig. 6, which illustrates the graph of $f(F)$ for a typical pair of values of ν_1 and ν_2. Let F_1 denote the value of F for which $P[F < F_1] = 0.025$, and F_2 the

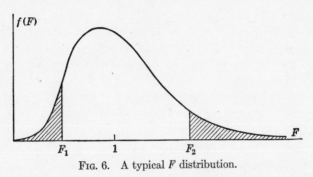

FIG. 6.   A typical F distribution.

value for which $P[F > F_2] = 0.025$. If the sample value of F falls outside the interval (F_1, F_2), the hypothesis of a common σ^2 will be rejected. For convenience of notation, let $F' = 1/F$. Since $F = \hat{\sigma}_x^2/\hat{\sigma}_y^2$ with ν_1 and ν_2 degrees of freedom, $F' = \hat{\sigma}_y^2/\hat{\sigma}_x^2$ with ν_2 and ν_1 degrees of freedom. By means of the reciprocal function, F', the probability of $F < F_1$ can be evaluated as follows:

$$0.025 = P[F < F_1] = P\left[\frac{1}{F} > \frac{1}{F_1}\right] = P\left[F' > \frac{1}{F_1}\right]$$

This result shows that the left critical point of the F distribution corresponds to the right critical point of the F' distribution. As a result, it is necessary to find only right critical points for F and F' to determine F_2 and F_1. Because of this property of F, only right critical points for F are tabulated. Unfortunately, only the 5% and 1% critical points have been tabulated in Table V; consequently it is necessary to interpolate roughly half way between these two values in order to obtain an approximate $2\frac{1}{2}\%$ critical point.

In view of this reciprocal property, the procedure to be followed is always to place the larger of the two unbiased variance estimates in the numerator of F; consequently $\hat{\sigma}_x^2$ will always denote the larger of the two estimates. If the hypothesis of a common σ^2 is rejected whenever the sample value of F exceeds its $2\frac{1}{2}\%$ point, the hypothesis will be rejected whenever the original F falls outside the interval (F_1, F_2), because, when $F > 1$, F_2 will serve as the critical value, and when $F < 1$, F' will be used instead and F_2' will serve as the critical value. But, as was demonstrated in the preceding paragraph, F_2' for F' corresponds to F_1 for F.

If this procedure is applied to the numerical problem being discussed, it will be found from Table V that the 5% critical value is

$$F_2 = 4.5, \quad \nu_1 = \nu_2 = 9$$

The sample value of $F = 2.63$ is therefore not significant. This result implies that the assumption of equal variances is a reasonable one and that the significant value of t obtained in connection with this problem when testing the hypothesis $m_x = m_y$ may not be reasonably attributed to a lack of the assumption $\sigma_x = \sigma_y$ being satisfied. This check on the reasonableness of the assumption that $\sigma_x = \sigma_y$ should be carried out whenever the t test is used to test the difference between two means. It does not follow, however, that, if the hypothesis $\sigma_x = \sigma_y$ is not substantiated, a significant value of t will be due to a lack of this assumption's being satisfied.

2. Testing the Homogeneity of a Set of Means

Problems similar to the one that arose in connection with Table 2 are rather common, but in the early stages of experimentation there may be several means for comparison rather than just two. For example, phosphorus in several different amounts may have been applied to equal numbers of plots, or various compounds may have been tried as possible fertilizers to equal numbers of plots. For such experiments it is incorrect to use the difference-of-two-means technique on any two selected means because these differences will be a function of the number of means available for comparison. If there were a large number of such means, the smallest and largest differences would differ considerably by chance, even if all the means had been drawn from the same population. A set of more than two means can be legitimately compared by means of the F distribution in the following manner.

Consider a set of n values of the statistical variable x arranged into a rows and b columns. For convenience of notation, let x_{ij} represent the value found in the ith row and jth column, $\bar{x}_{.j}$ the mean of the jth column, and $\bar{x}_{i.}$ the mean of the ith row. This arrangement and notation is indicated in Table 4.

TABLE 4

x_{11}	x_{12}	$\cdots$	x_{1j}	$\cdots$	x_{1b}	$\bar{x}_{1\cdot}$
x_{21}	x_{22}	$\cdots$	x_{2j}	$\cdots$	x_{2b}	$\bar{x}_{2\cdot}$
$\cdot$	$\cdot$		$\cdot$		$\cdot$	$\cdot$
$\cdot$	$\cdot$		$\cdot$		$\cdot$	$\cdot$
$\cdot$	$\cdot$		$\cdot$		$\cdot$	$\cdot$
x_{i1}	x_{i2}	$\cdots$	x_{ij}	$\cdots$	x_{ib}	$\bar{x}_{i\cdot}$
$\cdot$			$\cdot$		$\cdot$	$\cdot$
$\cdot$			$\cdot$		$\cdot$	$\cdot$
$\cdot$			$\cdot$			$\cdot$
x_{a1}	x_{a2}	$\cdots$	x_{aj}	$\cdots$	x_{ab}	$\bar{x}_{a\cdot}$
$\bar{x}_{\cdot 1}$	$\bar{x}_{\cdot 2}$	$\cdots$	$\bar{x}_{\cdot j}$	$\cdots$	$\bar{x}_{\cdot b}$	$\bar{x}$

Suppose that these values of x are random sample values from a normal population with mean m and variance σ^2 and that the arrangement of the values into rows and columns is a random one. Then the variance of x may be analyzed as follows.

$$(20) \quad \sum_{i=1}^{a} \sum_{j=1}^{b} (x_{ij} - \bar{x})^2 = \sum_{i=1}^{a} \sum_{j=1}^{b} [(x_{ij} - \bar{x}_{\cdot j}) + (\bar{x}_{\cdot j} - \bar{x})]^2$$

$$= \sum_{i=1}^{a} \sum_{j=1}^{b} (x_{ij} - \bar{x}_{\cdot j})^2 + \sum_{i=1}^{a} \sum_{j=1}^{b} (\bar{x}_{\cdot j} - \bar{x})^2$$

$$+ 2 \sum_{i=1}^{a} \sum_{j=1}^{b} (x_{ij} - \bar{x}_{\cdot j})(\bar{x}_{\cdot j} - \bar{x})$$

If the cross-product term is summed with respect to i first, $\bar{x}_{\cdot j} - \bar{x}$ will be a constant; hence this sum may be written as

$$2 \sum_{j=1}^{b} [(\bar{x}_{\cdot j} - \bar{x}) \sum_{i=1}^{a} (x_{ij} - \bar{x}_{\cdot j})]$$

Since the sum with respect to i is the sum of the deviations of the elements of the jth column from their mean, this cross-product term vanishes; consequently (20) reduces to

$$(21) \quad \sum_{i=1}^{a} \sum_{j=1}^{b} (x_{ij} - \bar{x})^2 = \sum_{i=1}^{a} \sum_{j=1}^{b} (x_{ij} - \bar{x}_{\cdot j})^2 + a \sum_{j=1}^{b} (\bar{x}_{\cdot j} - \bar{x})^2$$

Now the x_{ij} are merely random-sample values of the variable x; therefore by Theorem II it follows that

$$(22) \qquad \frac{1}{\sigma^2} \sum_{i=1}^{a} \sum_{j=1}^{b} (x_{ij} - \bar{x})^2$$

possesses a χ^2 distribution with $ab - 1$ degrees of freedom. Since the elements of any given column are also random-sample values of the variable x, it follows from Theorem II and Theorem III that

$$(23) \qquad \frac{1}{\sigma^2} \sum_{i=1}^{a} \sum_{j=1}^{b} (x_{ij} - \bar{x}_{.j})^2$$

possesses a χ^2 distribution with $b(a - 1)$ degrees of freedom. Theorem II applies to each column sum of squares, while Theorem III permits the combining of these quantities. Finally, because the $\bar{x}_{.j}$ constitute a set of b random means, it follows from Theorem II that

$$(24) \qquad \frac{a}{\sigma^2} \sum_{j=1}^{b} (\bar{x}_{.j} - \bar{x})^2$$

possesses a χ^2 distribution with $b - 1$ degrees of freedom. The factor a occurs here because the variable $\bar{x}_{.j}$ is a mean with variance σ^2/a and therefore the sum of squares must be divided by σ^2/a rather than by σ^2.

It is clear from (21) that not all three of these quantities possessing χ^2 distributions are independent. If the first term on the right were unusually large, for example, the left side would be made unusually large unless the second term on the right became small to compensate for the increase in the first term. However, it can be shown that the two terms on the right of (21) are independently distributed. The proof of this fact is fairly complicated and therefore will not be considered here. If the fact is assumed here, it follows that of these three quantities only (23) and (24) are independently distributed. It therefore follows from Theorem V that

$$(25) \qquad F = \frac{a \sum_{j=1}^{b} (\bar{x}_{.j} - \bar{x})^2}{\sigma^2 (b - 1)} \div \frac{\sum_{i=1}^{a} \sum_{j=1}^{b} (x_{ij} - \bar{x}_{.j})^2}{\sigma^2 b(a - 1)}$$

$$= \frac{ab(a - 1) \sum_{j=1}^{b} (\bar{x}_{.j} - \bar{x})^2}{(b - 1) \sum_{i=1}^{a} \sum_{j=1}^{b} (x_{ij} - \bar{x}_{.j})^2}$$

possesses an F distribution with $\nu_1 = b - 1$ and $\nu_2 = b(a - 1)$ degrees of freedom.

In applying (25) to problems, the arrangement of the sample values into columns will be with respect to some criterion that the experimenter is interested in testing. For example, as suggested at the beginning of this section, each column may correspond to a different amount of phosphorus added, or to a different compound. However, under the hypothesis that the variable x is independent of the criterion used for the classification, the columns may be treated as random samples and the F distribution may be applied to (25). If F exceeds its critical value, the hypothesis would be rejected and the experimenter would have evidence for believing that his criterion for classifying the data into columns was pertinent. This conclusion follows from the fact that, if the means of columns vary more than could be reasonably attributed to the random sampling variation of a normal variable, the value of the numerator in (25) would tend to be too large but the value of the denominator would not be so affected, with the result that F would tend to be too large. In a problem of this type, only the right tail of the F distribution is used for determining a critical value because the experimenter is interested only in knowing whether the means of columns vary too much and hence always applies (25) directly rather than considering its reciprocal also as is done when testing the hypothesis $\sigma_x = \sigma_y$. In applying (25), one therefore chooses the 5% value of F in Table V when using a 5% level of significance.

As a numerical illustration, consider the data of Table 5 on the yield of potatoes in pounds per plot in which 5 different treatments were used on 4 plots each. Although there appear to be treatment differences here, in order to test this belief it will be assumed that the 20 yields may be considered random-sample values of a normal variable. This assumption implies that the 5 treatments do not differ in their effects on yield and also that the 4 plots do not differ in fertility.

TABLE 5

Treatment

Plot		A	B	C	D	E
	1	306	349	442	295	457
	2	288	297	434	268	415
	3	307	304	419	310	467
	4	268	308	404	166	428

For computing purposes, the sums in (24) and (23) may be written

$$a \sum_{j=1}^{b} (\bar{x}._j - \bar{x})^2 = \frac{1}{a} \sum_{j=1}^{b} \left(\sum_{i=1}^{a} x_{ij} \right)^2 - \frac{1}{ab} \left(\sum_{i=1}^{a} \sum_{j=1}^{b} x_{ij} \right)^2$$

and

$$\sum_{i=1}^{a} \sum_{j=1}^{b} (x_{ij} - \bar{x}._j)^2 = \sum_{i=1}^{a} \sum_{j=1}^{b} x_{ij}^2 - \frac{1}{a} \sum_{j=1}^{b} \left(\sum_{i=1}^{a} x_{ij} \right)^2$$

These computing forms are readily verified by expanding the left sides and expressing all means in terms of sums. On a calculating machine the sums and sums of squares of elements for each column are calculated, then the sum of squares of these column totals is obtained. Calculations for this problem give

$$4 \sum_{j=1}^{5} (\bar{x}._j - \bar{x})^2 = 2,509,384 - 2,402,631 = 106,753$$

and

$$\sum_{i=1}^{4} \sum_{j=1}^{5} (x_{ij} - \bar{x}._j)^2 = 2,527,292 - 2,509,384 = 17,908$$

Then when (25) is applied,

$$F = \frac{15(106,753)}{4(17,908)} = 22, \quad \nu_1 = 4, \quad \nu_2 = 15$$

From Table V it is clear that this result is highly significant; therefore the 5 treatments undoubtedly differ in their effect on yield. A statistical test would hardly have been necessary here because an inspection of Table 5 will reveal that treatments C and E are superior to the others. However, if the differences had not been quite so pronounced, the experimenter would not have been able to make a valid judgment without some statistical test.

3. Testing the Homogeneity of Rows and Columns

In the last section, interest was centered on the variation of column means because the amount of this variation determined whether the classification with respect to columns was significant. However, the technique of breaking down the fundamental sum of squares into components of experimental interest, as was done in (21), can be generalized. It is known as the *analysis-of-variance* technique. In this method the fundamental sum of squares is analyzed into components such that one component measures that part of the variation that is being tested and another component measures what is often called the *experimental error*, that is, the variation in the fundamental variable after the effects of the controlled variables have been eliminated. For the classification considered in the last section, the fundamental sum of squares on the left side of (21) is broken down into two sums of squares. The second term on the right measures the variation between columns and hence measures that part of the variation being tested. The first term measures the variation within columns and is not influenced by the variation between columns; consequently this term measures what may be thought of as the natural variation after column effects have been eliminated, or as experimental error.

Consider the analysis-of-variance technique when both row and column variation are of interest. The fundamental sum of squares is broken down as follows.

$$
\sum_{i=1}^{a} \sum_{j=1}^{b} (x_{ij} - \bar{x})^2 = \sum_{i=1}^{a} \sum_{j=1}^{b} [(\bar{x}_{.j} - \bar{x}) + (\bar{x}_{i.} - \bar{x})
$$
$$
+ (x_{ij} - \bar{x}_{.j} - \bar{x}_{i.} + \bar{x})]^2
$$
$$
= \sum_{i=1}^{a} \sum_{j=1}^{b} (\bar{x}_{.j} - \bar{x})^2 + \sum_{i=1}^{a} \sum_{j=1}^{b} (\bar{x}_{i.} - \bar{x})^2
$$
$$
+ \sum_{i=1}^{a} \sum_{j=1}^{b} (x_{ij} - \bar{x}_{.j} - \bar{x}_{i.} + \bar{x})^2
$$

This result follows from the fact that all cross-product terms vanish on summation. Of the three terms on the right, the first measures the variation between columns, the second measures the variation between rows, and the last measures the variation after row and column effects have been eliminated. This fundamental identity simplifies somewhat into

$$
(26) \quad \sum_{i=1}^{a} \sum_{j=1}^{b} (x_{ij} - \bar{x})^2 = a \sum_{j=1}^{b} (\bar{x}_{.j} - \bar{x})^2 + b \sum_{i=1}^{a} (\bar{x}_{i.} - \bar{x})^2
$$
$$
+ \sum_{i=1}^{a} \sum_{j=1}^{b} (x_{ij} - \bar{x}_{.j} - \bar{x}_{i.} + \bar{x})^2
$$

If, as in the preceding section, it is assumed that x is normally distributed with variance σ^2 and the classification into rows and columns is a random classification, then it can be shown that all three quantities on the right of (26) when divided by σ^2 possess independent χ^2 distributions with $b - 1$, $a - 1$, and $(a - 1)(b - 1)$ degrees of freedom, respectively. If the experimenter were interested in the means of columns, he would apply Theorem V to

$$\frac{u}{\nu_1} = \frac{a \sum_{j=1}^{b}(\bar{x}_{\cdot j} - \bar{x})^2}{\sigma^2(b-1)}$$

and

$$\frac{v}{\nu_2} = \frac{\sum_{i=1}^{a}\sum_{j=1}^{b}(x_{ij} - \bar{x}_{\cdot j} - \bar{x}_{i \cdot} + \bar{x})^2}{\sigma^2(a-1)(b-1)}$$

If he were interested in the means of rows, he would apply the F test to

$$\frac{u}{\nu_1} = \frac{b \sum_{i=1}^{a}(\bar{x}_{i \cdot} - \bar{x})^2}{\sigma^2(a-1)}$$

and

$$\frac{v}{\nu_2} = \frac{\sum_{i=1}^{a}\sum_{j=1}^{b}(x_{ij} - \bar{x}_{\cdot j} - \bar{x}_{i \cdot} + \bar{x})^2}{\sigma^2(a-1)(b-1)}$$

Although the proofs that the F distribution may be applied as indicated are fairly involved, the mechanics of applying the F test is straightforward.

If the columns in the preceding test differ significantly, the F test may still be applied to testing the homogeneity of the rows, provided that a further assumption concerning the linearity of means is made. The meaning of this assumption will not be discussed here; however, it is a very plausible assumption.

As a numerical illustration of these ideas, consider once more the problem of Table 5. From (26) it is clear that the last sum is most easily calculated by subtraction after the remaining sums have been calculated. Calculations here give

$$\sum_{i}\sum_{j}(x_{ij} - \bar{x})^2 = \sum_{i}\sum_{j}x_{ij}^2 - \frac{1}{ab}\left(\sum_{i}\sum_{j}x_{ij}\right)^2 = 124{,}661$$

$$a\sum_{j}(\bar{x}_{\cdot j} - \bar{x})^2 = \frac{1}{a}\sum_{j}\left(\sum_{i}x_{ij}\right)^2 - \frac{1}{ab}\left(\sum_{i}\sum_{j}x_{ij}\right)^2 = 106{,}753$$

$$b\sum_{i}(\bar{x}_{i \cdot} - \bar{x})^2 = \frac{1}{b}\sum_{i}\left(\sum_{j}x_{ij}\right)^2 - \frac{1}{ab}\left(\sum_{i}\sum_{j}x_{ij}\right)^2 = 9{,}035$$

Hence

$$\sum_i \sum_j (x_{ij} - \bar{x}_{\cdot j} - \bar{x}_{i\cdot} + \bar{x})^2 = 8{,}873$$

The test for homogeneity of columns yields

$$F = \frac{12(106{,}753)}{4(8{,}873)} = 36, \quad \nu_1 = 4, \quad \nu_2 = 12$$

If this result is compared with that obtained by the analysis following Table 5, it will be observed that the present analysis is sharper than that of the previous section, implying that the elimination of row variability reduced the error variance in the denominator. The test for homogeneity of rows gives

$$F = \frac{12(9{,}035)}{3(8{,}873)} = 4.1, \quad \nu_1 = 3, \quad \nu_2 = 12$$

From Table V it will be found that the critical value of F at the 5% level of significance is 3.49; consequently the value 4.1 is barely significant. This result indicates that an explanation other than sampling variation should be sought to account for the row variability. Experience with experiments of this type shows that there is considerable variation of soil fertility in experimental plots unless the plots are small and close together. The lack of homogeneity in plot yields may therefore be caused by differences of fertility in the 4 plots.

DISTRIBUTION OF THE RANGE

In certain fields of applied statistics, the amount of routine computation becomes burdensome unless methods are chosen that involve only a small amount of it. In industrial quality control work, for example, the repeated computation of standard deviations as measures of the variability of a product is undesirable. It is customary in such work to take the range as the measure of variability. Not only is the range easy to compute, but also it is simple to explain as a measure of variability to individuals without a statistical background. For small samples from a normal population, it can be shown that the range is nearly as efficient, in a certain sense, for estimating σ as is the sample standard deviation; consequently for small samples the range is a highly useful statistic.

Consider a random sample, $x_1', x_2', \cdots, x_n'$, drawn from the population whose distribution function will be denoted by $p(x)$. Let these sample values be arranged in order of increasing magnitude, and denote the ordered set by $x_1, x_2, \cdots, x_n$. Now consider the problem of finding the probability that the smallest value, x_1, and the largest value, x_n, will fall within specified intervals. The distribution function of the range can be found quite easily by means of this probability.

Let the x axis be divided into the five intervals $(-\infty, u)$, $(u, u + \Delta u)$, $(u + \Delta u, v)$, $(v, v + \Delta v)$, $(v + \Delta v, \infty)$, where $u < v$ are any two values of x. The probability that x will fall in any particular one of these intervals is given by the integral of $p(x)$ over that interval; hence the probabilities corresponding to these five intervals can be written down even though they cannot be evaluated unless the form of $p(x)$ is known. In this connection, let

$$(27) \quad p_2 = \int_u^{u+\Delta u} p(x)\, dx, \quad p_3 = \int_{u+\Delta u}^v p(x)\, dx, \quad p_4 = \int_v^{v+\Delta v} p(x)\, dx$$

and determine the probability that in a sample of n values of x one will obtain no value in the first interval, one value in the second interval, $n - 2$ values in the third interval, one value in the fourth interval, and no value in the fifth interval. This procedure is equivalent to finding the probability that the smallest value in the sample will fall between u and $u + \Delta u$ while the largest value falls between v and $v + \Delta v$. The desired probability can be obtained directly from the multinomial distribution given by (39), Chapter III, by treating x as a discrete variable which can assume only one of five possible values corresponding to the five intervals. If p_1 and p_5 denote the probabilities that x will fall in the first and fifth intervals, respectively, the desired probability is given by

$$\frac{n!}{0!\,1!\,(n-2)!\,1!\,0!} p_1{}^0 p_2{}^1 p_3{}^{n-2} p_4{}^1 p_5{}^0$$

which reduces to

$$(28) \qquad n(n-1)p_2 p_4 p_3{}^{n-2}$$

Expression (28) can be simplified somewhat by simplifying the integrals of (27). Since $p(x)$ is assumed to be a continuous function, the mean-value theorem for integrals may be applied here. This theorem states that, if $p(x)$ is continuous on the interval (α, β), then

$$\int_\alpha^\beta p(x)\, dx = (\beta - \alpha)p(X)$$

where X is some number in the interval (α, β). A direct application of this theorem to (27) shows that

$$p_2 = \Delta u p(u + \theta_1 \Delta u), \quad 0 \le \theta_1 \le 1$$

and

$$p_4 = \Delta v p(v + \theta_2 \Delta v), \quad 0 \le \theta_2 \le 1$$

The first of these two results when applied to p_3 yields

$$p_3 = \int_{u+\Delta u}^{v} p(x)\, dx = \int_{u}^{v} p(x)\, dx - \int_{u}^{u+\Delta u} p(x)\, dx$$

$$= \int_{u}^{v} p(x)\, dx - \Delta u p(u + \theta_1 \Delta u)$$

If these values for p_2, p_3, and p_4 are inserted in (28), it becomes

$$(29) \quad n(n-1)p(u + \theta_1 \Delta u)p(v + \theta_2 \Delta v)$$

$$\left[\int_{u}^{v} p(x)\, dx - \Delta u p(u + \theta_1 \Delta u) \right]^{n-2} \Delta u\, \Delta v$$

This expression gives the probability that the smallest and largest values of a sample of size n will yield a point in the u, v plane that lies within the rectangle of dimensions Δu and Δv which has the vertex nearest the origin at the point (u, v). Since u and v are arbitrary, they may be treated as statistical variables. In order to find the probability density function of these two variables, it is necessary to divide this probability by the area of the rectangle, namely $\Delta u\, \Delta v$, and take the limit of the resulting quotient as Δu and Δv approach zero. If this desired distribution function is denoted by $f(u, v)$, it follows from (29) that

$$(30) \qquad f(u, v) = n(n-1)p(u)p(v)\left[\int_{u}^{v} p(x)\, dx \right]^{n-2}$$

The preceding developments prove the following theorem.

Theorem VI. *If u and v denote the smallest and largest values, respectively, in a random sample of size n from the population with the continuous distribution function $p(x)$, then the joint distribution function of u and v is given by*

$$f(u, v) = n(n-1)p(u)p(v)\left[\int_{u}^{v} p(x)\, dx \right]^{n-2}$$

The distribution function of the range can be obtained very quickly from this result. Let $R = v - u$ represent a change of variable from v to R with u held fixed. Then, by (7) and (30),

$$f(u, R) = f(u, v)$$

$$(31) \qquad = n(n - 1)p(u)p(u + R)\left[\int_u^{u+R} p(x)\, dx\right]^{n-2}$$

Consequently,

$$f(R) = \int_a^{b-R} f(u, R)\, du$$

where a, b is the range for which $p(x)$ is defined. The upper limit of $b - R$ arises from the fact that $u = v - R$; therefore, for R fixed, u cannot exceed the value obtained by giving v its maximum value b. If the explicit expression for $f(u, R)$ as given by (31) is inserted in this integral, the following formula for the distribution function of the range results.

$$(32) \quad f(R) = n(n - 1)\int_a^{b-R} p(u)p(u + R)\left[\int_u^{u+R} p(x)\, dx\right]^{n-2} du$$

Unless the integral of $p(x)$ is quite simple, this expression is likely to be difficult to work with, even numerically. As an illustration of a simple problem, consider the range for a sample of size n from the horizontal distribution which is defined for $0 \leq x \leq b$ by $p(x) = 1/b$. Here

$$\int_u^{u+R} p(x)\, dx = \frac{R}{b}$$

Therefore by (32)

$$f(R) = n(n - 1)\int_0^{b-R} \frac{1}{b}\cdot\frac{1}{b}\left[\frac{R}{b}\right]^{n-2} du$$

$$= n(n - 1)b^{-n}R^{n-2}(b - R)$$

APPLICATIONS OF THE RANGE

In the introduction to the last section it was remarked that the range was useful as a substitute for the standard deviation as a measure of variability in certain routine operations. It should therefore be of interest to know what the relationship is between the range and the standard deviation. This relationship may be found from the mean of R. Since

$$m_R = \int_0^{b-a} Rf(R)\, dR$$

it is clear from (32) that the evaluation of the relationship will give rise to a complicated double integral unless $p(x)$ is a convenient function. Unfortunately, if x is normally distributed, these integrations cannot be performed directly; therefore numerical methods of integration are required. Tables are available for the normal variable case which express m_R in terms of σ, corresponding to different values of n. Table 6 gives a few entries from such a table to indicate the nature of the relationship.

TABLE 6

n	2	3	4	5	10	50	100	1,000
$\dfrac{m_R}{\sigma}$	1.128	1.693	2.059	2.326	3.078	4.498	5.015	6.483

As an illustration of the use of such tables, consider once more the technique of constructing a quality control chart for $\bar{x}$ as given in the section on the distribution of $\bar{x}$ for non-normal populations in Chapter IV. There a $3\sigma_{\bar{x}}$ band was constructed for controlling $\bar{x}$. If the range is taken as the measure of variability, $3\sigma_{\bar{x}} = 3\sigma/\sqrt{n}$ will be replaced by $3m_R/d_n\sqrt{n}$, where d_n is the value obtained from the table from which Table 6 was extracted. The value of m_R can be approximated from the mean of sample values of R based on samples of size n each. For such charts, n is usually chosen to be an integer near 4; consequently a fairly large number of such samples is needed before a precise estimate of either m or m_R will be available.

If n is chosen less than 10, the estimation of σ by means of the range rather than the standard deviation of a sample is quite efficient. Investigations have shown that it requires approximately 115 sample ranges based on 6 observations each to yield the same precision as 100 sample standard deviations based on 6 observations each, provided the variable is normally distributed.

REFERENCES

For students who have studied advanced calculus, the change-of-variable technique employed in arriving at the t distribution, for example, could be simplified by using Jacobians and making a change of both variables at once. The role of the Jacobian in such transformations, as well as for several variables, is displayed in:

WILKS, S. S., *Mathematical Statistics*, Princeton University Press, pp. 23–29.

A proof of the independence of $\bar{x}$ and s^2 for a normal population may be found in the preceding reference beginning on page 108.

A useful application of the χ^2 distribution arises in connection with the problem of testing the homogeneity of a set of k sample variances from normal populations. A test of this hypothesis is derived in Chapter XII.

For observations ordered in time, the statistic

$$\frac{\sum_{i=1}^{n}(x_{i+1} - x_i)^2}{\sum_{i=1}^{n}(x_i - \bar{x})^2}$$

where $x_{n+1} = x_1$, has proved to be useful for detecting trends in the observations. The numerator alone serves as a measure of variation that is only slightly affected by trends. These two statistics would therefore be expected to be of value in studying the variability of data which are subject to possible trend effects. The theory required to obtain the distribution functions of these statistics is advanced; however, one of the more readable papers is:

> von Neumann, Kent, Bellinson, and Hart, "The Mean Square Successive Difference," *The Annals of Mathematical Statistics*, vol. xii (1941), pp. 153–162.

A proof of the χ^2 distribution of $\Sigma(Y_i - Y_i')^2/\sigma^2$, which is needed to justify the use of the t distribution on regression coefficients, may be found in:

> Wilks, *op. cit.*, pp. 157–159.

The t distribution can be applied to such problems as testing the significance of simple and partial correlation coefficients and to finding confidence limits for multiple regression coefficients. Some of these applications are illustrated in:

> Rider, P., *An Introduction to Modern Statistical Methods*, John Wiley & Sons, pp. 88–98.

The mathematical theory behind the general analysis of variance technique for complex situations is quite advanced; however, it may be found in:

> Wilks, *op. cit.*, pp. 176–186.

Further applications of the analysis of variance may be found in:

> Rider, *op. cit.*, pp. 137–192.
> Freeman, *Industrial Statistics*, John Wiley & Sons, pp. 52–95.

The F distribution can be applied to such problems as testing the significance of multiple correlation coefficients and correlation ratios, and testing the linearity of regression. Some of those applications are illustrated in:

> Rider, *op. cit.*, pp. 117–157.

The tables for ranges from which Table 6 was extracted, as well as a derivation of the theory behind those tables, will be found in:

> Tippett, L. H. C., "On the Extreme Individuals and the Range of Samples Taken from a Normal Population," *Biometrika*, vol. 17 (1925), pp. 364–387.

The application of the range to quality control charts, as well as a discussion of various quality control techniques, may be found in:

Control Chart Method of Controlling Quality During Production, American War Standards, Z1.3—1942, New York: American Standards Association.

EXERCISES

1. For a certain observed distribution, $n = 20$, $\bar{x} = 42$, and $s = 5$. Assuming that x is normally distributed: (a) test the hypothesis that $\sigma = 8$; (b) find 98% confidence limits for σ^2; (c) test the hypothesis that $m = 50$; (d) find 99% confidence limits for m.

2. For the data of problem 10, Chapter IV, determine 96% confidence limits for σ^2.

3. If a quality control chart were to be constructed for controlling s^2 based on samples of 5 each for the data of problem 10, Chapter IV, what control limits for s^2 should be set if s^2 for all the data is assumed to be equal to σ^2?

4. The following data give the amounts of corrosion of pipe coatings for underground use in a series of field tests in different types of soil. Taking differences of similar pairs to eliminate differences due to soil type, test the hypothesis that the two kinds of pipe do not differ in their resistance to corrosion, that is, that $m = 0$ for such differences.

Soil type	A	B	C	D	E	F	G	H	I	J	K	L	M	N
Lead-coated steel pipe	27.3	18.4	11.9	28.7	11.3	14.8	20.8	21.6	17.9	7.8	18.6	14.7	19.0	65.3
Bare steel pipe	41.3	18.9	21.7	9.8	16.8	9.0	19.3	11.1	32.1	7.4	68.3	20.7	34.4	76.2

5. The following data give the gains of 10 pairs of rats, half of which received their protein from raw peanuts while the other half received their protein from roasted peanuts. Test to see whether roasting the peanuts had any effect on their protein value.

Raw	61	60	56	63	56	63	59	56	44	61
Roasted	55	54	47	59	51	61	57	54	62	58

6. In an industrial experiment a job was performed by 30 workmen according to method I and by 40 workmen according to method II. The two groups were equally skilled. The following data give the results of the experiment. Determine by means of 95% confidence limits how much time on the average the plant could be expected to save by using method I.

Time	50	51	52	53	54	55	56	57	58	59	60
I	1	3	5	4	7	5	3	1	1	0	0
II	0	1	2	5	8	9	6	3	3	1	2

7. The following data give the intelligence quotients of 25 male juvenile delinquents and 25 male non-delinquents matched by age, family income, and place of residence. (a) Taking differences of matched pairs, test the hypothesis that the mean difference is zero. (b) Treating the two sets as independent, test the hypothesis that the difference of the two means is zero. (c) Note any difference in these two results, and comment on the advantages and disadvantages of this matching technique.

Delinquent	103	80	114	100	91	73	105	98	86
Non-delinquent	99	92	106	104	88	80	109	94	90

Delinquent	101	92	86	93	90	79	108	82	95
Non-delinquent	97	89	91	90	97	84	96	91	86

Delinquent	74	102	105	97	88	94	99
Non-delinquent	83	97	99	103	91	84	106

8. For the data of problem 2, Chapter V, determine confidence limits for β in the regression equation for estimating tensile strength from hardness.

9. The following table gives the condensation of data on the hardness and bending strength of wood stored outside and inside. Test to see whether either the mean or variability of hardness or of bending strength is affected by weathering.

	Hardness		Bending Strength	
	Outside	Inside	Outside	Inside
Number	40	100	40	100
Mean	117	132	6,184	6,270
Sum of squares about mean	8,655	27,244	16,799,390	30,459,499

10. For the data of problem 10, Chapter IV, calculate s^2 for the first 30 and the last 30 entries. (a) Test these two values for homogeneity. (b) Would it be legitimate to select the samples from the tenth and twelfth hours and test them against the remaining samples for homogeneity?

11. The following table gives the gains of 4 different types of hogs fed 3 different rations. Test to see whether the rations or the hog types differ in their effect on weight.

Type

		I	II	III	IV
	A	7.0	16.0	10.5	13.5
Ration	B	14.0	15.5	15.0	21.0
	C	8.5	16.5	9.5	13.5

12. The following data give the impact-strength readings in foot-pounds on 5 lots of insulating material. One specimen from each of 20 different sheets was tested from each of the 5 lots. The first 10 specimens were cut along the lengthwise direction of the sheets; the remaining 10 were cut along the crosswise direction. Test for differences between (a) lots (b) lengthwise and crosswise specimens.

	Lengthwise					Crosswise			
I	II	III	IV	V	I	II	III	IV	V
1.15	1.16	0.79	0.96	0.49	0.89	0.86	0.52	0.86	0.52
0.84	0.85	.68	.82	.61	.69	1.17	.52	1.06	.53
.88	1.00	.64	.98	.59	.46	1.18	.80	.81	.47
.91	1.08	.72	.93	.51	.85	1.32	.64	.97	.47
.86	0.80	.63	.81	.53	.73	1.03	.63	.90	.57
.88	1.01	.59	.79	.72	.67	0.84	.58	.93	.54
.92	1.14	.81	.79	.67	.78	0.89	.65	.87	.56
.87	0.87	.65	.86	.47	.77	0.84	.60	.88	.55
.93	0.97	.64	.84	.44	.80	1.03	.71	.89	.45
.95	1.09	.75	.92	.48	.79	1.06	.59	.82	.60

13. For problem 10, Chapter IV, express control limits in terms of the range.

14. Find the distribution function of R if x has the distribution function e^{-x}, $x \geq 0$.

15. Find the probability that in a sample of 10 random numbers drawn from the numbers between 0 and 1 the range will exceed 0.8.

16. Find how many random numbers between 0 and 1 would need to be drawn in order that the probability will exceed 0.95 that the range will exceed 0.90.

17. Suppose that samples of size 4 are taken from the population given by e^{-x}, $x \geq 0$. (a) Determine the mean value of R. (b) Determine σ, and then compare the ratio m_R/σ with that given by Table 6 for a normal variable. (c) Determine limits, R_1 and R_2, for R such that $P[R < R_1] = 0.025$ and $P[R > R_2] = 0.025$.

18. Derive a formula for the variance of $z = c_1 x_1 + \cdots + c_k x_k$ in terms of the variances and correlations of the x's (*a*) if the x_i are independent, (*b*) if the x_i are correlated.

19. If $f(x) = e^{-x}$, $x \geq 0$, find $f(y)$ where $y = 1/x$.

20. If $f(x) = e^{-x}$, $x \geq 0$: (*a*) determine $f(\bar{x})$; (*b*) determine $f(z)$, where $z = u/v$ and u and v are successive pairs of independent sample values of x; (*c*) determine $f(x^2)$.

21. Determine a formula for confidence limits for α in the regression equation $y = \alpha + \beta x$ by using the methods for finding confidence limits for β.

22. If x and y possess independent standard normal distributions, derive the distribution function of z where $z = \sqrt{x^2 + y^2}$. The variable z represents the radial error in gunnery and bombing problems in which x and y represent independent coordinate axes errors of equal variability.

23. Using the expression for $f(ns^2/\sigma^2)$, derive the formula $\sigma_{s^2} = \sigma^2 \sqrt{2(n-1)/n^2}$ for the standard deviation of a sample variance, if the sample variance is based on a random sample of size n from a normal population.

24. Using the results of problem 18, determine the variance of $z = \sum_1^k a_i s_i^2 / \sum_1^k a_i$, in which the a_i are constants and the s_i^2 are independent sample variances based on samples of size n_i.

25. Using the results of problems 23 and 24, determine the a_i so as to minimize the variance of z under the assumption that the k sample variances were from k independent normal populations having the same variance. Compare your result with (5).

CHAPTER IX

NON-PARAMETRIC METHODS

Most significance tests of statistical theory require certain assumptions concerning the form of some distribution function. In the small-sample methods of the preceding chapter, it was usually assumed that the basic variable was normally distributed. It will be recalled that in the chapter on large-sample methods significance tests involving means were considered accurate without the customary normality assumption. However, some statistics possess distributions that depend heavily upon the form of the basic variable distribution even for large samples; consequently the use of such statistics is restricted to situations in which the necessary assumptions are satisfied fairly well. For situations in which very little is known about the distribution of the basic variable or for which it is known that the necessary assumptions are not satisfied, it is necessary to develop methods that do not require those assumptions. For complete generality of application, it would be highly desirable to have methods that do not require any knowledge concerning the form of the basic distribution function.

A second reason for considering such methods is that certain significance tests that have proved useful in industrial statistics are of this type. Such tests are usually based on the qualitative order relationships of data as distinguished from the quantitative relationships employed in most tests.

A significance test that requires no assumption about the form of the basic distribution function could hardly be expected to be as efficient as one that needs some such assumption. To compensate somewhat for this decrease in efficiency, there is the advantage of complete generality in applications without the necessity of checking to see whether certain assumptions are satisfied.

Methods of the type just described are usually called *non-parametric* methods because they do not involve the estimation of parameter values of a distribution function. Although non-parametric techniques are numerous, only a few of the more common ones will be considered here.

TCHEBYCHEFF'S INEQUALITY

Consider the problem of determining what the probability is that a variable x will assume a value more than k standard deviations away from its mean. Assume that $f(x)$ is a continuous distribution function which possesses a finite variance. Then the integral defining its variance may be treated as follows.

$$\sigma^2 = \int_a^b (x - m)^2 f(x) \, dx$$

$$= \int_a^{m-k\sigma} (x - m)^2 f(x) \, dx + \int_{m-k\sigma}^{m+k\sigma} (x - m)^2 f(x) \, dx$$

$$+ \int_{m+k\sigma}^b (x - m)^2 f(x) \, dx$$

Since the middle integral is a positive quantity for $k > 0$,

$$\sigma^2 \geq \int_a^{m-k\sigma} (x - m)^2 f(x) \, dx + \int_{m+k\sigma}^b (x - m)^2 f(x) \, dx$$

In each of these integrals the quantity $(x - m)^2$ will assume its minimum value for that value of x in the range of integration which is nearest m. For the first integral this value is the upper limit, and for the second integral it is the lower limit; consequently

$$\sigma^2 \geq \int_a^{m-k\sigma} (k\sigma)^2 f(x) \, dx + \int_{m+k\sigma}^b (k\sigma)^2 f(x) \, dx$$

$$\geq (k\sigma)^2 \left[\int_a^{m-k\sigma} f(x) \, dx + \int_{m+k\sigma}^b f(x) \, dx \right]$$

The first integral gives the probability that x will be to the left of $m - k\sigma$, and the second that x will be to the right of $m + k\sigma$; hence this inequality is equivalent to the inequality

$$\sigma^2 \geq k^2 \sigma^2 P[\, | \, x - m \, | > k\sigma]$$

If σ^2 is divided out, this expression yields

(1)   *Tchebycheff's Inequality:* $P[\, | \, x - m \, | > k\sigma] \leq \dfrac{1}{k^2}$

Since no assumption was made regarding the form of $f(x)$, any test based upon Tchebycheff's inequality would be a non-parametric test.

By replacing integrals with sums, it is easily demonstrated that this inequality holds for a discrete variable as well.

For the purpose of observing the decrease in sensitivity in using (1) when the form of $f(x)$ is known, consider the case in which $f(x)$ is a normal distribution function. Computations by means of (1) and Table II yield the probabilities in Table 1. From this table it is clear

TABLE 1

k	Tchebycheff	Normal
1	$P \leq 1$	$P = 0.32$
2	$P \leq 0.25$	$P = 0.05$
3	$P \leq 0.11$	$P = 0.003$

that the normality assumption, if it can be legitimately made, greatly increases the sensitivity of such probability statements. By making further assumptions about $f(x)$ which do not involve a knowledge of its form, it is possible to obtain more refined inequalities of this type. Tchebycheff's inequality is not of much practical value except for very large samples.

As an illustration, consider the problem of determining how large a sample would be needed to reject at the 5% level of significance a deviation of 3 units in a sample mean if $m = 50$ and $\sigma = 5$. Here the variable is $\bar{x}$; hence $\sigma_{\bar{x}} = 5/\sqrt{n}$. In order that P shall not exceed 0.05, it is necessary that k be chosen to satisfy $1/k^2 = 0.05$; therefore $k = \sqrt{20}$. With this choice of k, Tchebycheff's inequality becomes

$$P\left[\, |\, \bar{x} - 50\, | > \sqrt{20}\,\frac{5}{\sqrt{n}}\right] \leq 0.05$$

Since $|\, \bar{x} - 50\, | = 3$ in this problem, the inequality will be satisfied if n exceeds the root of the equation

$$3 = \sqrt{20}\,\frac{5}{\sqrt{n}}$$

which is $n = 55.6$. Thus, a sample of size 56 will suffice here.

LAW OF LARGE NUMBERS

An interesting application of Tchebycheff's inequality arises when the variable x is the success ratio, p', in n trials of an event for which the probability of success in a single trial is p. Here $m = p$ and $\sigma = \sqrt{pq/n}$; therefore (1) becomes

$$P\left[\, |\, p' - p\, | > k\sqrt{\frac{pq}{n}}\right] \leq \frac{1}{k^2}$$

Now choose a number $\epsilon > 0$, and choose $k = \epsilon / \sqrt{pq/n}$. Then the preceding inequality reduces to

$$P[\,|\,p' - p\,|\, > \epsilon] \leq \frac{pq}{\epsilon}\frac{1}{n}$$

No matter how small ϵ may have been chosen, by allowing the number of trials, n, to increase sufficiently, P can be made as small as desired. This conclusion, which is called the *law of large numbers*, shows the probability nature of the convergence of a sample success ratio to its expected value. This probability type of convergence is often called *stochastic convergence* to distinguish it from ordinary mathematical convergence. The law of large numbers does not guarantee, for example, that the success ratio for a true coin will approach ½ as a limit, but rather that the probability of the success ratio differing from ½ by more than any given amount will approach zero as a limit. It is customary here to say that the success ratio converges stochastically to ½.

TOLERANCE LIMITS

The problem of determining the variability of a normal variable was solved in the preceding chapter by finding confidence limits for σ^2. If the form of the distribution function is unknown, a different approach to the problem is necessary. One approach consists in finding two numbers, L_1 and L_2, which are based upon the results of sampling and between which a high percentage of the population may be expected to lie. Such numbers are called *tolerance limits*. The name arose in connection with the industrial problem of controlling a quality characteristic of a product by finding limits within which with respect to this characteristic a high percentage of the product could be expected to lie.

If the numbers L_1 and L_2 are chosen as the smallest and largest values, respectively, to be found in the sample, it will be found that the percentage of the population which can be expected to lie between L_1 and L_2 does not depend upon the form of the distribution function of the variable being considered. This is also true of certain other common choices for L_1 and L_2, but they will not be considered here.

Let the variable x possess the continuous distribution function $p(x)$. Then by Theorem VI, Chapter VIII, if u and v denote the smallest and largest values respectively in a random sample of size n, the joint distribution of u and v will be given by

$$(2) \qquad f(u, v) = n(n - 1)p(u)p(v)\left[\int_u^v p(x)\,dx\right]^{n-2}$$

Now the integral within the brackets is precisely the desired proportion of the population lying between the extreme values of the sample; therefore consider the change of variable from v to z with u held fixed, where

$$(3) \qquad z = \int_u^v p(x)\, dx$$

By means of the calculus theorem stated after (5), Chapter VI, it follows that $dz/dv = p(v)$ and therefore by (7), Chapter VIII, that

$$f(u, z) = f(u, v) \frac{1}{p(v)}$$

Hence, from (2),

$$(4) \qquad f(u, z) = n(n-1)p(u)z^{n-2}$$

Now hold z fixed and consider the change of variable from u to w, where

$$(5) \qquad w = \int_a^u p(x)\, dx$$

Here $dw/du = p(u)$; consequently

$$f(w, z) = f(u, z) \frac{1}{p(u)}$$

Hence, from (4),

$$(6) \qquad f(w, z) = n(n-1)z^{n-2}$$

In order to obtain the distribution function of z, it is merely necessary to integrate this function with respect to w over its range of values for z fixed. From (3) and (5) it will be observed that $w + z$ equals the probability that x will not exceed v; therefore $w + z \leq 1$. Since z is being held fixed, w can assume values from 0 to $1 - z$ only; consequently, from (6),

$$f(z) = \int_0^{1-z} f(w, z)\, dw$$

$$= \int_0^{1-z} n(n-1)z^{n-2}\, dw$$

$$= n(n-1)z^{n-2}(1-z)$$

This demonstrates the following theorem.

Theorem I. *If a variable possesses a continuous distribution function and if z denotes the proportion of the population that lies between the* *extreme values of a random sample of size n drawn from this population, then the distribution function of z is given by*

$$f(z) = n(n-1)z^{n-2}(1-z)$$

As an illustration of the application of this theorem, consider the problem of determining how large a sample must be taken in order to be certain with a probability of 0.95 that at least 99% of the population will lie between the extreme values of the sample. The solution is given by determining the value of n which satisfies the equation

$$\int_{0.99}^{1.00} f(z)\, dz = 0.95$$

If the value of $f(z)$ given by Theorem I is inserted and the integration is performed, this equation becomes

$$n(n-1)\left\{ \frac{1}{n-1} - \frac{1}{n} - \frac{(0.99)^{n-1}}{n-1} + \frac{(0.99)^n}{n} \right\} = 0.95$$

which simplifies to

$$(0.99)^n = \frac{4.95}{n+99}$$

It will be found by trial that the integer that most nearly satisfies this equation is $n = 473$; consequently a sample of this size is required to obtain the desired coverage and certainty from the extreme values of the sample as tolerance limits. It is clear from this example that a very large sample is necessary before the extreme values of a sample will suffice to set limits within which practically all the population would be expected to lie.

The transcendental equation which arises in determining the value of n for problems of this type is not easy to solve; consequently a simple approximate solution would be highly desirable. Such an approximation exists in the formula

$$n \doteq \frac{1}{4}\chi_\alpha^2 \frac{1+\delta}{1-\delta} + \frac{1}{2}$$

where δ is the proportion of the population to be covered by the sample range, α is 1 minus the desired probability, and χ_α^2 is the value of χ^2 for 4 degrees of freedom for which $P[\chi^2 > \chi_\alpha^2] = \alpha$. If this formula is applied to the problem that was just solved, to the nearest integer

$$n \doteq \frac{1}{4}(9.488)\frac{1.99}{0.01} + \frac{1}{2} = 473$$

RANDOMNESS OF SEQUENCES

Most of the statistical methods that have been considered thus far were designed to be applied to data for which no useful information was gained by preserving the order of the observations. Some of these methods nevertheless proved to be valuable for situations in which order was important. For example, quality control charts for percentages and for means employed such methods.

Situations arise, however, in quality control work in which the control-chart technique fails to capitalize on the information available in the time-order relationships of the data. For example, the occurrence of numerous slight erratic shifts in the mean might continue unnoticed in the customary control chart. Methods are available which concern themselves with such behavior patterns and which therefore serve as additional tools in discovering a lack of randomness in sequences of observations when it exists. These methods assume that the observations constitute a random sequence and then determine a function of the observations for testing the randomness of the sequence. Some of these methods also have the desirable property of being non-parametric. Two such methods will be discussed in this chapter.

1. Runs

Consider the following set of values of a variable:

$$20, 23, 18, 17, 24, 16, 17, 21, 22, 26, 15, 16$$

If each value is assigned the letter a provided that it is less than the median 19 and the letter b provided that it is greater than 19, this set of values will give rise to the following set of letters:

$$b, b, a, a, b, a, a, b, b, b, a, a$$

A sequence of i identical letters which is preceded and followed by a different letter or no letter is called a run of length i. The runs of a's and b's in this example have the lengths 2, 2, 1, 2, 3, 2.

If a set of values of a variable has been obtained by taking samples at regular time intervals, and if there is, say, a trend or a cyclical pattern in the sequence of values, the fact can be discovered by studying the runs of a's and b's that result from the sequence when a value less than the median is assigned the letter a and a value greater than the median is assigned the letter b. In the event of an upward trend, there would be a tendency for long runs of a's to be followed by long runs of b's. In a regular cyclical pattern, the runs would tend to be of uniform length. It appears from illustrations such as these that the study of runs would prove particularly useful in testing for randomness of data that have been ordered with respect to time.

For the purpose of deriving a test of randomness, consider a sample of size n containing n_a a's and n_b b's where $n = n_a + n_b$. Let r_a and r_b denote the total number of runs of a's and b's, respectively. Now consider the basic problem of finding the probability of obtaining specified values of r_a and r_b under the assumption that all possible permutations of the a's and b's have the same probability of occurring. The desired probability will be given by the ratio of the number of permutations possible when n, n_a, n_b, r_a, and r_b are held fixed to the number of permutations possible when n, n_a, and n_b are held fixed. This assumes that only samples of size n which give rise to n_a a's and n_b b's are being considered and that the two statistical variables here are r_a and r_b.

The denominator of this probability ratio, which is the number of permutations when n, n_a, and n_b are held fixed, is equal to the number of ways of permuting n things of which n_a are alike and n_b are alike. By (22), Chapter III, the denominator is

$$(7) \qquad \frac{n!}{n_a! n_b!}$$

For the purpose of counting the number of permutations when r_a and r_b are also held fixed, concentrate first upon the a's. The permutations of the a's will be obtained in two steps. First the number of permutations for a fixed set of run lengths which total r_a will be determined. Then these permutations will be summed for all possible sets of run lengths which total r_a. In this connection it is convenient to study the multinomial

$$(8) \qquad (p_1 + p_2 + \cdots + p_{n_a})^{r_a}$$

Consider the general term in the expansion of this multinomial, namely,

$$C p_1{}^{n_1} p_2{}^{n_2} \cdots p_{n_a}{}^{n_{n_a}}$$

where the explicit value of C is given by (39), Chapter III, and where

$$(9) \qquad \sum_{i=1}^{n_a} n_i = r_a$$

Each run of a's of length i may be thought of as being replaced by the letter x_i; then the first step is to count the number of permutations of the x's. If p_i is associated with x_i, and n_i denotes the number of runs of length i, then from (39), Chapter III, it follows that C gives precisely the number of such permutations. This concludes the first step in the counting procedure. The second step consists in summing coefficients like C for all sets of run lengths which satisfy (10). Because n_a is also being held fixed here, it follows that the n_i must satisfy

$$(10) \qquad \sum_{i=1}^{n_a} i n_i = n_a$$

in addition to (9). To accomplish the summing of coefficients like C, replace p_i by p^i in (8). Then (8) will assume the form

$$(11) \qquad (p + p^2 + p^3 + \cdots + p^{n_a})^{r_a}$$

and the general term will assume the form

$$(12) \qquad C p^{n_1 + 2n_2 + 3n_3 + \cdots + n_a n_a}$$

From (12) it will be observed that the term in the expansion of (11) which contains p^{n_a} satisfies condition (10). Since this is the only term for which (10) is satisfied, the coefficient of p^{n_a} gives the sum of coefficients like C satisfying both (9) and (10). But this is precisely the sum of the permutations of the a's for a fixed set of run lengths summed over all sets of run lengths satisfying (9) and (10). The coefficient of p^{n_a} therefore gives the desired permutations. This coefficient may be found by means of the identity

$$(p + p^2 + p^3 + \cdots)^{r_a} = \frac{p^{r_a}}{(1 - p)^{r_a}}$$

$$= p^{r_a} \sum_{j=0}^{\infty} \frac{(r_a - 1 + j)! p^j}{j!(r_a - 1)!}$$

The coefficient of p^{n_a} in (11) is the same as the coefficient of p^{n_a} on the left side of this identity and hence is the same as the coefficient of p^{n_a} on the right side. The latter coefficient is given by the term for which $j = n_a - r_a$ and is

$$\frac{(n_a - 1)!}{(r_a - 1)!(n_a - r_a)!}$$

This expression gives the desired number of permutations of the a's for r_a and n_a held fixed. By analogy the number of permutations of the b's for r_b and n_b held fixed is

$$\frac{(n_b - 1)!}{(r_b - 1)!(n_b - r_b)!}$$

If a sequence of a's and b's begins and ends with the same letter, r_a and r_b will differ by 1. If the sequence begins with one letter and ends with the other, r_a and r_b will be equal. In the latter case, a given arrangement of the a's can be fitted together with a given arrangement of the b's in two ways by beginning with either an a or a b. If k denotes the number of ways in which the a's and b's can be fitted together, the number of permutations of the a's and b's together will be

$$k \frac{(n_a - 1)!}{(r_a - 1)!(n_a - r_a)!} \cdot \frac{(n_b - 1)!}{(r_b - 1)!(n_b - r_b)!}$$

If this result is combined with that in (7), the following theorem results.

Theorem II. *If the various permutations of n_a letters a and n_b letters b have the same probability of occurring and if r_a and r_b denote the total number of runs of a's and b's respectively, then the joint distribution function of r_a and r_b is given by*

$$P(r_a, r_b) = k \frac{(n_a - 1)!(n_b - 1)!n_a!n_b!}{(r_a - 1)!(n_a - r_a)!(r_b - 1)!(n_b - r_b)!n!}$$

where $k = 2$ if $r_a = r_b$ and $k = 1$ if $r_a \neq r_b$.

Although the a's and b's were introduced by means of the relationship of sample values to their median, the derivation of this theorem does not place any restriction on what value of a variable should be selected for assigning letters to the sample values.

It will be observed that this theorem is not concerned with the form of any basic variable distribution function; consequently any test derived directly from this theorem will be a non-parametric test.

One of the interesting and useful applications of this theorem arises in connection with finding the probability of obtaining $u = r_a + r_b$ total runs of a's and b's when n_a and n_b are fixed. In order to find this probability, which will be denoted by $P(u)$, it is necessary to sum $P(r_a, r_b)$ over all values of r_a and r_b that give rise to this value of u. If u is even, $r_a = r_b = u/2$; consequently there is but one pair of values to be considered. If u is odd, $r_a = (u \pm 1)/2$ and $r_b = (u \mp 1)/2$; consequently there are but two pairs of values to be considered. It therefore follows from Theorem II that

$$P(u) = 2 \frac{(n_a - 1)!(n_b - 1)!n_a!n_b!}{\left(\frac{u}{2} - 1\right)!\left(\frac{u}{2} - 1\right)!\left(n_a - \frac{u}{2}\right)!\left(n_b - \frac{u}{2}\right)!n!}$$

if u is even, and

$$P(u) = \frac{(n_a - 1)!(n_b - 1)!n_a!n_b!}{\left(\dfrac{u-1}{2}\right)!\left(\dfrac{u-3}{2}\right)!n!}\left[\frac{1}{\left(n_a - \dfrac{u+1}{2}\right)!\left(n_b - \dfrac{u-1}{2}\right)!}\right.$$

$$\left. + \frac{1}{\left(n_a - \dfrac{u-1}{2}\right)!\left(n_b - \dfrac{u+1}{2}\right)!}\right]$$

if u is odd.

These probabilities have been used to construct tables of $\sum\limits_{u=2}^{u'} P(u)$ for various values of n_a, n_b, and u'. Such tables enable one to test whether a sample value of u is unusually large or small as compared to what would be expected if the sequence of values constituted a random sequence. In order to illustrate the use of such tables, a few entries have been extracted from one of them and have been recorded in Table 2. In this table $u_{0.05}$ and $u_{0.95}$ are the largest and smallest integers, respectively, such that $P[u \leq u_{0.05}] \leq 0.05$ and $P[u \leq u_{0.95}] \geq 0.95$. These values may therefore be used as 5% critical values for testing whether u is unusually small or unusually large, respectively. Table 2 requires that $n_a = n_b$; however, if the median of a set of

TABLE 2

$n_a = n_b$	5	10	15	20	25	30	40	50	60	70	80	90	100
$u_{0.05}$	3	6	11	15	19	24	33	42	51	60	70	79	88
$u_{0.95}$	8	15	20	26	32	37	48	59	70	81	91	102	113
$u_{0.025}$	2	6	10	14	18	22	31	40	49	58	68	77	86
$u_{0.975}$	6	15	21	27	33	39	50	61	72	83	93	104	115

observations is chosen for assigning letters, and if the sample is fairly large, this requirement will usually be approximately satisfied.

As a numerical illustration, consider the data introduced at the beginning of the section on runs. There $u = 6$, $n_a = 6$, and $n_b = 6$. It is clear from interpolating in Table 2 that the value of u is not significant; consequently there is no reason for doubting the randomness of the sequence as far as this test is concerned.

As a second illustration, consider the data of problem 24, Chapter III. There are reasons for believing that the expected percentage may be shifting here from time to time; hence consider testing the hypothesis of randomness against the alternative of too many long runs. If these percentages are assigned letters on the basis of lying below or above 2.55, it will be found that the resulting sequence of a's and b's is

$$a, a, a, a, b, a, a, a, a, b, a, b, b, b, a, b, b, b, b,$$

$$b, b, b, a, b, a, a, a, a, a, a, a, a, b, b, a, b, b, b$$

Here $n_a = 20$, $n_b = 18$, and $u = 14$. Interpolation in Table 2 for $n_a = n_b = 19$ would give $u_{0.05} = 14$. Since this result is significant at the 5% level for a one-sided test, the hypothesis of randomness would be rejected. There appear to be too few runs because of too many very long runs; consequently an investigation of the long runs should be made.

Several other tests for randomness are based on functions of runs. One such test, for example, is based upon the probability of obtaining at least one run of a length greater than a specified length. Such a test might be helpful in the problem just considered, since a run of length 8 for such a short sequence seems unlikely.

2. Serial Correlation

Another approach to testing the randomness of a sequence of observations can be made by means of correlation methods. If a set of observations is ordered with respect to time and if time is irrelevant to the variable being considered, no correlation would be expected to exist, for example, between successive pairs of values of the sequence. If the distribution function of a correlation coefficient of this type could be found, it would be possible to test the hypothesis that the population correlation was zero and thus test the sequence for randomness. The derivation of such distribution functions is complicated; consequently only the results of one such derivation will be described here.

If $x_1, x_2, \cdots, x_n$ denotes the sequence to be tested, it is clear that the cross-product term

$$(13) \qquad\qquad R = \sum_{i=1}^{n} x_i x_{i+1}$$

where $x_{n+1} = x_1$, differs considerably from the cross-product term $\sum_{i=1}^{n} x_i y_i$ in the ordinary correlation coefficient. The x_i and x_{i+1} no longer constitute a set of random sample pairs of values of two variables; consequently it is hardly to be expected that the correlation coefficient of successive pairs, which is called the *serial correlation coefficient* with lag 1, will possess the same distribution function as the ordinary correlation coefficient. It is therefore not possible to use the significance test for r explained in Chapter V to test serial correlations. Useful approximations to the distribution function of the serial correlation coefficient, however, are available for two different situations. Tables of critical values have been worked out under the assumption that the variable x is normally distributed. Formulas have also been worked out which are satisfactory for large samples but which require no assumption as to the form of $f(x)$. Since the latter approach is non-parametric, it alone will be discussed here.

If all possible permutations of the sequence being considered are treated as equally likely to occur, it is theoretically possible to determine the probability that R in (13) will assume any given value by calculating R for all possible permutations and then counting the number of such permutations that produce the given value. Such calculations become exceedingly lengthy except for small values of n. For large values of n, it turns out that R possesses an approximate normal distribution which may be used to test the hypothesis of zero serial correlation. For such a test, only the mean and variance of R are necessary. These values are given by the formulas

$$E(R) = \frac{S_1^2 - S_2}{n - 1}$$

and

$$\sigma_R^2 = \frac{S_2^2 - S_4}{n - 1} + \frac{S_1^4 - 4S_1^2 S_2 + 4S_1 S_3 + S_2^2 - 2S_4}{(n - 1)(n - 2)} - E^2(R)$$

where

$$S_k = x_1^k + x_2^k + \cdots + x_n^k$$

It can be shown that a test based upon R is equivalent to a test based upon the serial correlation coefficient with lag 1; consequently the test based upon R is selected because of its simpler form.

REFERENCES

A well-known inequality of the Tchebycheff type which is somewhat more sensitive than Tchebycheff's inequality, but which of course places further non-parametric restrictions on $f(x)$, is the Camp-Meidel inequality. A discussion of it may be found in:

CAMP, B. H., "A New Generalization of Tchebycheff's Statistical Inequality," *Bulletin of the American Mathematical Society*, vol. 28 (1922), pp. 427–432.

There are numerous variations of the law of large numbers, and an extensive field of probability study is concerned with problems of this kind. Material on the subject may be found in:

USPENSKY, J. V., *Introduction to Mathematical Probability*, McGraw-Hill Book Company.

An illustration of the loss of sensitivity in using tolerance limits when the form of the distribution function is known and is of the normal type, as well as a derivation of theory, may be found in:

WILKS, S. S., "Determination of Sample Sizes for Setting Tolerance Limits," *Annals of Mathematical Statistics*, vol. xii (1941), pp. 91–96.

The approximate solution to the transcendental equation involved in determining the size sample for setting tolerance limits will be found in:

SCHEFFÉ, H., and TUKEY, J., "A Formula for Sample Sizes for Population Tolerance Limits," *Annals of Mathematical Statistics*, vol. xv (1944), p. 217.

The tables from which Table 2 was extracted are available in:

SWED, F., and EISENHART, C., "Tables for Testing Randomness of Grouping in a Sequence of Alternatives," *Annals of Mathematical Statistics*, vol. xiv (1943), pp. 66–87.

Tables for testing the randomness of sequences by means of long runs, as well as a discussion of the technique of applying those tables, will be found in:

MOSTELLER, F., "Note on an Application of Runs to Quality Control Charts," *Annals of Mathematical Statistics*, vol. xii (1941), pp. 228–232.

The derivation of the formulas for serial correlation is based on advanced mathematics; however, it may be found in:

WALD, A., and WOLFOWITZ, J., "An Exact Test for Randomness in the Non-Parametric Case Based on Serial Correlation," *Annals of Mathematical Statistics*, vol. xiv (1945), pp. 378–388.

The formulas for serial correlation under the assumption that the basic variable is normally distributed are considerably easier to apply. These formulas and their derivation are available in:

ANDERSON, R. L., "Distribution of the Serial Correlation Coefficient," *Annals of Mathematical Statistics*, vol. xiii (1942), pp. 1–13.

An advanced but extensive discussion of non-parametric methods may be found in:

SCHEFFÉ, H., "Statistical Inference in the Non-Parametric Case," *Annals of Mathematical Statistics*, vol. xiv (1943), pp. 305–332.

EXERCISES

1. Compare the $P[|x - m| > 2\sigma]$ given by Tchebycheff's inequality with the actual value for (a) the rectangular distribution $f(x) = 1$, $0 \leq x \leq 1$, (b) $f(x) = e^{-x}$, $x \geq 0$.

2. Derive Tchebycheff's inequality for a discrete variable.

3. Use Tchebycheff's inequality to show that the $P[(\bar{x} - m)^2 > \epsilon] \to 0$ as $n \to \infty$.

4. For $f(x) = cx^k e^{-x}$, $x \geq 0$, determine the $P[|\, x - m\,| > 2\sigma]$. Compare this value with the value given by Tchebycheff's inequality.

5. For a sample of 200, determine what the probability is that at least 99% of the population will be included between the extreme values of the sample.

6. Determine how large a sample is necessary in order that the probability will be 0.80 that at least 99% of the population will be expected to lie between the extreme values of the sample.

7. Derive formulas for the mean and variance of z where z is the proportion of the population lying between the extreme values of the sample.

8. From the variance of z obtained in the preceding problem, would you expect the estimated percentage of the population lying between the extreme values of a sample of 100 to be an accurate estimate of the expected percentage?

9. Following the methods that were used to derive Theorem I, derive the distribution function of the proportion of the population which lies between the rth smallest and the rth largest values in a random sample of size n.

10. Toss a coin 30 times, recording the sequence of heads and tails, and then test for randomness by means of Table 2.

11. Write down a sequence of a's and b's totaling 50 letters which you feel is random. Test this sequence for randomness by means of Table 2.

12. The defective parts from a day's production of a certain machine were recorded as a if too narrow, and as b if too wide, with the following results: a, a, a, b, b, a, a, b, b, b, a, b, b, b, b, b, b, b, b, b. By means of the more complete tables for total runs found on page 70 of the March 1943 issue of *Annals of Mathematical Statistics*, determine whether the machine seems to be shifting slightly towards parts that are too wide.

13. Test the following set of measurements for a trend by means of serial correlation, applying the formulas to the measurements after reduction by a convenient common difference: 28, 32, 37, 25, 31, 29, 33, 28, 27, 28, 23, 22, 18, 17.

CHAPTER X

TESTING GOODNESS OF FIT

THE χ^2 DISTRIBUTION

1. Nature of χ^2

A problem that arises frequently in statistical work is the testing of the compatibility of a set of observed and theoretical frequencies. If it is reasonable on the basis of a test to assume that a set of observed frequencies might have been obtained in random sampling from a population that has a specified set of corresponding theoretical frequencies, the two sets of frequencies will be said to be compatible as far as that test is concerned. This type of problem was solved in Chapter III for the case in which the set consisted of only one pair of observed and theoretical frequencies and in which the binomial distribution was used to obtain the theoretical frequencies. A generalization of the binomial problem to k pairs of observed and theoretical frequencies will give rise to the multinomial distribution of Chapter III, and the solution of the problem will require a simple approximation to the multinomial distribution similar to the normal approximation to the binomial distribution. It turns out that the familiar χ^2 distribution function serves as an excellent approximation to the multinomial for large samples and therefore that tests of compatibility can be based upon it.

As a simple illustration of the type of problem being discussed, consider the problem of testing the "honesty" of a die. Suppose that a die is rolled 60 times and a record is kept of the number of times each face comes up. The statement that a die is honest means that each face has the probability $\frac{1}{6}$ of appearing in a single roll. Therefore each face would be expected to show 10 times in an experiment of this kind. Suppose that the first of a contemplated sequence of experiments produced the following result, where the rows labeled o and e represent the observed and theoretical frequencies respectively.

Face	1	2	3	4	5	6
o	6	15	7	4	17	11
e	10	10	10	10	10	10

Now, as a measure of the compatibility of such observed and expected frequencies, it is customary to calculate the statistic called χ^2, which is defined by

$$(1) \qquad \chi^2 = \sum_{i=1}^{k} \frac{(o_i - e_i)^2}{e_i}$$

where k is the number of pairs of frequencies to be compared, o_i and e_i denote these frequencies, and $\Sigma o_i = \Sigma e_i = n$. In this problem $k = 6$ and

$$\chi^2 = \frac{(6-10)^2}{10} + \frac{(15-10)^2}{10} + \frac{(7-10)^2}{10} + \frac{(4-10)^2}{10}$$

$$+ \frac{(17-10)^2}{10} + \frac{(11-10)^2}{10} = 13.6$$

A value of zero here would correspond to exact agreement with expectation, whereas increasingly large values of χ^2 may be thought of as corresponding to increasingly poor agreement. Now if this experiment were repeated a large number of times and each time the value of χ^2 were computed, a set of χ^2's would be obtained which could be classified into a relative frequency table of χ^2's. This relative frequency table would tell one approximately in what percentage of such experiments various ranges of values of χ^2 could be expected to be obtained. Then one would be able to judge whether the value of $\chi^2 = 13.6$ was unusually large as compared to the run of χ^2's in such experiments.

If the relative frequency table of χ^2's were graphed as a histogram, the histogram would serve as an approximation to the true frequency distribution of χ^2 for an unlimited number of such experiments. Now the true frequency distribution of χ^2 is discrete, and hence it would be represented by a histogram also because there are only a finite number of values that χ^2 can assume, since all the o_i are integers ranging from 0 to 60. For example, the smallest positive value that χ^2 can assume in this problem is 0.2, which is obtained when two of the observed frequencies are 9 and 11 and the remaining frequencies are 10 each. However, in most problems of this type, the number of possible values of χ^2 is large; consequently the histogram representing the true χ^2 distribution is usually quite regular and can therefore be approximated by means of a curve.

The preceding discussion has been concerned with how one could proceed empirically to find an approximation to the distribution function of χ^2. However, by using the multinomial distribution function and making certain approximations, it is possible to obtain an approximation to the distribution function of χ^2 by theoretical methods. Since the derivation of this approximation is not simple, it will not be considered here; however, such a derivation shows that for large samples an excellent approximation to the distribution function of χ^2 is given by

$$(2) \qquad g(\chi^2) = \frac{(\chi^2)^{\frac{k-3}{2}} e^{-\frac{\chi^2}{2}}}{2^{\frac{k-1}{2}} \Gamma\left(\frac{k-1}{2}\right)}$$

If this function is compared with that given by (8), Chapter VIII, it will be observed that (2) is what was previously called the χ^2 distribution function with $k - 1$ degrees of freedom. As a matter of fact, the name χ^2 was given to the function (8), Chapter VIII, because of its identity with (2).

Now consider the application of (2) to the particular problem being discussed. Since large values of χ^2 correspond to one's notion of poor experimental results, it is customary to select a value χ_0^2 such that $P[\chi^2 > \chi_0^2] = 0.05$ as a critical value for judging significance at the 5% level. Since $f(\chi^2)$ depends only on the parameter ν, called the number of degrees of freedom, there will correspond a χ^2 curve and a 5% critical value to each value of ν. The graph of $f(\chi^2)$ corresponding to various degrees of freedom is given in Fig. 4, Chapter VIII. Since (2) is $f(\chi^2)$ with $\nu = k - 1$ and $k = 6$ in this problem, the graph corresponding to $\nu = 5$ shows the distribution of χ^2's to be expected in this problem. From Table III it will be found that $\chi_0^2 = 11.1$ for 5 degrees of freedom; hence the value of $\chi^2 = 13.6$ is significant, and the honesty of the die is highly questionable. If the die were honest, and repeated experiments of rolling the die 60 times were conducted, then in less than 5% of such experiments would a value of χ^2 be obtained which exceeded this first experimental result.

2. Generality of χ^2

Since $f(\chi^2)$ depends only upon the parameter ν, which is always available in any given problem, the χ^2 test is a non-parametric test, although it is often applied to parametric problems. The χ^2 distribution is concerned with the values of the e_i but not with the form of the distribution function from which they might have been obtained as samples. This property of the χ^2 distribution permits it to be used on a wide variety of problems involving a comparison of observed and theoretical frequencies.

A second feature of the χ^2 distribution which makes the χ^2 test one of wide applicability arises from the theory which demonstrates that χ^2 as given by (1) possesses approximately the distribution function given by (8), Chapter VIII, with $\nu = k - 1$. In that theory it is shown that, for each independent linear restriction imposed upon the observations, o_i, the value of the parameter ν is decreased by unity; otherwise the function is unchanged.

In the die problem, it was assumed that in each experiment the die was rolled 60 times; consequently the o_i always satisfied the single linear restriction $\sum_{1}^{6} o_i = 60$. In the light of the second feature of the χ^2 distribution just discussed, this restriction explains why ν was equal to 5 in the preceding problem. For most problems the determination of the value of ν can be made intuitively by counting the number of independent cell frequencies. Since these 6 cell frequencies must total 60, there are only 5 independent cell frequencies, which is therefore the number of the degrees of freedom here. This connection between the physical idea of degrees of freedom and the parameter ν in $f(\chi^2)$ explains why that parameter is called the number of degrees of freedom.

3. Applications

In experiments on the breeding of flowers of a certain species, an experimenter obtained 120 magenta flowers with a green stigma, 48 magenta flowers with a red stigma, 36 red flowers with a green stigma, and 13 red flowers with a red stigma. Theory predicts that flowers of these types should be obtained in the ratio of 9:3:3:1. Are these experimental results compatible with the theory? On the basis of this theory, the observed and expected frequencies, correct to the nearest integer, are given by

o	120	48	36	13
e	122	41	41	14

Calculations give

$$\chi^2 = \frac{(120 - 122)^2}{122} + \frac{(48 - 41)^2}{41} + \frac{(36 - 41)^2}{41} + \frac{(13 - 14)^2}{14} = 1.9$$

From Table III the 5% critical value of χ^2 for 3 degrees of freedom is $\chi_0^2 = 7.8$; consequently the result is not significant. There is no reason on the basis of this test for doubting the theory here.

As a second application, consider the following data on the number of aircraft accidents that occurred during the various days of the week for a given period of time at certain training bases. First, consider

Sunday	Monday	Tuesday	Wednesday	Thursday	Friday	Saturday
14	16	8	12	11	9	14

the question whether accidents are uniformly distributed over the week. Since the total number of accidents under consideration is 84, the expected frequencies are 12 each. Computations with $e_i = 12$ give $\chi^2 = 4.2$. Since $\chi_0^2 = 12.6$ for 6 degrees of freedom, the observed frequencies are compatible with those based on the assumption of homogeneity. Second, consider the question whether social activities of the week end affect the accident rate. If Saturday, Sunday, and Monday are treated as the days that would be so affected, the problem reduces to a comparison of frequencies after the data have been combined into the two groups

Week end	Remaining days
44	40

On the basis of a uniform distribution over the week, the expected frequencies are now 36 and 48 respectively. Computations then give $\chi^2 = 3.1$. Since this value is so near the critical value of 3.8 for 1 degree of freedom, one would prefer to suspend judgment until further data were made available.

4. Limitations

Since the χ^2 curve is only an approximation to the true distribution for problems of this type, care must be exercised so that the χ^2 test will be used only when this approximation is good. Experience and theoretical investigations indicate that the approximation is usually satisfactory provided that the $e_i \geq 5$ and $k \geq 5$. If $k < 5$, it is best to have the e_i somewhat larger than 5.

If some of the cell frequencies, e_i, do not exceed 5, they may possibly be combined with other cell frequencies until the condition is satisfied. In the illustration on aircraft accidents, such a combination was made in the second part of the problem for the purpose of testing a second hypothesis, but it could equally well have been made of necessity if the cell frequencies had been too small to satisfy the above conditions. In any such reduction, of course, it is necessary to calculate the value of χ^2 and to determine the number of degrees of freedom after the reduction.

Methods are available for some of the other applications about to be presented which permit the χ^2 test to be applied with slightly greater confidence when the above conditions are barely satisfied.

CONTINGENCY TABLES

A slightly more complicated problem arises in testing the compatibility of sets of observed and expected frequencies when the frequencies occur in a two-way table rather than in a one-way table like those considered thus far. Such two-way tables are often called contingency tables. As an illustration of a contingency table, consider Table 1 in which are recorded the frequencies, corresponding to the indicated classifications, from a sample of 400 individuals.

A contingency table is usually constructed for the purpose of studying the relationship between the two variables of classification. If the variables are unrelated, that fact can be tested by means of an adaptation of the χ^2 test. The problem here is to test whether there is any relationship between an individual's education and his adjustment to marriage; therefore set up the hypothesis that there is no relationship.

TABLE 1

MARRIAGE-ADJUSTMENT SCORE

		Very low	Low	High	Very high	Totals
Education	College	18 (27)	29 (39)	70 (64)	115 (102)	232
	High school	17 (13)	28 (19)	30 (32)	41 (51)	116
	Grades only	11 (6)	10 (9)	11 (14)	20 (23)	52
	Totals	46	67	111	176	400

Now consider repeated sampling experiments of the type from which these data were obtained. Each experiment consists in selecting 400 people at random from the population in question and classifying them with respect to their education and marriage-adjustment score. Out of all such experiments, consider only those which give the same row and column totals as for this first experiment for which the frequencies are given in Table 1. For such experiments the percentage of individuals with some college education, for example, will remain constant. Now, if there is no relationship between the two variables, the percentage of individuals with some college education should be the same for all four of the categories of marriage adjustment. Since there are 232 college people out of the 400 sampled and the totals do not change from experiment to experiment, the percentage of college people to be expected in each of the four categories is 58%, correct to the nearest per cent. Since the column totals do not change, this percentage of the column totals will yield the number of college people to be expected in each of the four columns. The resulting expected frequencies, 27, 39, 64, and 102, correct to the nearest integer, have been inserted in parentheses in Table 1 next to their corresponding observed frequencies. The expected frequencies for the other two rows were obtained in a similar manner from the marginal totals. A check on the calculations may be obtained by verifying the row and column totals. It should be clearly understood that, unless the marginal totals are held fixed, the frequencies in parentheses would vary from experiment to experiment and therefore could not be treated as expected frequencies. By considering only the experiments that yield the same marginal totals, the problem is reduced to testing the compatibility of a set of observed and expected frequencies. By restricting the class of experiments for consideration in this manner, an experiment is judged by comparison with experiments very similar to it with respect to certain unimportant characteristics rather than by comparison with a wider class of experiments. The characteristic of possessing the same marginal totals is unimportant because it does not influence the relationship of the two variables.

In order to determine the number of degrees of freedom in this problem, it is necessary to know how many independent linear restrictions are imposed because of the marginal restrictions. If the observed frequency in the ith row and the jth column is denoted by o_{ij}, the restriction that the row and column totals shall remain fixed can be expressed as

$$\sum_1^4 o_{1j} = 232, \qquad \sum_1^4 o_{2j} = 116, \qquad \sum_1^4 o_{3j} = 52$$

$$\sum_1^3 o_{i1} = 46, \qquad \sum_1^3 o_{i2} = 67, \qquad \sum_1^3 o_{i3} = 111, \qquad \sum_1^3 o_{i4} = 176$$

It would appear from this that there are 7 independent linear restrictions here; however, the sum of the first 3 of these sums equals the sum of the remaining 4 sums because they both equal the total sample size. Thus, there are but 6 independent linear restrictions and hence the number of degrees of freedom here is $12 - 6 = 6$. This result can be obtained very easily by counting independent cell frequencies. Since the frequencies in the first row must total 232, only 3 of the 4 cell frequencies are free to vary. Similarly for the second row. The third-row frequencies, however, are now completely determined because the column totals are fixed; consequently there are only 6 independent cell frequencies and hence 6 degrees of freedom. In general, for a contingency table of a rows and b columns, there will be $(a - 1)(b - 1)$ degrees of freedom.

The value of χ^2 for Table 1 will be found to be 20.7. Since $\chi_0^2 = 12.6$ for 6 degrees of freedom, this result is highly significant. An inspection of the table shows that individuals with some college education appear to adjust themselves to marriage more readily than those with less education.

FREQUENCY CURVE FITTING

If a theoretical frequency distribution has been fitted to an observed frequency distribution, the question naturally arises whether the fit is satisfactory. This question arose, for example, in the exercise on fitting a normal curve to a histogram in Chapter III. When a normal curve is fitted to a histogram, it is usually assumed that the data represent a sample selected at random from a normal population and that the fitted normal curve is an approximation to the population curve. From this point of view, the question whether a fit is satisfactory can be answered only if one knows what sort of histograms will be obtained in random samples from a normal population.

Now the χ^2 test can be employed to give a partial answer to this question. Since the χ^2 test is concerned only with comparing sets of observed and expected frequencies, it is capable of testing only those features of the fitted distribution that are affected by a lack of compatibility in the compared sets. For example, the χ^2 test is not capable of differentiating between a normal curve with a given set of expected frequencies and any other curve with the same expected frequencies. With this understanding, consider the problem of testing the adequacy of the normal curve fit found in Chapter III by means of the last two columns of Table 1 of that chapter.

If the theoretical frequencies of this table are treated as the expected frequencies, e_i, it will be found that $\chi^2 = 8.4$. There are 10 pairs of frequencies to be compared in this problem, but there are not 9 degrees of freedom here as one might expect by analogy with the previous applications of the test. In this problem the expected frequencies would change from experiment to experiment because the fitted normal curve uses the mean and variance of the data rather than their population values, which are unknown. However, if repeated samples of size n are drawn from the same normal population and only those results are retained that give rise to the same mean and variance as for this one experiment, then the expected frequencies will not change. But now there will be 3 independent linear restrictions on the o_i because

$$\sum_1^k o_i = n, \qquad \sum_1^k x_i o_i = n\bar{x}, \qquad \sum_1^k (x_i - \bar{x})^2 o_i = ns^2$$

The first equality requires that the sample size be n, the second that the mean be $\bar{x}$, and the third that the variance be s^2; consequently the number of degrees of freedom would be $\nu = k - 3$. In this particular problem $\nu = 10 - 3 = 7$ and $\chi_0^2 = 14.1$. Since $\chi^2 = 8.4$, there is no reason for doubting that the data might have been obtained from sampling a normal population, as far as compatibility of corresponding sets of frequencies is concerned, and so the fit in Fig. 4, Chapter III, would be considered satisfactory from this point of view.

The situation that was met in this problem is the common one in fitting theoretical frequency distributions to observed distributions because the parameters specifying the theoretical distribution are seldom known and must be estimated from the data. In most problems of this type, these estimates are determined by means of moments, which give rise to linear restrictions; consequently the χ^2 test may be applied provided that 1 degree of freedom is deducted for each parameter that is replaced by its sample estimate.

If a binomial distribution were fitted to an observed frequency distribution by determining the 3 independent parameters in $N(q + p)^n$, where N is the sample size, from the observations, the number of degrees of freedom in the χ^2 test would be $k - 3$ just as in normal curve fitting; however, it often happens in binomial problems that one or more of the parameters will be specified from other considerations. For example, suppose that one were interested in studying the sex distribution in families of 8 children each. Here the value of $n = 8$ does not place any restriction on the o_i; consequently the number of degrees of freedom would be $k - 2$. If one were to assume equal sex distribution rather than determine p from the observations, the number of degrees of freedom would be $k - 1$.

Since the fitting of a Poisson distribution involves only two parameters, the χ^2 test will involve $k - 2$ or $k - 1$ degrees of freedom, depending upon whether m is replaced by its sample value or is known from other considerations. The illustrative example discussed in Chapter III in the section on the Poisson distribution is an example in which $k - 2$ is the correct number of degrees of freedom.

The preceding discussion in which only those sampling experiments that give rise to the same sample mean and variance as for the first experiment are considered is an attempt to describe what corresponds to the theory of the χ^2 distribution in this case. A theoretical discussion would involve probability densities and conditional distributions like those of Chapter VI. The possibility of obtaining sampling experiments with precisely the same mean and variance as for the first experiment therefore need not give one concern since this approach is merely a method of describing sampling from a conditional distribution.

INDICES OF DISPERSION

It frequently happens that an experimenter has a set of data that he believes can be treated as having come from a binomial distribution, or a Poisson distribution, but which contains so few values that it is useless to attempt to fit a binomial, or Poisson, distribution to the observed distribution. In such situations it is customary to test the hypothesis that the data came from a distribution of the assumed type by testing the variability of the data. Since these tests can be treated as special cases of the χ^2 test, they will be introduced from that point of view.

Let $x_1, x_2, \cdots, x_k$ represent the number of successes in n trials each in taking k samples from a binomial distribution with probability p. These numbers may be treated as the observed frequencies in the first row of the following two-rowed contingency table.

(3)

x_1	x_2	$\cdots$	x_k
$n - x_1$	$n - x_2$	$\cdots$	$n - x_k$

If this table is treated as though it were an ordinary contingency table like the contingency table in the second section preceding this one, the expected frequencies of the cells in the first row will become

$$e_i = \frac{\Sigma x_i}{nk} n = \bar{x} \qquad (i = 1, 2, \cdots, k)$$

and therefore those of the second row will become $n - \bar{x}$. As a result, the value of χ^2 will reduce to

$$\chi^2 = \sum_1^k \frac{(x_i - \bar{x})^2}{\bar{x}} + \sum_1^k \frac{(x_i - \bar{x})^2}{n - \bar{x}}$$

$$= \left(\frac{1}{\bar{x}} + \frac{1}{n - \bar{x}} \right) \sum_1^k (x_i - \bar{x})^2$$

(4)
$$= \sum_1^k \frac{(x_i - \bar{x})^2}{\bar{x}[1 - (\bar{x}/n)]}$$

The contingency table upon which this result is based differs slightly from the ordinary contingency table treated previously. For the ordinary table, successive observations were free to fall in any one of the cells. Then out of such experimental results only those experiments were considered that possessed the fixed marginal totals of the first experiment. Among such restricted experiments, the χ^2 distribution is known to represent approximately the relative frequency of possible values of χ^2. For this binomial contingency table, however, successive observations are not free to fall in any one of the cells. The first n observations must fall in one of the two cells of the first column, the second n observations in one of the two cells of the second column, etc. It is therefore necessary to consider only those sampling experiments that produce the same order of experimental results in addition to the same marginal totals. Since the sampling is random, this ordering does not affect the relative distribution of values in the various cells; consequently the ordinary contingency table methods for applying χ^2 are applicable.

The expression (4) is called the *binomial index of dispersion*. It is used to test the hypothesis that the k sample frequencies, x_i, came from the same binomial population. Since the sample size is fixed, the binomial index actually tests the hypothesis that the probability of a success is the same for all k samples. This is but one of many such tests that could be designed to check on the experimenter's belief that the value of p remains unchanged from sample to sample. It is clear from the nature of χ^2 that the binomial index will exceed its critical value only if there is excessive variability in the observed frequencies.

As an illustration of the application of (4), consider the following data on the number of infected plants per plot for 12 plots and 90 plants in each plot: 19, 6, 9, 18, 15, 13, 14, 15, 16, 20, 22, 14. The problem here is to determine whether it is reasonable to assume that the infection is distributed at random over the 12 plots. Calculations give, to the indicated accuracy,

$$\bar{x} = 15.1, \quad \sum_{1}^{12}(x_i - \bar{x})^2 = 223, \quad \chi^2 = 18$$

For 11 degrees of freedom, $\chi_0^2 = 19.7$; consequently there is some doubt whether the infection is distributed at random. For data of this type, it sometimes happens that the infection is localized and gradually spreads from the center of concentration; however, the number of plots here is not sufficiently large to investigate such possibilities.

If the value of p is very small and the value of n is very large, the value of $\bar{x}/n$, which is the sample estimate of p, will be very small; consequently the value of $1 - \bar{x}/n$ will be very nearly 1. If this approximation is used in (4), the binomial index of dispersion reduces to what is known as the *Poisson index of dispersion*, namely,

$$\sum_{1}^{k} \frac{(x_i - \bar{x})^2}{\bar{x}}$$

It would appear that the Poisson index is merely a special case of the χ^2 test of compatibility given earlier for those situations in which the expected frequencies are equal; however, there is a distinction in the nature of the variables. The sum of the frequencies in the ordinary χ^2 test represents the total number of observations made, whereas in applications of the Poisson index there are but k observations, each observation yielding a result that happens to be a frequency number. It is important to distinguish between these two types of problems in order to avoid the mistake of applying the ordinary χ^2 test to the first row only of the binomial frequencies in (3). Such an application would be equivalent to assuming that the data came from a Poisson rather than a binomial population. The value of χ^2 would then tend to be too small.

As an illustration of the Poisson index, consider the problem of testing whether the following data on the number of defective parts found in samples of 1,000 parts each are homogeneous: 15, 13, 8, 6, 11, 9, 14, 10, 16, 9, 12. Since the probability of a part's being defective is very small and n is very large, these frequencies will be treated as having come from a Poisson population. Calculations give

$$\bar{x} = 11.2, \quad \Sigma(x_i - \bar{x})^2 = 97.6, \quad \Sigma \frac{(x_i - \bar{x})^2}{\bar{x}} = 8.7$$

For 10 degrees of freedom, $\chi_0^2 = 18.3$; consequently the result is not significant.

REFERENCES

The derivation of the χ^2 distribution from the multinomial distribution has been expounded in an interesting elementary manner in:

GREENHOOD, E. R., *A Detailed Proof of the Chi-Square Test of Goodness of Fit*, Harvard University Press.

A direct derivation requiring slightly more mathematical maturity may be found in:

KENNEY, J. F., *Mathematics of Statistics*, D. Van Nostrand Company, pp. 164–168.

For 2 × 2 contingency tables there is available a correction to χ^2 which makes the χ^2 test slightly more accurate when some of the e_i are small. This correction is illustrated in:

RIDER, P., *An Introduction to Modern Statistical Methods*, John Wiley & Sons, pp. 112–115.

If the relationship between the two variables of a contingency table is obvious or highly significant, it may be of interest to obtain a measure of the strength of the relationship comparable to the correlation coefficient. Such a measure exists in what is known as the coefficient of contingency. A reference to its derivation and an illustration of its use will be found in:

KENDALL, M. G., *The Advanced Theory of Statistics*, vol. 1, Griffin and Company, pp. 318–322.

Investigations have shown that the χ^2 test must be applied with discretion when any of the e_i are small, particularly for the binomial index of dispersion and when fitting theoretical frequency distributions to observed distributions. An interesting example to illustrate the errors that may arise in fitting theoretical distributions is given in:

GUMBEL, E. J., "On the Reliability of the Classical Chi-Square Test," *Annals of Mathematical Statistics*, vol. xiv (1943), pp. 253–263.

In this article, the author advocates the use of a transformation to circumvent some of the drawbacks of the standard χ^2 test in such cases.

EXERCISES

1. Toss a coin 100 times, and apply the χ^2 test to see whether the coin is biased.

2. Roll a die 66 times, recording the various number of points obtained, and apply the χ^2 test to see whether the die is symmetrical.

3. In a breeding experiment it was expected that ducks would be hatched in the ratio of 1 duck with a white bib to each 3 ducks without bibs. Of 86 ducks hatched, 17 had white bibs. Is this a reasonable result?

4. In an epidemic of infantile paralysis, 927 children contracted the disease. Of these, 408 received no serum, and of these 104 became paralyzed. Of those who did receive serum, 166 became paralyzed. Was the serum effective?

5. Is there any relation between the mentality and weight of criminals as judged by the following data?

Weight

Mentality	90–120	120–130	130–140	140–150	150–
Normal	21	51	94	106	124
Weak	15	18	34	15	15

6. Show that for a 2×2 contingency table with cell frequencies a, b, c, and d, respectively,

$$\chi^2 = \frac{(a + b + c + d)(ad - bc)^2}{(a + b)(c + d)(b + d)(a + c)}$$

7. Use Tippett's random-sampling numbers to sample from the population expressed by

x	0	1	2
f	0.4	0.4	0.2

taking samples of 25 and performing 20 (or more) such sampling experiments. Calculate χ^2 for each experiment, then classify the 20 (or more) values into a frequency table. Compare the resulting histogram with the χ^2 curve for $\nu = 2$. This class exercise is intended to make the stated χ^2 theory seem plausible.

8. Apply the χ^2 test to the normal curve fit for the following 500 determinations of the width of a spectral band of light. Here e denotes the fitted normal curve frequencies.

o	5	12	43	61	105	103	89	54	19	7	2
e	5	14	36	71	102	109	85	50	21	7	2

9. Apply the χ^2 test for goodness of fit to the results of problem 23, Chapter III.

10. Apply the χ^2 test for goodness of fit to the results of problem 27, Chapter III.

11. The following data give the number of colonies of bacteria which developed on 15 different plates from the same dilution. Is one justified in claiming that the dilution technique was satisfactory in the sense that the bacteria behave as though they were randomly distributed in the dilution? The number of colonies were: 193, 168, 161, 153, 183, 152, 171, 156, 159, 140, 151, 152, 133, 164, 157.

12. On the basis of a given hypothesis, show that if an experiment yields a value of $\chi^2 = \chi_1^2$ with ν degrees of freedom, and if the experiment is repeated with approximately the same results, then the two experiments combined yield a different degree of confidence in the hypothesis from the first experiment alone.

13. Find m, σ, α_3, and α_4 for $f(\chi^2)$, and comment on its normal approximation.

14. Show that, when $\nu = 1$, the variable χ possesses a normal distribution.

15. Show that the large-sample method of Chapter IV for testing the difference of percentages is equivalent to the χ^2 test when applied to the 2×2 contingency table of successes and failures.

CHAPTER XI

TESTING STATISTICAL HYPOTHESES

NATURE OF STATISTICAL HYPOTHESES

A large part of the material presented in the preceding chapters has been concerned with testing various statistical hypotheses. These hypotheses were tested by means of distribution functions that were derived for such purposes or that seemed to be applicable to the given problem. The F distribution, for example, was derived to test the hypothesis that two independent normal samples came from populations with equal variances; however, the F distribution was found to be applicable for testing many other hypotheses as well. In all these problems the particular distribution function used and the particular critical region selected were based on intuitive arguments rather than upon any logical principle. For example, the 5% critical region for the simple χ^2 test of the preceding chapter was selected as the 5% right-hand tail of the χ^2 curve. This choice was based on the reasoning that, the larger the value of χ^2 in a sampling experiment, the less faith an experimenter would have in the truth of the hypothesis of compatibility between observed and expected frequencies. Although such intuitive arguments often yield highly efficient tests for testing the hypothesis in question, some logical principle for selecting the proper test is necessary if one is to be certain of the efficiency of a test. Two such principles will be considered very briefly in this chapter.

A consideration of the various hypotheses that were tested in the preceding chapters will show that most of them consisted in the specification of, or the equality of, certain parameter values in the distribution function representing the population being sampled. For example, the first application of Student's t distribution was the testing of the hypothesis that the mean of the normal population from which the sample was taken had a specified value. The second application of this distribution was testing the hypothesis that the means of two normal populations having equal variances were equal. In all these tests, the normality assumption was not a part of the hypothesis. A *statistical hypothesis* is usually regarded as a statement that specifies the value of one or more, or a relationship between two or more, of the parameters that determine the assumed distribution function.

A *test* of a statistical hypothesis is a rule for accepting or rejecting the hypothesis, this rule consisting in the selection of a critical region for the statistic being used and agreeing to reject the hypothesis if and only if the sample gives a value of this statistic that falls in the critical region. For example, in testing the hypothesis that the mean of a normal population has a specified value, as was done in the example discussed in the derivation of Student's t distribution, the critical region consisted of that part of the t axis lying to the right of the point $t_{0.10}$. In similar problems in which there is no reason for preferring one tail of Student's t distribution, the critical region might consist of the two regions $t > t_{0.05}$ and $t < -t_{0.05}$. It will be recalled that $t_{0.05}$ is a value of t such that $P[\,|\,t\,| > t_{0.05}] = 0.05$.

TWO TYPES OF ERROR

In following a procedure for testing hypotheses, there are two possibilities for error. If the hypothesis is true but the test rejects the hypothesis, an error known as a type I error is made. On the other hand, if the hypothesis is false but the test accepts the hypothesis, an error known as a type II error is made. The relative importance of these two kinds of errors depends upon what action is to be taken as a result of the test.

As an illustration, suppose that an innocent man is being tried for a crime and that his sentence hinges on the result of a certain experiment. If a hypothesis corresponding to innocence was set up and was rejected by the experiment, then an innocent man would be convicted and a type I error would result. On the other hand, if the man were guilty but the experimental result accepted the hypothesis corresponding to innocence, then a guilty man would be freed and a type II error would result. Here a type I error would be considered by society as more serious than a type II error.

As another illustration, suppose that a new industrial process which is superior to the standard process is being tested by means of an experiment. If the hypothesis of no improvement was set up and was accepted, then a valuable improvement would be lost. This would usually be more serious than making the mistake of advocating a new process that in reality is no improvement. Here a type II error would be more serious than a type I error. The relative importance of these two types of error is usually not as simple a matter as the above discussion might indicate. For example, suppose that employees are being screened by means of a test. The test may be quite good at selecting the potentially undesirable employee provided that its standards are sufficiently high; however, these standards may also eliminate a fairly large percentage of potentially desirable employees. If labor is scarce, the problem of deciding on the most economical score to choose for screening becomes quite complex.

A logical procedure for selecting efficient tests of statistical hypotheses can be designed by means of these two types of error. The procedure consists in first specifying that all the tests under consideration shall have the same-size type I error and then selecting that test for which the type II error is a minimum. Since the size of the type I error is the probability that the sample will yield a value falling in the critical region, the size of this error can be regulated by changing the size of the critical region. Thus, all tests under consideration can be made to have the same-size type I error, say α, by choosing all critical regions to be of size α. The problem is then reduced to determining which test, if any, minimizes the type II error. For most of the tests that were employed in the preceding chapters, the solution of this problem is not simple.

As an illustration of this procedure for designing an efficient test, consider the problem of testing the hypothesis that the mean of a certain normal population with unit variance has the value m_0. The procedure employed in Chapter IV for testing this hypothesis on the basis of a sample of size n was to calculate the quantity

$$(1) \qquad u = (\bar{x} - m_0)\sqrt{n}$$

which would be normally distributed with zero mean and unit variance provided the hypothesis was true, and accept the hypothesis if and only if u satisfied the inequality

$$-1.96 < u < 1.96$$

In order to determine whether this is an efficient test, it is necessary to compare it with other tests. For the sake of simplicity, consider only those tests that agree to accept the hypothesis if and only if u satisfies the inequality

$$t_1 < u < t_2$$

where t_1 and t_2 are two numbers such that

$$(2) \qquad \frac{1}{\sqrt{2\pi}} \int_{t_1}^{t_2} e^{-\frac{t^2}{2}} \, dt = 0.95$$

The restriction (2) guarantees that all these tests will have a type I error of size 0.05.

Now the problem is to determine the values of t_1 and t_2 that will minimize the type II error. If the hypothesis is false with the mean of the population equal to $m \neq m_0$, the variable

$$(3) \qquad v = (\bar{x} - m)\sqrt{n}$$

will be normally distributed with zero mean and unit variance. If (3) is used in (1), u can be written in the form

$$u = v + \sqrt{n}(m - m_0)$$

consequently the variable u will now be normally distributed with mean $\sqrt{n}(m - m_0)$ and unit variance. The probability that u will fall in the interval (t_1, t_2) is therefore given by

$$(4) \qquad P = \frac{1}{\sqrt{2\pi}} \int_{t_1}^{t_2} e^{-\frac{1}{2}[u - \sqrt{n}(m - m_0)]^2} \, du$$

This integral gives the type II error, which it is desired to minimize subject to the restriction (2).

For the purpose of calculating the derivative of P, it is convenient to write P in the form

$$(5) \quad P = \frac{1}{\sqrt{2\pi}} \int_0^{t_2} e^{-\frac{1}{2}[u - \sqrt{n}(m - m_0)]^2} \, du$$

$$- \frac{1}{\sqrt{2\pi}} \int_0^{t_1} e^{-\frac{1}{2}[u - \sqrt{n}(m - m_0)]^2} \, du$$

If t_1 is treated as the independent variable, t_2 will be a function of t_1 because of condition (2). Now the derivative of P with respect to t_1 may be obtained by means of the calculus formula used previously and given after (5), Chapter VI. Application of this formula to (5) gives

$$(6) \quad \frac{dP}{dt_1} = \frac{1}{\sqrt{2\pi}} e^{-\frac{1}{2}[t_2 - \sqrt{n}(m - m_0)]^2} \frac{dt_2}{dt_1} - \frac{1}{\sqrt{2\pi}} e^{-\frac{1}{2}[t_1 - \sqrt{n}(m - m_0)]^2}$$

The integral in (2) may be treated in the same manner to give

$$(7) \qquad \frac{1}{\sqrt{2\pi}} e^{-\frac{t_2^2}{2}} \frac{dt_2}{dt_1} - \frac{1}{\sqrt{2\pi}} e^{-\frac{t_1^2}{2}} = 0$$

If the value of dt_2/dt_1 from (7) is substituted in (6), (6) will reduce to

$$\frac{dP}{dt_1} = \frac{1}{\sqrt{2\pi}} e^{-\frac{1}{2}[t_2 - \sqrt{n}(m - m_0)]^2 - \frac{1}{2}[t_1^2 - t_2^2]} - \frac{1}{\sqrt{2\pi}} e^{-\frac{1}{2}[t_1 - \sqrt{n}(m - m_0)]^2}$$

This simplifies into

$$(8) \qquad \frac{dP}{dt_1} = \frac{1}{\sqrt{2\pi}} \, e^{-\frac{1}{2}[t_1^2 + n(m-m_0)^2]} \left\{ e^{t_2\sqrt{n}(m-m_0)} - e^{t_1\sqrt{n}(m-m_0)} \right\}$$

Since $t_2 > t_1$, it follows from (8) that $dP/dt_1 \gtrless 0$ according as $m \gtrless m_0$. This means that P is an increasing function of t_1 for $m > m_0$ and a decreasing function for $m < m_0$; consequently the maximum and minimum values of P are assumed when t_1 takes on its extreme values. Thus, for $m > m_0$ the minimum value of P occurs when $t_1 = -\infty$ and its maximum value occurs when $t_2 = \infty$, since t_1 assumes its largest value then. For $m < m_0$ the maximum value of P occurs when $t_1 = -\infty$ and its minimum value occurs when $t_2 = \infty$. There is therefore no pair of numbers, t_1 and t_2, which will minimize the type II error for all possible values of $m \neq m_0$.

If t_1 and t_2 are held fixed and P in (4) is treated as a function of m, its graph will show how the type II error changes with m. From the preceding discussion it follows that the two curves corresponding to $t_1 = -\infty$ and $t_2 = \infty$ will determine a region in the P, m plane within which all other test curves will lie. From (4) it will be observed that, for $t_1 = -\infty$, $P \to 1$ as $m \to -\infty$, and $P \to 0$ as $m \to \infty$, whereas, for $t_2 = \infty$, $P \to 0$ as $m \to -\infty$ and $P \to 1$ as $m \to \infty$. These results follow readily if one thinks geometrically of a standard normal curve which moves off to infinity. The preceding results show that the two boundary curves in the P, m plane have the lines $P = 0$ and $P = 1$ as horizontal asymptotes. These two boundary curves are represented graphically by a and b in Fig. 1. The curve corresponding to the test given in (1) is labeled c. Other pairs of values of t_1 and t_2 satisfying (2) would yield curves lying between the curves a and b.

From the preceding discussion and Fig. 1, it is clear that there is no best test among the class of tests considered for testing the hypothesis $m = m_0$ because there is no curve lying below all other curves for all values of $m \neq m_0$. However, if only values of $m < m_0$ were considered as possible alternatives to $m = m_0$, then the curve b would correspond to the best possible test because the type II error would be less than that for any other test for every value of $m < m_0$. Since the minimizing curve b corresponds to the value $t_2 = \infty$, from (2) it follows that the 5% critical region here is determined by the inequality $u < -1.64$. This value merely determines the 5% left tail of the standard normal curve. It may be recalled that this is precisely the critical region that was selected on intuitive grounds in the first problem on applications of Theorem I, Chapter IV. The procedure followed in the solution of that problem was therefore a highly efficient one from this point of view.

From Fig. 1 it appears that the test corresponding to curve c is a fairly efficient test provided that all values of $m \neq m_0$ are assumed as possible alternatives to the hypothesis of $m = m_0$. Unless further restrictions are placed on the nature of the tests that should be con-

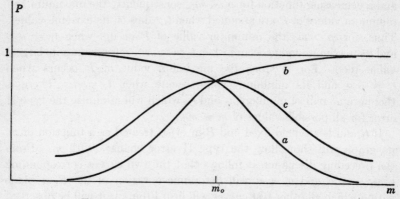

FIG. 1.   Type II error treated as a function of m.

sidered, there does not appear to be any test more efficient than this symmetrical test for this case. These considerations help to justify the intuitive procedure in problems of the type indicated in (1).

It can be shown with considerably more difficulty that Student's t test has efficiency properties analogous to those of the one-sided and symmetrical normal curve tests for testing the hypothesis $m = m_0$ when the value of σ is unspecified. Such investigations justify the use of the t test in previous applications.

MAXIMUM LIKELIHOOD

The illustration of the preceding section gives an indication of the difficulties that are met in designing efficient tests. Although the hypothesis in that illustration was very simple, no test existed that minimized the type II error for all possible alternatives. For more complex hypotheses, the occurrence of tests with this minimizing property is infrequent. It is often possible in such situations to place further restrictions on the class of tests that will be considered and thereby determine a best test from among this restricted set; however, such ideas will not be discussed here.

A second basis for selecting efficient tests is one called the principle of maximum likelihood. This principle is justified partly on its strong intuitive appeal but mostly on the desirable properties the tests it produces are found to possess.

1. Maximum Likelihood Estimation

Suppose that the variable x has a distribution function $f(x; \theta)$ which depends upon the single parameter θ. The distribution function of a random sample of size n will therefore be given by

$$(9) \qquad P = f(x_1; \theta)f(x_2; \theta) \cdots f(x_n; \theta)$$

For a given sample, P represents the probability density at the sample point $x_1, x_2, \cdots, x_n$, or the probability of obtaining the sample, depending upon whether x is a continuous or a discrete variable. In either case, P represents a function of θ which is called the *likelihood* function for the sample. This name corresponds to one's intuitive belief that an estimate of θ that makes P relatively large is likely to be a good estimate of the parameter. If this belief is capitalized upon, it gives rise to a technique of estimating population parameters that is known as the method of *maximum likelihood*. The technique is often quite simple since it is merely necessary to solve the equation $dP/d\theta = 0$ for θ.

As an illustration of the maximum-likelihood technique, consider the problem of estimating the mean m in the Poisson function

$$f(x; m) = \frac{e^{-m}m^x}{x!}$$

Here, the likelihood function given by (9) reduces to

$$P = \frac{e^{-m}m^{x_1}}{x_1!} \frac{e^{-m}m^{x_2}}{x_2!} \cdots \frac{e^{-m}m^{x_n}}{x_n!}$$

$$= \frac{e^{-mn} \cdot m^{\bar{x}n}}{x_1! x_2! \cdots x_n!}$$

Therefore,

$$\frac{dP}{dm} = \frac{e^{-mn} \cdot \bar{x}n m^{\bar{x}n-1} - e^{-mn} \cdot nm^{\bar{x}n}}{x_1! x_2! \cdots x_n!}$$

$$= \frac{e^{-mn} \cdot nm^{\bar{x}n}}{x_1! x_2! \cdots x_n!}\left[\frac{\bar{x}}{m} - 1\right]$$

The solution of $dP/dm = 0$ is evidently $m = \bar{x}$. This result shows that the probability of obtaining a given set of sample values from a Poisson population is a maximum when the population mean is equal to the sample mean.

The preceding technique can be extended directly to distribution functions of more than one parameter and more than one variable.

2. Simple Hypotheses

The principle of maximum likelihood can also be applied to the problem of selecting efficient tests for testing statistical hypotheses. For simplicity of explanation, suppose as before that the distribution function of the variable x depends upon a single parameter θ and that the hypothesis to be tested is that $\theta = \theta_0$. If the sample values of x are held fixed, P in (9) is a function of θ only. Let $P_m(\theta)$ denote the maximum value of this function, and let $P(\theta_0)$ denote its value for $\theta = \theta_0$. Then the ratio

$$(10) \qquad \lambda = \frac{P(\theta_0)}{P_m(\theta)}$$

is a function of the sample values $x_1, \cdots, x_n$ only. Since $P(\theta)$ includes $P(\theta_0)$ as one of its possible values, its maximum value must be at least as great as the value of $P(\theta_0)$; consequently λ satisfies the inequality $0 \le \lambda \le 1$. This ratio is called the *likelihood ratio* for the hypothesis being tested. If λ is close to 1, the probability density of the sample point could not be increased much by allowing θ to assume values other than θ_0; consequently a value of λ near 1 corresponds intuitively to considerable belief in the truth of the hypothesis that $\theta = \theta_0$. If increasing values of λ are treated as corresponding to increasing degrees of belief in the truth of the hypothesis, and if the distribution function of λ can be found, then a critical value of λ, say λ_0, could be determined such that the hypothesis would be rejected if and only if $P[\lambda \le \lambda_0] = 0.05$.

Although this method of selecting a test is based largely on intuitive arguments as contrasted with the preceding method, it is highly useful for those hypotheses for which a minimum type II error does not exist and for complicated hypotheses. Experience and theory indicate that likelihood tests possess many desirable properties.

As an illustration of the application of the likelihood principle, consider the same hypothesis as for the illustrative example of the preceding section. Since $\sigma = 1$ in that example, the only parameter is $\theta = m$; consequently

$$P(m) = \frac{1}{\sqrt{2\pi}} e^{-\frac{1}{2}(x_1 - m)^2} \cdots \frac{1}{\sqrt{2\pi}} e^{-\frac{1}{2}(x_n - m)^2}$$

$$(11) \qquad = \left(\frac{1}{\sqrt{2\pi}}\right)^n e^{-\frac{1}{2} \sum_{i=1}^{n} (x_i - m)^2}$$

The hypothesis to be tested is that $m = m_0$; therefore

$$P(m_0) = \left(\frac{1}{\sqrt{2\pi}}\right)^n e^{-\frac{1}{2}\sum_{i=1}^{n}(x_i-m_0)^2}$$

By differentiating (11), the maximum likelihood value of m will be found to be $m = \bar{x}$; consequently

$$P_m(m) = \left(\frac{1}{\sqrt{2\pi}}\right)^n e^{-\frac{1}{2}\sum_{1}^{n}(x_i-\bar{x})^2}$$

If these two values are substituted in (10), it will reduce to

$$\lambda = e^{-\frac{1}{2}\left[\sum_{1}^{n}(x_i-m_0)^2 - \sum_{1}^{n}(x_i-\bar{x})^2\right]}$$

$$= e^{-\frac{1}{2}[-2n\bar{x}+nm_0^2+n\bar{x}^2]}$$

(12) $$= e^{-\frac{n}{2}[\bar{x}-m_0]^2}$$

Since n and m_0 are known constants, this equation expresses a relationship between λ and $\bar{x}$. By means of this relationship it would be possible to find the distribution function of λ from that of $\bar{x}$; however, for the purpose of testing hypotheses it is merely necessary to know how to find the critical region for the distribution function of λ from that for $\bar{x}$. Now from (12) it is clear that to each value of λ there correspond two values of $\bar{x}$ and that these values of $\bar{x}$ are symmetrical with respect to $\bar{x} = m_0$. There will therefore be two values of $\bar{x}$ corresponding to the critical value of $\lambda = \lambda_0$. Furthermore, increasingly small values of λ correspond to increasingly large values of $|\bar{x} - m_0|$. Therefore the 5% critical region for λ consisting of the interval $0 \le \lambda \le \lambda_0$ will correspond to the two $2\frac{1}{2}\%$ tails of the $\bar{x}$ normal distribution. The critical region for $\bar{x}$ therefore consists of the two intervals given by $|\bar{x} - m_0|\sqrt{n} > 1.96$. A comparison of this result with (1) shows that the likelihood ratio test is merely the commonly employed test for this hypothesis.

3. Composite Hypotheses

When a distribution function of one variable depends upon more than one parameter and not all of them are specified by the hypothesis, the hypothesis is called *composite* and the likelihood ratio is defined more generally in the following manner.

Let $P(x_1, \cdots, x_n; \theta_1, \cdots, \theta_k)$ denote the probability density (or probability) function given in (9) when this function depends upon k

parameters, and let $P(x_1, \cdots, x_n; \theta_1', \cdots, \theta_k')$ represent this function when those values of the parameters that are specified by the hypothesis have been inserted. Then the likelihood ratio is defined as

$$(13) \qquad \lambda = \frac{P_m(x_1, \cdots, x_n; \theta_1', \cdots, \theta_k')}{P_m(x_1, \cdots, x_n; \theta_1, \cdots, \theta_k)}$$

where, as before, the subscript m on P denotes its maximum value with respect to the parameters involved. It is clear that (10) is a special case of (13) when $k = 1$. The same intuitive arguments employed to justify the use of λ in (10) as a basis for testing a simple hypothesis may be employed to justify the use of λ in (13) for testing a composite hypothesis.

As an illustration of how (13) may be used to design tests of more complicated hypotheses, consider the problem of deciding whether a set of variances is homogeneous. In measuring the variability of industrial processes, for example, it is necessary to know whether the process variability has changed; consequently a test of homogeneity is required.

Consider k normal populations with respective means and variances given by m_i and σ_i^2 $(i = 1, \cdots, k)$. Let random samples of sizes n_i be drawn from these populations. Then the hypothesis to be tested here is that

$$(14) \qquad \sigma_1 = \sigma_2 = \cdots = \sigma_k$$

For simplicity of notation, the probability density will be denoted by $P(x_{ij}; m_i, \sigma_i)$, where x_{ij} represents the $\sum_1^k n_i = n$ variables, and m_i and σ_i represent the $2k$ parameters. Here

$$(15) \qquad P(x_{ij}; m_i, \sigma_i) = \frac{e^{-\frac{1}{2}\sum\limits_{i=1}^{k}\sum\limits_{j=1}^{n_i}\left(\frac{x_{ij}-m_i}{\sigma_i}\right)^2}}{(2\pi)^{\frac{n}{2}}\sigma_1^{n_1}\cdots\sigma_k^{n_k}}$$

When the hypothesis (14) is true, (15) reduces to

$$(16) \qquad P(x_{ij}; m_i, \sigma) = \frac{e^{-\frac{1}{2}\sum\limits_{i=1}^{k}\sum\limits_{j=1}^{n_i}\left(\frac{x_{ij}-m_i}{\sigma}\right)^2}}{(2\pi)^{\frac{n}{2}}\sigma^n}$$

where σ represents the common value of the σ_i. In order to apply (13), it is necessary to maximize (15) and (16) with respect to their parameters. This is accomplished by first taking logarithms of both sides. If (15) and (16) are denoted by P and P', respectively, then

$$\frac{\partial \log P}{\partial m_i} = -\frac{1}{\sigma_i{}^2} \sum_{j=1}^{n_i} (x_{ij} - m_i)$$

$$\frac{\partial \log P}{\partial \sigma_i} = -\frac{n_i}{\sigma_i} + \frac{1}{\sigma_i{}^3} \sum_{j=1}^{n_i} (x_{ij} - m_i)^2$$

$$\frac{\partial \log P'}{\partial m_i} = -\frac{1}{\sigma^2} \sum_{j=1}^{n_i} (x_{ij} - m_i)$$

$$\frac{\partial \log P'}{\partial \sigma} = -\frac{n}{\sigma} + \frac{1}{\sigma^3} \sum_{i=1}^{k} \sum_{j=1}^{n_i} (x_{ij} - m_i)^2$$

From the first and third of these derivatives, it follows that the maximum likelihood estimates for m_i are in each case given by $m_i = \bar{x}_i$. From the second and fourth of these derivatives, it follows that the respective maximum likelihood estimates for σ_i are given by

$$\sigma_i{}^2 = \sum_{j=1}^{n_i} \frac{(x_{ij} - \bar{x}_i)^2}{n_i} = s_i{}^2$$

and

$$\sigma^2 = \sum_{i=1}^{k} \sum_{j=1}^{n_i} \frac{(x_{ij} - \bar{x}_i)^2}{n} = \sum_{i=1}^{k} \frac{n_i s_i{}^2}{n}$$

If these estimates are substituted in (15) and (16), respectively, P and P' will become

$$P_m = \frac{e^{-\frac{n}{2}}}{(2\pi)^{\frac{n}{2}} s_1{}^{n_1} \cdots s_k{}^{n_k}}$$

and

$$P_m' = \frac{e^{-\frac{n}{2}}}{(2\pi)^{\frac{n}{2}} \left[\dfrac{n_1 s_1{}^2 + \cdots + n_k s_k{}^2}{n} \right]^{\frac{n}{2}}}$$

The likelihood ratio given by (13) therefore reduces to

(17)
$$\lambda = \frac{s_1{}^{n_1} \cdots s_k{}^{n_k}}{\left[\dfrac{n_1 s_1{}^2 + \cdots + n_k s_k{}^2}{n} \right]^{\frac{n}{2}}}$$

If both sides of this expression are raised to the power $2/n$, it will be observed that $\lambda^{\frac{2}{n}}$ is the ratio of the geometric and arithmetic means of the sample variances.

If now the distribution function of λ were available, it would be possible to find critical values of λ for deciding whether to accept the hypothesis of equal variances. Because of the complexity of this distribution function, it is necessary to resort to convenient approximations. If the values of the n_i are fairly large, it turns out that the quantity $-2 \log_e \lambda$ has a distribution that can be approximated fairly well by the χ^2 distribution with $k - 1$ degrees of freedom; consequently critical values of λ may be obtained from the corresponding critical values of χ^2.

A somewhat more accurate test, particularly for small values of the n_i, than the likelihood test just discussed is available. In this test each n_i in λ is interpreted as the number of degrees of freedom in s_i^2, and s_i^2 is interpreted as the unbiased estimate of σ_i^2. If the resulting value of λ is denoted by μ, this test consists in treating

$$(18) \qquad \frac{-2 \log_e \mu}{1 + \dfrac{1}{3(k - 1)} \left\{ \sum_1^k \dfrac{1}{n_i} - \dfrac{1}{n} \right\}}$$

as a variable with a χ^2 distribution with $k - 1$ degrees of freedom. These changes in the interpretation of n_i and s_i^2 will not affect the value of λ appreciably if the n_i are large; however, for small samples this correction becomes important. For the special case in which all the n_i are equal, it can easily be shown that

$$(19) \qquad \log_e \mu = \frac{n_i{}'}{n_i} \log_e \lambda$$

where $n_i{}'$ denotes the number of degrees of freedom corresponding to n_i. Thus, this correction is much like that used to eliminate the bias in large-sample estimates of variances. This improved version of the likelihood ratio test was designed when investigations showed that the likelihood ratio test was slightly biased.

Maximum likelihood estimates and tests are known to possess desirable properties for large samples; however, many of them turn out to be biased for small samples and need to be corrected accordingly if they are to be used on small samples.

As a numerical illustration of this test, consider once more the second problem on applications of the χ^2 distribution in Chapter VIII. In that problem, five sample variances were combined to yield a single estimate of σ^2 on the assumption that the variances were homogeneous. Here

$$n_1 s_1^2 = 1,185, \qquad n_4 s_4^2 = 1,478$$

$$n_2 s_2^2 = 1,599, \qquad n_5 s_5^2 = 705$$

$$n_3 s_3^2 = 4,214, \qquad \sum_1^5 n_i s_i^2 = 9,181$$

Since each variance was based on five measurements, $n_i = 5$ if λ is used and $n_i = 4$ if μ is used. The value of $n_i s_i^2$ is the same for λ and μ. Calculations give $-2 \log_e \lambda = 2.00$; therefore by (19) and (18), $-2 \log_e \mu = 1.60$ and

$$\frac{-2 \log_e \mu}{1 + \dfrac{1}{3(k-1)} \left\{ \displaystyle\sum_1^k \frac{1}{n_i} - \frac{1}{n} \right\}} = \frac{1.60}{1.1} = 1.45$$

Since $\chi_0^2 = 9.5$ for $k - 1 = 4$ degrees of freedom, this result is not significant. The assumption of homogeneity appears to have been a reasonable one.

REFERENCES

The method of constructing tests of hypotheses by means of the two types of error is known as the Neyman-Pearson theory of testing hypotheses. Further material on this approach to the testing of hypotheses, which, however, requires considerable mathematical experience, may be found in the references 71–74 given in:

WILKS, S. S., *Mathematical Statistics*, Princeton University Press.

The maximum-likelihood approach to the testing of hypotheses is a few years older than the Neyman-Pearson approach; although it often possesses the advantage of simplicity, it lacks the desirable efficiency property of that approach. Further material on this topic may be found in the preceding reference.

The derivation of the correction to the likelihood ratio test for testing the homogeneity of a set of variances will be found in:

BARTLETT, M. S., "Properties of Sufficiency and Statistical Tests," *Proceedings of the Royal Society of London*, series A, vol. 160 (1937), pp. 273 ff.

There are other approaches to the testing of hypotheses in addition to the two discussed in this chapter; however, a consideration of their relative merits would be out of place here.

EXERCISES

1. Find the maximum likelihood estimate of p for a binomial distribution based on a sample of size n.

2. Find the maximum likelihood estimates of m and σ for a normal distribution.

3. Calculate the type II error if the hypothesis $\sigma = 10$ is tested against the single alternative $\sigma = 20$ on the basis of a sample of size 4 from a normal population and if the critical region consists of the 5% right tail of the distribution of s^2.

4. Prove that the likelihood ratio test of the hypothesis $m = m_0$ for a normal population of unknown variance σ^2 is equivalent to Student's t test for this hypothesis.

CHAPTER XII

STATISTICAL DESIGN IN EXPERIMENTS

It is a common occurrence for experimenters who are unacquainted with statistical principles to seek statistical assistance when their experiments fail to produce the results anticipated by them. In some experiments the data were obtained in such a manner as to exclude any valid conclusions of the type desired; in others, there is little that can be done to extract further information from the data because the experiment was not designed with a statistical analysis in mind. Only rarely are the experiments that give valid conclusions as efficient as they would have been if a standard statistical design had been employed. Too many experimenters do not seem to appreciate the obvious injunction that the time to design an experiment is before the experiment is begun.

In this chapter, the statistical design of experiments will be considered from the point of view of validity and efficiency. Although an experimental design that does not yield valid results may be considered inefficient, it is convenient to distinguish between these two concepts because a valid design need not be an efficient one. Only a few of the many techniques available in statistical literature for assisting in the designing of experiments will be considered in this chapter.

VALIDITY

In most experiments there are several variables in addition to the one or more being investigated that need to be controlled if the experiment is to give valid conclusions. In some cases these interfering variables can be controlled by laboratory techniques; in others such control may be possible only through statistical design. As a simple illustration, consider an agricultural experiment in which two different seed varieties are to be tested on a piece of land. If the piece of land were divided into two equal pieces and one variety planted on each, the difference in yields could not be used as a valid estimate of the differential effect of the two seed varieties because of the possible difference in soil fertility of the two pieces.

Experiments can often be made valid by applying the principles of *randomization* and *replication*. Thus, in the present illustration, if the piece of land were divided into a number of small plots of equal size, and if one variety of seed were planted on half of those plots and the other variety on the remaining half, with the selection of plots determined by a random process, then the varying fertility of the land would affect the two varieties approximately equally and therefore the difference in varietal yields would represent a valid estimate of the differential effects of the two seed varieties.

Randomization by itself is not necessarily sufficient to yield a valid experiment. For example, if one merely tossed a coin to determine which half of the original piece of land should be planted with one of the seed varieties, the selection would be random but it would not permit the two seed varieties to be equally affected by any varying fertility. In order to insure validity, it would be necessary that the piece of land be divided into a sufficiently large number of similar plots so that the probability will be very small of having one of the seed varieties largely located on the more fertile plots. This repetition of an experiment or experimental unit is called replication. Thus, to insure validity in an experiment, randomization should be accompanied by sufficient replication.

Not only are randomization and replication useful techniques for assisting in the construction of valid experiments, but they are often essential to certain classes of experiments whose conclusions depend upon the use of distribution functions. Since all the distribution functions in this book were derived upon the basis of random sampling, it follows that the methods employed in the preceding chapters are applicable to such samples only; consequently any experiment whose conclusions depend upon such methods requires randomization. Replication is also necessary for the application of any method that obtains its measure of variability directly from the data because at least two observations are needed to measure variability. For example, the illustrative experiment just discussed requires randomization and replication if the difference between mean yields is to be tested by means of Student's t distribution, because the t distribution is based on random sampling and because sample variances are needed to evaluate t.

The requirement of random samples for the applicability of most statistical methods is not always easy to satisfy. For example, if the product of a machine is sampled every hour for several days, it may easily happen that the product of the machine changes during the day because of the operator's working pattern and also from day to day because of wear. For situations like this in which observations are ordered with respect to time, one of the previous methods for testing randomness should be applied before methods based upon random samples are used.

EFFICIENCY

In the preceding illustration, the techniques of randomization and replication removed much of the danger of obtaining biased results; however, these techniques did not remove the effect of differences in soil fertility on the variability of yields. If the variation in fertility is increased, the variation in yield is thereby increased. As a consequence, if Student's t distribution for testing the difference between two means were applied, a considerably larger sample might be needed to produce a significant difference with large fertility differences between plots than if the plots were of uniform fertility because of the larger estimate of variance involved in the denominator of t. Such an experiment could therefore be made more efficient by selecting plots of uniform fertility. Very often, however, it is not feasible to control the fertility in this manner. Nevertheless, by arranging the plots into small homogeneous groups, it is often possible to eliminate statistically the greater share of the fertility variability effects in the t test and thereby make the experiment more efficient. This approach to efficiency will be treated in the next section.

No attempt will be made here to state what is meant by an efficient experiment; however, certain common aspects of efficiency will be treated. For experiments of fixed size, methods for increasing the sensitivity of an experiment will be considered, whereas, for experiments of variable size, methods for minimizing the amount of sampling needed to insure the desired sensitivity will be considered.

ANALYSIS OF VARIANCE

One of the most useful techniques for increasing the sensitivity of an experiment is the designing of the experiment in such a way that the total variation of the variable being studied can be separated into components that are of experimental interest. This technique, which is called the analysis of variance, was introduced in Chapter VIII as an application of the F test. It enables the experimenter to utilize statistical methods to eliminate the effects of certain interfering variables.

An example of such an experiment occurred in the third application of the F distribution in Chapter VIII. In that experiment 4 equal plots of land were each divided into 5 equal subplots. Then the 5 different treatments being tested were assigned to the 5 subplots in each of the 4 plots by a random process. The advantage of assigning treatments at random within a plot rather than assigning them at random throughout all 20 subplots lies in the fact that the fertility of the soil is likely to be more homogeneous in small neighboring groups of 5 subplots than it is throughout all 20 subplots and that it may therefore be possible to measure and hence eliminate some of the interfering soil variability by this procedure. For the purpose of observing the advantage of this technique, consider the difference in approach in testing for differences among treatments before and after the 4 plots are segregated. Before segregation the variation in yield was broken down according to (21), Chapter VIII, into the variation within treatments and between treatments. After segregation the variation in yield was broken down according to (26), Chapter VIII, into the variation between treatments, between plots, and the remainder. The F distribution was applied in each case to test the hypothesis of no treatment differences. The computations there gave the values

$$F = 22, \quad \nu_1 = 4, \quad \nu_2 = 15$$

and

$$F = 36, \quad \nu_1 = 4, \quad \nu_2 = 12$$

respectively. Since the change in ν_2 has only a slight effect upon the critical value of F, it is clear that the elimination of plot differences in the second F test enabled the treatment differences to be recognized more easily and thus produced a more sensitive experiment.

If there had been other variables in addition to soil fertility that were believed to influence yield and that could be controlled statistically in much the same manner as fertility was, then a further reduction in the variance could be made with a corresponding increase in the sensitivity of the experiment for detecting treatment differences. For example, if similar experiments were conducted at different experimental farms or regions, a loss in experimental sensitivity would result if the variability arising from farm or region differences were not eliminated by the proper analysis of variance.

TWO TYPES OF ERROR

If the conclusions to be obtained from an experiment depend upon the results of a test of a statistical hypothesis, the best test available for testing this hypothesis should be used to increase the sensitivity of the experiment. From the preceding chapter, such a test, if it exists, is one that minimizes the type II error. Although only a few of the tests of hypotheses presented in this book actually minimize the type II error, most of them are considered highly efficient tests for testing the hypothesis in question.

In addition to its use to increase the sensitivity of an experiment, the type II error can also assist the experimenter in deciding how large his experiment should be. Before consideration can be given to the size of an experiment, it is necessary to determine rather carefully what the experiment is expected to accomplish. Frequently the experiment is expected to decide which of two or more procedures or qualities is preferable. The experimenter would like to be fairly certain that the experiment will indicate a difference if and only if a real difference is present. This assurance can be obtained by making the probabilities of the two types of error arising in the significance test to be used sufficiently small. If the probabilities of the two types of error are denoted by α and β, respectively, the experiment should be designed to be sufficiently large to insure that the test will yield values of α and β that will satisfy the experimenter.

As a simple illustration of how to determine the size of an experiment by means of the two types of error, consider a variation of the problem proposed as an application of Theorem I, Chapter IV. There, experience gave a mean of 15.6 pounds and a standard deviation of 2.2 pounds for the breaking strength of samples of a certain brand of string. Then a time-saving process was tried which seemed to lower the mean somewhat. Suppose, now, that the manufacturer will tolerate a drop in the mean to 14.6 pounds but no lower. How large a sample will be necessary if the manufacturer desires the probability of a type I error to be 0.01 and the probability of a type II error to be 0.05? The critical region here will correspond to the 1% left tail of the normal curve for $\bar{x}$ and is determined by the inequality

$$\bar{x} < m_0 - \tau_{0.02}\sigma_{\bar{x}}$$

where $\tau_{0.02}$ is the standard normal deviate. For the problem under consideration, this inequality becomes

(1) $$\bar{x} < 15.6 - 2.33 \frac{2.2}{\sqrt{n}}$$

Now the probability of a type II error is the probability that $\bar{x}$ will not fall in this critical region when the hypothesis is false. It is often more convenient to treat it as 1 minus the probability that $\bar{x}$ will fall in the critical region when the hypothesis is false. Here it will be assumed that the hypothesis to be tested is $m = m_0 = 15.6$ and that the only alternative is $m = m_1 = 14.6$. It is clear that, if $m < 14.6$, the type II error would be decreased. In order to make the type II error equal 0.05, it is therefore necessary that the probability be 0.95 that $\bar{x}$ will satisfy (1) when the population mean has dropped to 14.6. Since $\bar{x}$ is now normally distributed with mean 14.6 and standard deviation $2.2/\sqrt{n}$, this requirement may be written in the form

$$\frac{\sqrt{n}}{2.2\sqrt{2\pi}} \int_{-\infty}^{15.6 - 2.33\frac{2.2}{\sqrt{n}}} e^{-\frac{n}{2}\left(\frac{\bar{x} - 14.6}{2.2}\right)^2} \, d\bar{x} = 0.95$$

Let $y = \sqrt{n}(\bar{x} - 14.6)/2.2$; then this equation reduces to

$$\frac{1}{\sqrt{2\pi}} \int_{-\infty}^{\frac{\sqrt{n}}{2.2} - 2.33} e^{-\frac{y^2}{2}} \, dy = 0.95$$

From Table II it follows that n must satisfy the equation

$$\frac{\sqrt{n}}{2.2} - 2.33 = 1.64$$

The solution of this equation is $n = 76$; consequently a sample of this size will give the manufacturer the specified protection against an incorrect decision.

Unless the difference between the hypothetical value of a population parameter and its alternative value is rather large, the experimenter will discover that a considerably larger sample is required than he had anticipated. The size of the experiment can be decreased, of course, if the probabilities of the two types of error are increased.

If the experiment can be placed on the basis of a day-to-day accumulation of data, there are methods which require on the average smaller samples than those indicated in the procedure just discussed; however, if the experiment is such that it is not feasible or convenient to design it on other than a fixed-size basis, the preceding procedure yields the desired information. The accumulation-of-data method referred to will be considered briefly in a later section.

SAMPLING INSPECTION

The discussion thus far has been concerned with techniques for designing valid experiments and for increasing the sensitivity of such experiments. Although there are many other such techniques, they will not be considered here. Consideration will now be given to the second feature of efficiency that was introduced in the section on efficiency, namely, minimizing the amount of sampling.

One of the most useful applications of the design of experiments to minimize the amount of sampling occurs in industrial sampling inspection. If a certain type of sampling procedure is agreed upon, the notion of the two types of error can be used to advantage to design an efficient inspection procedure.

It is a common practice in industry to accept or reject lots of merchandise on the basis of a sample drawn from the lot. This practice arises from the fact that it is often more economical to tolerate a small percentage of defectives than to bear the cost of 100% inspection. The basis for accepting a lot of merchandise usually consists in specifying the maximum number of defective pieces that will be tolerated in a random sample of a given size. By means of such samples and specifications the purchaser is protected against receiving bad lots of merchandise.

Sampling inspection is quite different from quality control. It is a method for protecting the purchaser against poor quality after the product has been manufactured rather than a method for finding and correcting flaws in the manufacturing process, as in quality control methods. When sampling inspection methods are applied to continuous manufacturing processes, however, they are often useful in helping to control the quality of the product.

From the consumer's point of view, there is a maximum percentage of defectives that he will tolerate. This percentage when expressed as a decimal is known as the *lot tolerance fraction defective* and is denoted by p_t. Without nearly 100% inspection, it may be impossible to be certain that the quality is better than p_t; however, it is possible to set up a sampling procedure that will insure this quality with a certain probability. To this end consider a lot of N pieces from which a random sample of n pieces is selected. Let c denote the maximum number of defective pieces in the sample for accepting the lot.

Although numerous sampling schemes are available, only one common type of sampling procedure, known as *single sampling*, will be considered here. This scheme proceeds as follows:

(2)
1. Inspect a sample of n pieces.
2. If the number of defective pieces does not exceed c, accept the lot; otherwise inspect the entire lot.
3. Replace all defective pieces found by non-defective pieces.

Now consider the probability that the consumer will receive a bad lot under this sampling procedure. If the lot being considered is one of precisely p_t fraction defective, there will be Np_t defective and $N - Np_t$ non-defective pieces in the lot. Then the probability of obtaining x defectives in a sample of size n is given by the ratio of the number of ways of obtaining x things from Np_t things and $n - x$ things from $N - Np_t$ things to the number of ways of obtaining n things from N things. By means of the familiar college algebra combination formula

$$\binom{s}{r} = \frac{s!}{r!(s - r)!}$$

which gives the number of ways of obtaining r things from s things, this probability may be expressed as

$$(3) \qquad \frac{\binom{Np_t}{x}\binom{N - Np_t}{n - x}}{\binom{N}{n}}$$

The probability that the consumer will be led to accept a lot of quality p_t will therefore be

$$(4) \qquad P_c = \sum_{x=0}^{c} \frac{\binom{Np_t}{x}\binom{N - Np_t}{n - x}}{\binom{N}{n}}$$

This probability is known as the *consumer's risk*. By demanding a small value of P_c, the consumer is adequately protected against poor quality. The consumer's risk would be still smaller if the fraction defective were below the consumer's tolerance value p_t.

From the producer's point of view, any sampling scheme for deciding on the quality of a lot possesses the disadvantage of occasionally rejecting a lot of satisfactory quality. If the producer has standardized his quality at a level denoted by $\bar{p}$, which is called the *process average fraction defective*, then from (4) the probability that a lot of his will be unjustly rejected is

$$(5) \qquad P_p = 1 - \sum_{x=0}^{c} \frac{\binom{N\bar{p}}{x}\binom{N - N\bar{p}}{n - x}}{\binom{N}{n}}$$

This probability is known as the *producer's risk*. It is clear that P_p can be made small by making $\bar{p}$ sufficiently small; however, it may often be more economical for the producer to admit a fairly large risk than to attempt to decrease $\bar{p}$.

It will be observed that the consumer and producer risks correspond to the two types of error in testing hypotheses. For example, if $\bar{p}$ is the hypothetical value of p, and p_t is the alternative value, then P_p represents the type I error and P_c represents the type II error. As a matter of fact, consumer and producer risks preceded the use of the two types of error in statistical literature.

1. Minimum Single Sampling

Thus far nothing has been said concerning the method of selecting values of n and c. The consumer's requirements fix the values of p_t and P_c in (4). Since N is specified, (4) places a single restriction on n and c. Now, from the producer's point of view, one desirable method of approach is to select that pair of values which minimizes the amount of inspection. Since a sample of size n is always inspected and the remainder of the lot is inspected with a relative frequency given by (5), the average number of pieces inspected per lot under the sampling scheme (2) will be given by

$$(6) \qquad\qquad I = n + (N - n)P_p$$

In order to satisfy the consumer's demands and also minimize the amount of inspection, it is necessary to find that pair of values of n and c which satisfies (4) and minimizes (6). These quantities are difficult to manipulate; consequently the minimizing solution is obtained numerically for different values of N, p_t, $\bar{p}$, and for P_c chosen equal to 0.10. Extensive tables are available for the minimizing values of n and c under these conditions.

As an illustration, consider a lot of 1,000 pieces for which the process average is $\bar{p} = 0.01$ and for which the consumer is willing to assume a risk of $P_c = 0.10$ of accepting a lot with a fraction defective of $p_t = 0.05$. Upon consulting the proper tables, or working numerically by allowing c to assume small integral values, it will be found that the minimum amount of inspection will occur if a sample of 130 is taken and if the maximum allowable number of defectives is 3. With these values it will also be found that the average number of pieces inspected per lot will be 164.

2. Average Outgoing Quality Limit

A somewhat different approach to the problem of protecting the consumer from an inferior product is to attempt to guarantee him a certain quality level of the product after inspection regardless of what quality level is being maintained by the producer. Toward this end, consider the problem of determining the mean value of the fraction defective after inspection if the producer's fraction defective is p.

From (2) it is clear that there will be no defectives left in a lot of N if the sample gives a number of defectives, x, greater than c because then the entire lot will be inspected. It also follows from (2) that the number of defectives left in a lot of N after inspection when $x \leq c$ will be $Np - x$ because now only the x defectives of the sample will be replaced by non-defectives. From (3) the probability of obtaining x defectives is

$$P(x) = \frac{\dbinom{Np}{x}\dbinom{N - Np}{n - x}}{\dbinom{N}{n}}$$

Since the mean value of a discrete variable x that takes on the values $x_1, \cdots, x_k$ is given by

$$m = \sum_{i=1}^{k} x_i P(x_i)$$

the mean value of the number of defectives after inspection will be given by

$$m = \sum_{x=0}^{c}(Np - x)P(x) + \sum_{x=c+1}^{N} 0 \cdot P(x)$$

$$= \sum_{x=0}^{c} \frac{(Np - x)\dbinom{Np}{x}\dbinom{N - Np}{n - x}}{\dbinom{N}{n}}$$

If this expression is divided by N, it will give the mean fraction defective in lots of N when following the inspection procedure (2). If this mean value is denoted by $\tilde{p}$, it follows that

$$(7) \qquad \tilde{p} = \sum_{x=0}^{c} \frac{\left(p - \dfrac{x}{N}\right)\dbinom{Np}{x}\dbinom{N - Np}{n - x}}{\dbinom{N}{n}}$$

If the sampling procedure (2) has been specified, the values of N, n, and c may be treated as given. The consumer, however, is not likely to be willing to accept the producer's claim that his fraction defective is p; consequently p may not be treated as given. If $\tilde{p}$ is considered a function of p, it will be found that $\tilde{p}$ possesses a maximum value. This maximum value, which will be denoted by $\tilde{p}_L$, is called the *average outgoing quality limit*. It is a number such that, regardless of what the producer's fraction defective may be, the average fraction defective after inspection never exceeds $\tilde{p}_L$. It might appear offhand that the value of $\tilde{p}$ would continue to increase with p; however, as p increases a greater percentage of lots will be sampled 100%, with a resulting eventual decrease in the average percentage of defectives remaining.

The average outgoing quality limit has a certain appeal to many consumers that is not possessed by the protection afforded through a specified consumer's risk.

It is usually possible to select several pairs of values of c and n that will yield functions, $\tilde{p}$, having approximately the same value of $\tilde{p}_L$. From the producer's point of view, it would be highly desirable to select that pair of values which minimizes the amount of inspection given by (6). As in the minimum single sampling of the preceding section, the minimizing pair of values of c and n is obtained numerically. Tables are available for determining these minimizing values corresponding to useful ranges of values of N, $\tilde{p}_L$, and $\bar{p}$. It should be noted that the value of $\bar{p}$ is required in order to minimize I, just as it was in minimum single sampling.

As an illustration, consider the problem that was used as an illustration for minimum single sampling. Then $N = 1,000$, $p_t = 0.05$, $\bar{p} = 0.01$, and $P_c = 0.10$. The Dodge and Romig tables referred to at the end of this chapter show that $\tilde{p}_L = 0.013$ for this problem. If the consumer wishes an average outgoing quality limit of, say, $\tilde{p}_L = 0.03$, these tables give $c = 2$ and $n = 44$ as the values that will minimize the amount of inspection.

STRATIFIED SAMPLING

The technique of breaking down the variation of a variable into useful components in order to decrease the experimental variation, as was done in the analysis of variance, can also be used to advantage in designing experiments for estimating means of populations. It turns out that a more accurate estimate of the mean can often be obtained by taking restricted random samples than by taking completely random samples. For example, suppose that an accurate estimate of the mean weight of fifth-grade pupils was desired for a school system. By taking the proper-size random samples in the various age groups, or in the various schools of the system, a more accurate estimate of the population mean will usually be obtained than by taking the same total sample at random in the system. In order to determine the proper size subsamples, consider the following general problem.

Let a population be divided into k distinct subpopulations. Further, let the mean and variance of this population be m and σ^2 and of the ith subpopulation be m_i and σ_i^2. Then consider as estimates of m the quantities $\bar{x}$ and $\bar{x}_R$, where $\bar{x}$ is the mean of a random sample of size n and where

$$(8) \qquad \bar{x}_R = \frac{n_1}{n}\,\bar{x}_1 + \cdots + \frac{n_k}{n}\,\bar{x}_k$$

in which $\bar{x}_i$ is the mean of a random sample of size n_i drawn from the ith subpopulation and $\sum_1^k n_i = n$. This restricted type of random sampling is called *stratified sampling*.

For the purpose of comparing the relative precision of these two estimates of m, consider their respective variances. The variance of $\bar{x}$ is given by $\sigma_{\bar{x}}^2 = \sigma^2/n$. Since the $\bar{x}_i$ are independent, the variance of (8) is given by

$$(9) \qquad \sigma_{\bar{x}_R}^2 = \sum_1^k \left(\frac{n_i}{n}\right)^2 \sigma_{\bar{x}_i}^2 = \sum_1^k \left(\frac{n_i}{n}\right)^2 \frac{\sigma_i^2}{n_i} = \sum_1^k \frac{n_i \sigma_i^2}{n^2}$$

In order to express the variance of $\bar{x}$ in terms of the σ_i^2, it is necessary to express the distribution function of the population in terms of those of the subpopulations. This may be done by applying the two basic rules of probability to the problem of determining the probability that x will assume a value within any specified interval. If p_i denotes the probability that x will come from the ith subpopulation and $f_i(x)$ denotes the distribution function for this subpopulation,

$$p_i \int_\alpha^\beta f_i(x)\,dx$$

represents the probability that x will come from the ith subpopulation and will assume a value between α and β. Since these subpopulations are mutually exclusive, the probability that x will assume a value between α and β is the sum of all such probabilities; hence

$$\int_\alpha^\beta f(x)\,dx = p_1 \int_\alpha^\beta f_1(x)\,dx + \cdots + p_k \int_\alpha^\beta f_k(x)\,dx$$

But α and β are arbitrary; consequently by the same reasoning as was followed on (5), Chapter VI,

$$f(x) = p_1 f_1(x) + \cdots + p_k f_k(x)$$

Now

$$(10) \quad m = \int_a^b f(x)\, dx = p_1 \int_a^b f_1(x)\, dx + \cdots + p_k \int_a^b f_k(x)\, dx$$

$$= p_1 m_1 + \cdots + p_k m_k$$

Furthermore

$$\sigma^2 + m^2 = \int_a^b x^2 f(x)\, dx$$

$$= p_1 \int_a^b x^2 f_1(x)\, dx + \cdots + p_k \int_a^b x^2 f_k(x)\, dx$$

$$= p_1[\sigma_1{}^2 + m_1{}^2] + \cdots + p_k[\sigma_k{}^2 + m_k{}^2]$$

If the value of m^2 is eliminated by means of (10) and the fact that $\sum_1^k p_i = 1$, this reduces to

$$\sigma^2 = \sum_1^k p_i[\sigma_i{}^2 + (m_i - m)^2]$$

From this result it follows that the variance of $\bar{x}$ can be written in the form

$$(11) \quad \sigma_{\bar{x}}{}^2 = \frac{1}{n} \sum_1^k p_i[\sigma_i{}^2 + (m_i - m)^2]$$

Now consider a special type of sampling called *representative sampling* in which the subpopulation sample sizes, n_i, are chosen so that $n_i/n = p_i$. For a finite population this means that the relative sizes of the subpopulation samples are chosen equal to the relative sizes of the subpopulations. For representative sampling, (11) may be reduced by means of (9) to the form

$$(12) \quad \sigma_{\bar{x}}{}^2 = \sigma_{\bar{x}_R}{}^2 + \sum_1^k \frac{n_i}{n^2} (m_i - m)^2$$

This shows that $\sigma_{\bar{x}}{}^2 > \sigma_{\bar{x}_R}{}^2$, unless the subpopulations have equal means. Representative sampling is of particular advantage for populations whose subpopulations have widely differing means.

Public-opinion polls are familiar examples of representative sampling. For such polls it is customary to stratify the population in several ways. For example, it may be divided into several income groups, into several vocational groups, etc. Then, within strata, random samples are taken proportional to the relative sizes of those strata.

Various other types of restricted random sampling are available, most of which have been developed by governmental agencies for their particular needs.

As an illustration of the increased precision of estimating m through the use of representative sampling, suppose for the sake of simplicity that a district is made up of 45% democrats and 55% republicans, and that 70% of the democrats will vote for a certain "non-partisan" candidate in a primary election but only 20% of the republicans will do so. Now suppose that a sample of size 200 is taken by each method. Although experience indicates that the precision of poll percentages is not as great as that given by binomial theory, the precisions here will be compared on a theoretical basis; consequently

$$\sigma_{\bar{x}}^2 = \sigma_p^2 = \frac{pq}{n} = \frac{(0.425)(0.575)}{200} = 0.00122$$

and

$$\sum_1^k \frac{n_i}{n^2} (m_i - m)^2 = \frac{90}{(200)^2} (0.70 - 0.425)^2 + \frac{110}{(200)^2} (0.20 - 0.425)^2$$
$$= 0.00031$$

Therefore from (12)

$$\sigma_{\bar{x}_R}^2 = 0.00091$$

Since $\sigma_{\bar{x}_R}^2 / \sigma_{\bar{x}}^2 = 0.75$ here, a considerable increase in precision would result from using representative sampling in preference to pure random sampling.

SEQUENTIAL ANALYSIS

The methods that have been presented thus far for minimizing the amount of sampling needed to attain certain objectives were designed on the assumption that the experiment was to be of fixed size, once the minimizing size had been determined. If the experiment can be conducted on an accumulation-of-information basis, there are methods that require considerably less sampling than even the best of the fixed-size methods. These methods are known as *sequential methods* because they operate upon the successive terms of the sequence of observations as they are received. These methods have been found to require only about 50% as much sampling on the average as the best fixed methods for some problems.

Sequential methods were designed to test hypotheses. In a sequential test, a rule of procedure is given for making one of the following three decisions at each stage of the experiment: (1) accept the hypothesis,

(2) reject the hypothesis, (3) continue the experiment by taking an additional observation.

For the purpose of describing a sequential test, consider a variable x whose probability function $f(x; \theta)$ depends upon the single parameter θ. If x is a continuous variable, $f(x; \theta)$ represents the probability density at the point x; if x is discrete, it represents the probability that the variable will assume the value x. Let the hypothesis to be tested be denoted by $\theta = \theta_0$, and let there be but the single alternative $\theta = \theta_1$. Then form the likelihood ratio

$$(13) \qquad \frac{p_{1m}}{p_{0m}} = \frac{f(x_1; \theta_1)f(x_2; \theta_1) \cdots f(x_m; \theta_1)}{f(x_1; \theta_0)f(x_2; \theta_0) \cdots f(x_m; \theta_0)}$$

where $x_1, x_2, \cdots, x_m$ represent m random-sample values of x. Finally, let α and β represent the probabilities of making a type I and type II error, respectively. Then the sequential test known as the *sequential probability ratio test* proceeds as follows:

$$(14) \quad \begin{cases} 1. \text{ If } \dfrac{p_{1m}}{p_{0m}} \le \dfrac{\beta}{1 - \alpha}, \text{ accept the hypothesis that } \theta = \theta_0. \\[3mm] 2. \text{ If } \dfrac{p_{1m}}{p_{0m}} \ge \dfrac{1 - \beta}{\alpha}, \text{ accept the alternative that } \theta = \theta_1. \\[3mm] 3. \text{ If } \dfrac{\beta}{1 - \alpha} < \dfrac{p_{1m}}{p_{0m}} < \dfrac{1 - \beta}{\alpha}, \text{ take an additional observation.} \end{cases}$$

This procedure is continued until either 1 or 2 is satisfied.

Because certain approximations were used to obtain these inequalities, it is not strictly true that the two types of error will be maintained at the levels given by α and β; however, since these approximations have been found to be excellent for ordinary applications, this test may be used with confidence.

For most applications there will be more than one alternative to the hypothesis; nevertheless the problem can often be solved satisfactorily by considering only one alternative. For example, in the section on sampling inspection, the producer's fraction defective $\bar{p}$ was contrasted with the consumer's tolerance fraction defective p_t on the grounds that the consumer's risk would be even smaller than that calculated if the fraction defective were smaller than p_t. In most applications there will be a difference $|\theta - \theta_0| = \Delta$ such that it will be profitable to make a change from θ_0 only if $|\theta - \theta_0| \ge \Delta$; consequently, if θ_1 is selected as that alternative value of θ for which $|\theta_1 - \theta_0| = \Delta$, any alternative satisfying the practical inequality will give rise to smaller type I or type II errors than those for θ_1.

Although the test given by (14) can be applied to numerous types of problems, it will be applied here only to the problem of testing a binomial probability. Consider the hypothesis $p = p_0$ and the single alternative $p = p_1$. If $x = 1$ for success and $x = 0$ for failure, $f(x; \theta)$ will reduce to $f(1; p) = p$ and $f(0; p) = q$. Now suppose that there are d_m successes in the first m trials of the event. Then (13) becomes

$$\frac{p_{1m}}{p_{0m}} = \frac{p_1^{d_m} q_1^{m-d_m}}{p_0^{d_m} q_0^{m-d_m}}$$

If this expression is substituted in (14) and the desired numerical values are assigned to p_0, p_1, α, and β, the test procedure will be determined.

As a numerical illustration, let $p_0 = 0.5$, $p_1 = 0.7$, $\alpha = 0.10$, and $\beta = 0.20$. These values may be thought of as those that might be used to test the honesty of a coin when that coin is suspected of giving too many heads. Here $\beta/(1 - \alpha) = \frac{2}{9}$, $(1 - \beta)/\alpha = 8$, and

$$\frac{p_{1m}}{p_{0m}} = \frac{(0.7)^{d_m}(0.3)^{m-d_m}}{(0.5)^{d_m}(0.5)^{m-d_m}} = \left(\frac{3}{5}\right)^m \left(\frac{7}{3}\right)^{d_m}$$

The first inequality in (14),

$$\left(\tfrac{3}{5}\right)^m \left(\tfrac{7}{3}\right)^{d_m} \leq \tfrac{2}{9}$$

can be written more conveniently in the form

$$d_m \leq \frac{\log \frac{2}{9}}{\log \frac{7}{3}} + m \frac{\log \frac{5}{3}}{\log \frac{7}{3}}$$

In a similar manner the second inequality becomes

$$d_m \geq \frac{\log 8}{\log \frac{7}{3}} + m \frac{\log \frac{5}{3}}{\log \frac{7}{3}}$$

If these logarithms are evaluated, the test will proceed as follows:

1. If $d_m \leq -1.78 + 0.603m$, accept $p = 0.5$.
2. If $d_m \geq \ \ \ 2.45 + 0.603m$, accept $p = 0.7$.
3. If neither inequality is satisfied, take another trial.

Tosses of a coin gave the results shown in the following table. For the purpose of determining when one of the inequalities is satisfied, it is convenient to represent these inequalities and the results of the successive trials graphically. If m and d_m are treated as the coordinates of a

m	1	2	3	4	5	6	7	8	9	10	11	12	13	14	15
x_m	0	0	1	1	1	0	1	1	0	1	0	0	1	0	0
d_m	0	0	1	2	3	3	4	5	5	6	6	6	7	7	7

point, the straight lines $d_m = -1.78 + 0.603m$ and $d_m = 2.45 + 0.603m$ will serve to divide the m, d_m plane into three regions corresponding to the three possible decisions at each trial. The graph corresponding

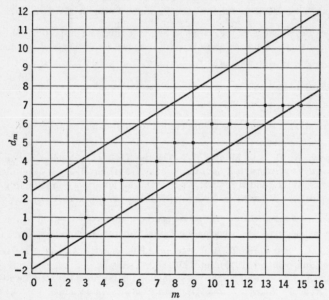

FIG. 1. Sequential test for testing $p = 0.5$ against $p = 0.7$.

to this problem is given in Fig. 1. From this graph it will be observed that the experiment terminated after 15 trials because inequality 1 was then satisfied. In accepting the hypothesis that $p = 0.5$, the experimenter does so in preference to accepting the hypothesis that $p = 0.7$.

If the alternative to $p = 0.5$ had been $p = 0.6$, say, a considerably larger number of trials would have been required on the average to arrive at a decision with these same values of α and β. By selecting the alternative value properly, the experimenter can design his experiment in such a manner as to discover profitable differences in p for a minimum amount of inspection.

REFERENCES

An extensive discussion of fundamental principles such as randomization and replication, as well as of many modern experimental designs, will be found in:

FISHER, R. A., *The Design of Experiments*, Oliver & Boyd.

Further material on the analysis-of-variance technique is illustrated in:

RIDER, P., *An Introduction to Modern Statistical Methods*, John Wiley & Sons, pp. 137–192.

The mathematical theory behind the more complex analysis of variance techniques is not simple; however, it may be found in:

WILKS, S. S., *Mathematical Statistics*, Princeton University Press, pp. 176–186.

Tables for assisting in the design of efficient sampling inspection schemes, as well as a discussion of some other types of sampling inspection, will be found in:

DODGE and ROMIG, *Sampling Inspection Tables*, John Wiley & Sons.

Further material on the efficiency of stratified sampling is available in:

WILKS, *op. cit.*, pp. 86–89.

A derivation of some of the theory related to non-random sampling may be found in:

MADOW, W. G., and MADOW, L., "On the Theory of Systematic Sampling," *Annals of Mathematical Statistics*, vol. xv (1944), pp. 1–24.

HANSEN, M. H., and HURWITZ, W. N., "On the Theory of Sampling from Finite Populations," *Annals of Mathematical Statistics*, vol. xiv (1943), pp. 333–362.

The mathematical theory behind sequential analysis is contained in the first of the two following papers, whereas the second paper is largely expository:

WALD, A., "Sequential Tests of Statistical Hypotheses," *Annals of Mathematical Statistics*, vol. xvi (1945), pp. 117–186.

WALD, A., "Sequential Method of Sampling for Deciding between Two Courses of Action," *Journal of the American Statistical Association*, vol. 40 (1945), pp. 277–306.

Tables of binomial coefficients for problems in which the normal or Poisson approximations are not sufficiently accurate are available in:

FRY, T., *Probability and Its Engineering Uses*, D. Van Nostrand Company.

EXERCISES

1. Using the table of binomials referred to in Fry's book, determine the percentage error in replacing the binomial sum given in (4) by

$$\sum_{x=0}^{c} \frac{e^{-np_t}(np_t)^x}{x!}$$

for the case in which $N = 50$, $n = 10$, $p_t = 0.1$, and $c = 2$.

2. Using the Poisson approximation

$$\sum_{x=0}^{c} \frac{e^{-np}(np)^x}{x!}$$

with p replaced by p_t and $\bar{p}$, respectively, for the probabilities given by (4) and (5), verify by trying neighboring values of the variables c and n that the values given in the illustrative example for minimum single sampling are approximately correct.

3. Using the Poisson approximations of the preceding problem, determine by numerical methods the values of n and c which minimize the amount of inspection for $N = 400$, $P_c = 0.10$, $p_t = 0.05$, and $\bar{p} = 0.02$. Proceed by assigning c a value, beginning with 1, then determining the value of n to satisfy (4), and finally selecting that pair of values which makes (6) a minimum.

4. Derive the sequential test for testing the hypothesis $m = m_0$ against the alternative $m = m_1$ for a Poisson distribution.

5. By the use of Tippett's random sampling numbers draw repeated samples from the Poisson population with $m = 2$. Use the test derived in the preceding problem on these sample values to test the hypothesis $m = 2$ against the alternative $m = 3$ for a Poisson distribution.

6. Derive the sequential test for testing the hypothesis $m = m_0$ against the alternative $m = m_1$ for a normal distribution with known variance σ^2.

7. How would you proceed if you wished to design an analysis-of-variance experiment for testing the speed of two (or more) different methods of performing a job with a certain type of machine. Consider different operators and different machines as variables to be incorporated in the design.

N	N²	√N	√10N	N	N²	√N	√10N
1.00	1.0000	1.00000	3.16228	**1.50**	2.2500	1.22474	3.87298
1.01	1.0201	1.00499	3.17805	1.51	2.2801	1.22882	3.88587
1.02	1.0404	1.00995	3.19374	1.52	2.3104	1.23288	3.89872
1.03	1.0609	1.01489	3.20936	1.53	2.3409	1.23693	3.91152
1.04	1.0816	1.01980	3.22490	1.54	2.3716	1.24097	3.92428
1.05	1.1025	1.02470	3.24037	1.55	2.4025	1.24499	3.93700
1.06	1.1236	1.02956	3.25576	1.56	2.4336	1.24900	3.94968
1.07	1.1449	1.03441	3.27109	1.57	2.4649	1.25300	3.96232
1.08	1.1664	1.03923	3.28634	1.58	2.4964	1.25698	3.97492
1.09	1.1881	1.04403	3.30151	1.59	2.5281	1.26095	3.98748
1.10	1.2100	1.04881	3.31662	**1.60**	2.5600	1.26491	4.00000
1.11	1.2321	1.05357	3.33167	1.61	2.5921	1.26886	4.01248
1.12	1.2544	1.05830	3.34664	1.62	2.6244	1.27279	4.02492
1.13	1.2769	1.06301	3.36155	1.63	2.6569	1.27671	4.03733
1.14	1.2996	1.06771	3.37639	1.64	2.6896	1.28062	4.04969
1.15	1.3225	1.07238	3.39116	1.65	2.7225	1.28452	4.06202
1.16	1.3456	1.07703	3.40588	1.66	2.7556	1.28841	4.07431
1.17	1.3689	1.08167	3.42053	1.67	2.7889	1.29228	4.08656
1.18	1.3924	1.08628	3.43511	1.68	2.8224	1.29615	4.09878
1.19	1.4161	1.09087	3.44964	1.69	2.8561	1.30000	4.11096
1.20	1.4400	1.09545	3.46410	**1.70**	2.8900	1.30384	4.12311
1.21	1.4641	1.10000	3.47851	1.71	2.9241	1.30767	4.13521
1.22	1.4884	1.10454	3.49285	1.72	2.9584	1.31149	4.14729
1.23	1.5129	1.10905	3.50714	1.73	2.9929	1.31529	4.15933
1.24	1.5376	1.11355	3.52136	1.74	3.0276	1.31909	4.17133
1.25	1.5625	1.11803	3.53553	1.75	3.0625	1.32288	4.18330
1.26	1.5876	1.12250	3.54965	1.76	3.0976	1.32665	4.19524
1.27	1.6129	1.12694	3.56371	1.77	3.1329	1.33041	4.20714
1.28	1.6384	1.13137	3.57771	1.78	3.1684	1.33417	4.21900
1.29	1.6641	1.13578	3.59166	1.79	3.2041	1.33791	4.23084
1.30	1.6900	1.14018	3.60555	**1.80**	3.2400	1.34164	4.24264
1.31	1.7161	1.14455	3.61939	1.81	3.2761	1.34536	4.25441
1.32	1.7424	1.14891	3.63318	1.82	3.3124	1.34907	4.26615
1.33	1.7689	1.15326	3.64692	1.83	3.3489	1.35277	4.27785
1.34	1.7956	1.15758	3.66060	1.84	3.3856	1.35647	4.28952
1.35	1.8225	1.16190	3.67423	1.85	3.4225	1.36015	4.30116
1.36	1.8496	1.16619	3.68782	1.86	3.4596	1.36382	4.31277
1.37	1.8769	1.17047	3.70135	1.87	3.4969	1.36748	4.32435
1.38	1.9044	1.17473	3.71484	1.88	3.5344	1.37113	4.33590
1.39	1.9321	1.17898	3.72827	1.89	3.5721	1.37477	4.34741
1.40	1.9600	1.18322	3.74166	**1.90**	3.6100	1.37840	4.35890
1.41	1.9881	1.18743	3.75500	1.91	3.6481	1.38203	4.37035
1.42	2.0164	1.19164	3.76829	1.92	3.6864	1.38564	4.38178
1.43	2.0449	1.19583	3.78153	1.93	3.7249	1.38924	4.39318
1.44	2.0736	1.20000	3.79473	1.94	3.7636	1.39284	4.40454
1.45	2.1025	1.20416	3.80789	1.95	3.8025	1.39642	4.41588
1.46	2.1316	1.20830	3.82099	1.96	3.8416	1.40000	4.42719
1.47	2.1609	1.21244	3.83406	1.97	3.8809	1.40357	4.43847
1.48	2.1904	1.21655	3.84708	1.98	3.9204	1.40712	4.44972
1.49	2.2201	1.22066	3.86005	1.99	3.9601	1.41067	4.46094
1.50	2.2500	1.22474	3.87298	**2.00**	4.0000	1.41421	4.47214
N	N²	√N	√10N	N	N²	√N	√10N

* Reprinted, by permission, from the *Wiley Trigonometric Tables*. John Wiley & Sons, 1945.

N	N²	√N	√10N	N	N²	√N	√10N
2.00	4.0000	1.41421	4.47214	**2.50**	6.2500	1.58114	5.00000
2.01	4.0401	1.41774	4.48330	2.51	6.3001	1.58430	5.00999
2.02	4.0804	1.42127	4.49444	2.52	6.3504	1.58745	5.01996
2.03	4.1209	1.42478	4.50555	2.53	6.4009	1.59060	5.02991
2.04	4.1616	1.42829	4.51664	2.54	6.4516	1.59374	5.03984
2.05	4.2025	1.43178	4.52769	2.55	6.5025	1.59687	5.04975
2.06	4.2436	1.43527	4.53872	2.56	6.5536	1.60000	5.05964
2.07	4.2849	1.43875	4.54973	2.57	6.6049	1.60312	5.06952
2.08	4.3264	1.44222	4.56070	2.58	6.6564	1.60624	5.07937
2.09	4.3681	1.44568	4.57165	2.59	6.7081	1.60935	5.08920
2.10	4.4100	1.44914	4.58258	**2.60**	6.7600	1.61245	5.09902
2.11	4.4521	1.45258	4.59347	2.61	6.8121	1.61555	5.10882
2.12	4.4944	1.45602	4.60435	2.62	6.8644	1.61864	5.11859
2.13	4.5369	1.45945	4.61519	2.63	6.9169	1.62173	5.12835
2.14	4.5796	1.46287	4.62601	2.64	6.9696	1.62481	5.13809
2.15	4.6225	1.46629	4.63681	2.65	7.0225	1.62788	5.14782
2.16	4.6656	1.46969	4.64758	2.66	7.0756	1.63095	5.15752
2.17	4.7089	1.47309	4.65833	2.67	7.1289	1.63401	5.16720
2.18	4.7524	1.47648	4.66905	2.68	7.1824	1.63707	5.17687
2.19	4.7961	1.47986	4.67974	2.69	7.2361	1.64012	5.18652
2.20	4.8400	1.48324	4.69042	**2.70**	7.2900	1.64317	5.19615
2.21	4.8841	1.48661	4.70106	2.71	7.3441	1.64621	5.20577
2.22	4.9284	1.48997	4.71169	2.72	7.3984	1.64924	5.21536
2.23	4.9729	1.49332	4.72229	2.73	7.4529	1.65227	5.22494
2.24	5.0176	1.49666	4.73286	2.74	7.5076	1.65529	5.23450
2.25	5.0625	1.50000	4.74342	2.75	7.5625	1.65831	5.24404
2.26	5.1076	1.50333	4.75395	2.76	7.6176	1.66132	5.25357
2.27	5.1529	1.50665	4.76445	2.77	7.6729	1.66433	5.26308
2.28	5.1984	1.50997	4.77493	2.78	7.7284	1.66733	5.27257
2.29	5.2441	1.51327	4.78539	2.79	7.7841	1.67033	5.28205
2.30	5.2900	1.51658	4.79583	**2.80**	7.8400	1.67332	5.29150
2.31	5.3361	1.51987	4.80625	2.81	7.8961	1.67631	5.30094
2.32	5.3824	1.52315	4.81664	2.82	7.9524	1.67929	5.31037
2.33	5.4289	1.52643	4.82701	2.83	8.0089	1.68226	5.31977
2.34	5.4756	1.52971	4.83735	2.84	8.0656	1.68523	5.32917
2.35	5.5225	1.53297	4.84768	2.85	8.1225	1.68819	5.33854
2.36	5.5696	1.53623	4.85798	2.86	8.1796	1.69115	5.34790
2.37	5.6169	1.53948	4.86826	2.87	8.2369	1.69411	5.35724
2.38	5.6644	1.54272	4.87852	2.88	8.2944	1.69706	5.36656
2.39	5.7121	1.54596	4.88876	2.89	8.3521	1.70000	5.37587
2.40	5.7600	1.54919	4.89898	**2.90**	8.4100	1.70294	5.38516
2.41	5.8081	1.55242	4.90918	2.91	8.4681	1.70587	5.39444
2.42	5.8564	1.55563	4.91935	2.92	8.5264	1.70880	5.40370
2.43	5.9049	1.55885	4.92950	2.93	8.5849	1.71172	5.41295
2.44	5.9536	1.56205	4.93964	2.94	8.6436	1.71464	5.42218
2.45	6.0025	1.56525	4.94975	2.95	8.7025	1.71756	5.43139
2.46	6.0516	1.56844	4.95984	2.96	8.7616	1.72047	5.44059
2.47	6.1009	1.57162	4.96991	2.97	8.8209	1.72337	5.44977
2.48	6.1504	1.57480	4.97996	2.98	8.8804	1.72627	5.45894
2.49	6.2001	1.57797	4.98999	2.99	8.9401	1.72916	5.46809
2.50	6.2500	1.58114	5.00000	**3.00**	9.0000	1.73205	5.47723
N	N²	√N	√10N	N	N²	√N	√10N

N	N²	√N	√10N	N	N²	√N	√10N
3.00	9.0000	1.73205	5.47723	**3.50**	12.2500	1.87083	5.91608
3.01	9.0601	1.73494	5.48635	3.51	12.3201	1.87350	5.92453
3.02	9.1204	1.73781	5.49545	3.52	12.3904	1.87617	5.93296
3.03	9.1809	1.74069	5.50454	3.53	12.4609	1.87883	5.94138
3.04	9.2416	1.74356	5.51362	3.54	12.5316	1.88149	5.94979
3.05	9.3025	1.74642	5.52268	3.55	12.6025	1.88414	5.95819
3.06	9.3636	1.74929	5.53173	3.56	12.6736	1.88680	5.96657
3.07	9.4249	1.75214	5.54076	3.57	12.7449	1.88944	5.97495
3.08	9.4864	1.75499	5.54977	3.58	12.8164	1.89209	5.98331
3.09	9.5481	1.75784	5.55878	3.59	12.8881	1.89473	5.99166
3.10	9.6100	1.76068	5.56776	**3.60**	12.9600	1.89737	6.00000
3.11	9.6721	1.76352	5.57674	3.61	13.0321	1.90000	6.00833
3.12	9.7344	1.76635	5.58570	3.62	13.1044	1.90263	6.01664
3.13	9.7969	1.76918	5.59464	3.63	13.1769	1.90526	6.02495
3.14	9.8596	1.77200	5.60357	3.64	13.2496	1.90788	6.03324
3.15	9.9225	1.77482	5.61249	3.65	13.3225	1.91050	6.04152
3.16	9.9856	1.77764	5.62139	3.66	13.3956	1.91311	6.04979
3.17	10.0489	1.78045	5.63028	3.67	13.4689	1.91572	6.05805
3.18	10.1124	1.78326	5.63915	3.68	13.5424	1.91833	6.06630
3.19	10.1761	1.78606	5.64801	3.69	13.6161	1.92094	6.07454
3.20	10.2400	1.78885	5.65685	**3.70**	13.6900	1.92354	6.08276
3.21	10.3041	1.79165	5.66569	3.71	13.7641	1.92614	6.09098
3.22	10.3684	1.79444	5.67450	3.72	13.8384	1.92873	6.09918
3.23	10.4329	1.79722	5.68331	3.73	13.9129	1.93132	6.10737
3.24	10.4976	1.80000	5.69210	3.74	13.9876	1.93391	6.11555
3.25	10.5625	1.80278	5.70088	3.75	14.0625	1.93649	6.12372
3.26	10.6276	1.80555	5.70964	3.76	14.1376	1.93907	6.13188
3.27	10.6929	1.80831	5.71839	3.77	14.2129	1.94165	6.14003
3.28	10.7584	1.81108	5.72713	3.78	14.2884	1.94422	6.14817
3.29	10.8241	1.81384	5.73585	3.79	14.3641	1.94679	6.15630
3.30	10.8900	1.81659	5.74456	**3.80**	14.4400	1.94936	6.16441
3.31	10.9561	1.81934	5.75326	3.81	14.5161	1.95192	6.17252
3.32	11.0224	1.82209	5.76194	3.82	14.5924	1.95448	6.18061
3.33	11.0889	1.82483	5.77062	3.83	14.6689	1.95704	6.18870
3.34	11.1556	1.82757	5.77927	3.84	14.7456	1.95959	6.19677
3.35	11.2225	1.83030	5.78792	3.85	14.8225	1.96214	6.20484
3.36	11.2896	1.83303	5.79655	3.86	14.8996	1.96469	6.21289
3.37	11.3569	1.83576	5.80517	3.87	14.9769	1.96723	6.22093
3.38	11.4244	1.83848	5.81378	3.88	15.0544	1.96977	6.22896
3.39	11.4921	1.84120	5.82237	3.89	15.1321	1.97231	6.23699
3.40	11.5600	1.84391	5.83095	**3.90**	15.2100	1.97484	6.24500
3.41	11.6281	1.84662	5.83952	3.91	15.2881	1.97737	6.25300
3.42	11.6964	1.84932	5.84808	3.92	15.3664	1.97990	6.26099
3.43	11.7649	1.85203	5.85662	3.93	15.4449	1.98242	6.26897
3.44	11.8336	1.85472	5.86515	3.94	15.5236	1.98494	6.27694
3.45	11.9025	1.85742	5.87367	3.95	15.6025	1.98746	6.28490
3.46	11.9716	1.86011	5.88218	3.96	15.6816	1.98997	6.29285
3.47	12.0409	1.86279	5.89067	3.97	15.7609	1.99249	6.30079
3.48	12.1104	1.86548	5.89915	3.98	15.8404	1.99499	6.30872
3.49	12.1801	1.86815	5.90762	3.99	15.9201	1.99750	6.31664
3.50	12.2500	1.87083	5.91608	**4.00**	16.0000	2.00000	6.32456
N	N²	√N	√10N	N	N²	√N	√10N

N	N²	√N	√10N	N	N²	√N	√10N
4.00	16.0000	2.00000	6.32456	4.50	20.2500	2.12132	6.70820
4.01	16.0801	2.00250	6.33246	4.51	20.3401	2.12368	6.71565
4.02	16.1604	2.00499	6.34035	4.52	20.4304	2.12603	6.72309
4.03	16.2409	2.00749	6.34823	4.53	20.5209	2.12838	6.73053
4.04	16.3216	2.00998	6.35610	4.54	20.6116	2.13073	6.73795
4.05	16.4025	2.01246	6.36396	4.55	20.7025	2.13307	6.74537
4.06	16.4836	2.01494	6.37181	4.56	20.7936	2.13542	6.75278
4.07	16.5649	2.01742	6.37966	4.57	20.8849	2.13776	6.76018
4.08	16.6464	2.01990	6.38749	4.58	20.9764	2.14009	6.76757
4.09	16.7281	2.02237	6.39531	4.59	21.0681	2.14243	6.77495
4.10	16.8100	2.02485	6.40312	4.60	21.1600	2.14476	6.78233
4.11	16.8921	2.02731	6.41093	4.61	21.2521	2.14709	6.78970
4.12	16.9744	2.02978	6.41872	4.62	21.3444	2.14942	6.79706
4.13	17.0569	2.03224	6.42651	4.63	21.4369	2.15174	6.80441
4.14	17.1396	2.03470	6.43428	4.64	21.5296	2.15407	6.81175
4.15	17.2225	2.03715	6.44205	4.65	21.6225	2.15639	6.81909
4.16	17.3056	2.03961	6.44981	4.66	21.7156	2.15870	6.82642
4.17	17.3889	2.04206	6.45755	4.67	21.8089	2.16102	6.83374
4.18	17.4724	2.04450	6.46529	4.68	21.9024	2.16333	5.84105
4.19	17.5561	2.04695	6.47302	4.69	21.9961	2.16564	6.84836
4.20	17.6400	2.04939	6.48074	4.70	22.0900	2.16795	6.85565
4.21	17.7241	2.05183	6.48845	4.71	22.1841	2.17025	6.86294
4.22	17.8084	2.05426	6.49615	4.72	22.2784	2.17256	6.87023
4.23	17.8929	2.05670	6.50384	4.73	22.3729	2.17486	6.87750
4.24	17.9776	2.05913	6.51153	4.74	22.4676	2.17715	6.88477
4.25	18.0625	2.06155	6.51920	4.75	22.5625	2.17945	6.89202
4.26	18.1476	2.06398	6.52687	4.76	22.6576	2.18174	6.89928
4.27	18.2329	2.06640	6.53452	4.77	22.7529	2.18403	6.90652
4.28	18.3184	2.06882	6.54217	4.78	22.8484	2.18632	6.91375
4.29	18.4041	2.07123	6.54981	4.79	22.9441	2.18861	6.92098
4.30	18.4900	2.07364	6.55744	4.80	23.0400	2.19089	6.92820
4.31	18.5761	2.07605	6.56506	4.81	23.1361	2.19317	6.93542
4.32	18.6624	2.07846	6.57267	4.82	23.2324	2.19545	6.94262
4.33	18.7489	2.08087	6.58027	4.83	23.3289	2.19773	6.94982
4.34	18.8356	2.08327	6.58787	4.84	23.4256	2.20000	6.95701
4.35	18.9225	2.08567	6.59545	4.85	23.5225	2.20227	6.96419
4.36	19.0096	2.08806	6.60303	4.86	23.6196	2.20454	6.97137
4.37	19.0969	2.09045	6.61060	4.87	23.7169	2.20681	6.97854
4.38	19.1844	2.09284	6.61816	4.88	23.8144	2.20907	6.98570
4.39	19.2721	2.09523	6.62571	4.89	23.9121	2.21133	6.99285
4.40	19.3600	2.09762	6.63325	4.90	24.0100	2.21359	7.00000
4.41	19.4481	2.10000	6.64078	4.91	24.1081	2.21585	7.00714
4.42	19.5364	2.10238	6.64831	4.92	24.2064	2.21811	7.01427
4.43	19.6249	2.10476	6.65582	4.93	24.3049	2.22036	7.02140
4.44	19.7136	2.10713	6.66333	4.94	24.4036	2.22261	7.02851
4.45	19.8025	2.10950	6.67083	4.95	24.5025	2.22486	7.03562
4.46	19.8916	2.11187	6.67832	4.96	24.6016	2.22711	7.04273
4.47	19.9809	2.11424	6.68581	4.97	24.7009	2.22935	7.04982
4.48	20.0704	2.11660	6.69328	4.98	24.8004	2.23159	7.05691
4.49	20.1601	2.11896	6.70075	4.99	24.9001	2.23383	7.06399
4.50	20.2500	2.12132	6.70820	5.00	25.0000	2.23607	7.07107
N	N² .	√N	√10N	N	N²	√N	√10N

N	N²	√N	√10N
5.00	25.0000	2.23607	7.07107
5.01	25.1001	2.23830	7.07814
5.02	25.2004	2.24054	7.08520
5.03	25.3009	2.24277	7.09225
5.04	25.4016	2.24499	7.09930
5.05	25.5025	2.24722	7.10634
5.06	25.6036	2.24944	7.11337
5.07	25.7049	2.25167	7.12039
5.08	25.8064	2.25389	7.12741
5.09	25.9081	2.25610	7.13442
5.10	26.0100	2.25832	7.14143
5.11	26.1121	2.26053	7.14843
5.12	26.2144	2.26274	7.15542
5.13	26.3169	2.26495	7.16240
5.14	26.4196	2.26716	7.16938
5.15	26.5225	2.26936	7.17635
5.16	26.6256	2.27156	7.18331
5.17	26.7289	2.27376	7.19027
5.18	26.8324	2.27596	7.19722
5.19	26.9361	2.27816	7.20417
5.20	27.0400	2.28035	7.21110
5.21	27.1441	2.28254	7.21803
5.22	27.2484	2.28473	7.22496
5.23	27.3529	2.28692	7.23187
5.24	27.4576	2.28910	7.23878
5.25	27.5625	2.29129	7.24569
5.26	27.6676	2.29347	7.25259
5.27	27.7729	2.29565	7.25948
5.28	27.8784	2.29783	7.26636
5.29	27.9841	2.30000	7.27324
5.30	28.0900	2.30217	7.28011
5.31	28.1961	2.30434	7.28697
5.32	28.3024	2.30651	7.29383
5.33	28.4089	2.30868	7.30068
5.34	28.5156	2.31084	7.30753
5.35	28.6225	2.31301	7.31437
5.36	28.7296	2.31517	7.32120
5.37	28.8369	2.31733	7.32803
5.38	28.9444	2.31948	7.33485
5.39	29.0521	2.32164	7.34166
5.40	29.1600	2.32379	7.34847
5.41	29.2681	2.32594	7.35527
5.42	29.3764	2.32809	7.36206
5.43	29.4849	2.33024	7.36885
5.44	29.5936	2.33238	7.37564
5.45	29.7025	2.33452	7.38241
5.46	29.8116	2.33666	7.38918
5.47	29.9209	2.33880	7.39594
5.48	30.0304	2.34094	7.40270
5.49	30.1401	2.34307	7.40945
5.50	30.2500	2.34521	7.41620

N	N²	√N	√10N
5.50	30.2500	2.34521	7.41620
5.51	30.3601	2.34734	7.42294
5.52	30.4704	2.34947	7.42967
5.53	30.5809	2.35160	7.43640
5.54	30.6916	2.35372	7.44312
5.55	30.8025	2.35584	7.44983
5.56	30.9136	2.35797	7.45654
5.57	31.0249	2.36008	7.46324
5.58	31.1364	2.36220	7.46994
5.59	31.2481	2.36432	7.47663
5.60	31.3600	2.36643	7.48331
5.61	31.4721	2.36854	7.48999
5.62	31.5844	2.37065	7.49667
5.63	31.6969	2.37276	7.50333
5.64	31.8096	2.37487	7.50999
5.65	31.9225	2.37697	7.51665
5.66	32.0356	2.37908	7.52330
5.67	32.1489	2.38118	7.52994
5.68	32.2624	2.38328	7.53658
5.69	32.3761	2.38537	7.54321
5.70	32.4900	2.38747	7.54983
5.71	32.6041	2.38956	7.55645
5.72	32.7184	2.39165	7.56307
5.73	32.8329	2.39374	7.56968
5.74	32.9476	2.39583	7.57628
5.75	33.0625	2.39792	7.58288
5.76	33.1776	2.40000	7.58947
5.77	33.2929	2.40208	7.59605
5.78	33.4084	2.40416	7.60263
5.79	33.5241	2.40624	7.60920
5.80	33.6400	2.40832	7.61577
5.81	33.7561	2.41039	7.62234
5.82	33.8724	2.41247	7.62889
5.83	33.9889	2.41454	7.63544
5.84	34.1056	2.41661	7.64199
5.85	34.2225	2.41868	7.64853
5.86	34.3396	2.42074	7.65506
5.87	34.4569	2.42281	7.66159
5.88	34.5744	2.42487	7.66812
5.89	34.6921	2.42693	7.67463
5.90	34.8100	2.42899	7.68115
5.91	34.9281	2.43105	7.68765
5.92	35.0464	2.43311	7.69415
5.93	35.1649	2.43516	7.70065
5.94	35.2836	2.43721	7.70714
5.95	35.4025	2.43926	7.71362
5.96	35.5216	2.44131	7.72010
5.97	35.6409	2.44336	7.72658
5.98	35.7604	2.44540	7.73305
5.99	35.8801	2.44745	7.73951
6.00	36.0000	2.44949	7.74597
N	N²	√N	√10N

N	N²	√N	√10N	N	N²	√N	√10N
6.00	36.0000	2.44949	7.74597	**6.50**	42.2500	2.54951	8.06226
6.01	36.1201	2.45153	7.75242	6.51	42.3801	2.55147	8.06846
6.02	36.2404	2.45357	7.75887	6.52	42.5104	2.55343	8.07465
6.03	36.3609	2.45561	7.76531	6.53	42.6409	2.55539	8.08084
6.04	36.4816	2.45764	7.77174	6.54	42.7716	2.55734	8.08703
6.05	36.6025	2.45967	7.77817	6.55	42.9025	2.55930	8.09321
6.06	36.7236	2.46171	7.78460	6.56	43.0336	2.56125	8.09938
6.07	36.8449	2.46374	7.79102	6.57	43.1649	2.56320	8.10555
6.08	36.9664	2.46577	7.79744	6.58	43.2964	2.56515	8.11172
6.09	37.0881	2.46779	7.80385	6.59	43.4281	2.56710	8.11788
6.10	37.2100	2.46982	7.81025	**6.60**	43.5600	2.56905	8.12404
6.11	37.3321	2.47184	7.81665	6.61	43.6921	2.57099	8.13019
6.12	37.4544	2.47386	7.82304	6.62	43.8244	2.57294	8.13634
6.13	37.5769	2.47588	7.82943	6.63	43.9569	2.57488	8.14248
6.14	37.6996	2.47790	7.83582	6.64	44.0896	2.57682	8.14862
6.15	37.8225	2.47992	7.84219	6.65	44.2225	2.57876	8.15475
6.16	37.9456	2.48193	7.84857	6.66	44.3556	2.58070	8.16088
6.17	38.0689	2.48395	7.85493	6.67	44.4889	2.58263	8.16701
6.18	38.1924	2.48596	7.86130	6.68	44.6224	2.58457	8.17313
6.19	38.3161	2.48797	7.86766	6.69	44.7561	2.58650	8.17924
6.20	38.4400	2.48998	7.87401	**6.70**	44.8900	2.58844	8.18535
6.21	38.5641	2.49199	7.88036	6.71	45.0241	2.59037	8.19146
6.22	38.6884	2.49399	7.88670	6.72	45.1584	2.59230	8.19756
6.23	38.8129	2.49600	7.89303	6.73	45.2929	2.59422	8.20366
6.24	38.9376	2.49800	7.89937	6.74	45.4276	2.59615	8.20975
6.25	39.0625	2.50000	7.90569	6.75	45.5625	2.59808	8.21584
6.26	39.1876	2.50200	7.91202	6.76	45.6976	2.60000	8.22192
6.27	39.3129	2.50400	7.91833	6.77	45.8329	2.60192	8.22800
6.28	39.4384	2.50599	7.92465	6.78	45.9684	2.60384	8.23408
6.29	39.5641	2.50799	7.93095	6.79	46.1041	2.60576	8.24015
6.30	39.6900	2.50998	7.93725	**6.80**	46.2400	2.60768	8.24621
6.31	39.8161	2.51197	7.94355	6.81	46.3761	2.60960	8.25227
6.32	39.9424	2.51396	7.94984	6.82	46.5124	2.61151	8.25833
6.33	40.0689	2.51595	7.95613	6.83	46.6489	2.61343	8.26438
6.34	40.1956	2.51794	7.96241	6.84	46.7856	2.61534	8.27043
6.35	40.3225	2.51992	7.96869	6.85	46.9225	2.61725	8.27647
6.36	40.4496	2.52190	7.97496	6.86	47.0596	2.61916	8.28251
6.37	40.5769	2.52389	7.98123	6.87	47.1969	2.62107	8.28855
6.38	40.7044	2.52587	7.98749	6.88	47.3344	2.62298	8.29458
6.39	40.8321	2.52784	7.99375	6.89	47.4721	2.62488	8.30060
6.40	40.9600	2.52982	8.00000	**6.90**	47.6100	2.62679	8.30662
6.41	41.0881	2.53180	8.00625	6.91	47.7481	2.62869	8.31264
6.42	41.2164	2.53377	8.01249	6.92	47.8864	2.63059	8.31865
6.43	41.3449	2.53574	8.01873	6.93	48.0249	2.63249	8.32466
6.44	41.4736	2.53772	8.02496	6.94	48.1636	2.63439	8.33067
6.45	41.6025	2.53969	8.03119	6.95	48.3025	2.63629	8.33667
6.46	41.7316	2.54165	8.03741	6.96	48.4416	2.63818	8.34266
6.47	41.8609	2.54362	8.04363	6.97	48.5809	2.64008	8.34865
6.48	41.9904	2.54558	8.04984	6.98	48.7204	2.64197	8.35464
6.49	42.1201	2.54755	8.05605	6.99	48.8601	2.64386	8.36062
6.50	42.2500	2.54951	8.06226	**7.00**	49.0000	2.64575	8.36660
N	N²	√N	√10N	N	N²	√N	√10N

N	N²	√N	√10N	N	N²	√N	√10N
7.00	49.0000	2.64575	8.36660	**7.50**	56.2500	2.73861	8.66025
7.01	49.1401	2.64764	8.37257	7.51	56.4001	2.74044	8.66603
7.02	49.2804	2.64953	8.37854	7.52	56.5504	2.74226	8.67179
7.03	49.4209	2.65141	8.38451	7.53	56.7009	2.74408	8.67756
7.04	49.5616	2.65330	8.39047	7.54	56.8516	2.74591	8.68332
7.05	49.7025	2.65518	8.39643	7.55	57.0025	2.74773	8.68907
7.06	49.8436	2.65707	8.40238	7.56	57.1536	2.74955	8.69483
7.07	49.9849	2.65895	8.40833	7.57	57.3049	2.75136	8.70057
7.08	50.1264	2.66083	8.41427	7.58	57.4564	2.75318	8.70632
7.09	50.2681	2.66271	8.42021	7.59	57.6081	2.75500	8.71206
7.10	50.4100	2.66458	8.42615	**7.60**	57.7600	2.75681	8.71780
7.11	50.5521	2.66646	8.43208	7.61	57.9121	2.75862	8.72353
7.12	50.6944	2.66833	8.43801	7.62	58.0644	2.76043	8.72926
7.13	50.8369	2.67021	8.44393	7.63	58.2169	2.76225	8.73499
7.14	50.9796	2.67208	8.44985	7.64	58.3696	2.76405	8.74071
7.15	51.1225	2.67395	8.45577	7.65	58.5225	2.76586	8.74643
7.16	51.2656	2.67582	8.46168	7.66	58.6756	2.76767	8.75214
7.17	51.4089	2.67769	8.46759	7.67	58.8289	2.76948	8.75785
7.18	51.5524	2.67955	8.47349	7.68	58.9824	2.77128	8.76356
7.19	51.6961	2.68142	8.47939	7.69	59.1361	2.77308	8.76926
7.20	51.8400	2.68328	8.48528	**7.70**	59.2900	2.77489	8.77496
7.21	51.9841	2.68514	8.49117	7.71	59.4441	2.77669	8.78066
7.22	52.1284	2.68701	8.49706	7.72	59.5984	2.77849	8.78635
7.23	52.2729	2.68887	8.50294	7.73	59.7529	2.78029	8.79204
7.24	52.4176	2.69072	8.50882	7.74	59.9076	2.78209	8.79773
7.25	52.5625	2.69258	8.51469	7.75	60.0625	2.78388	8.80341
7.26	52.7076	2.69444	8.52056	7.76	60.2176	2.78568	8.80909
7.27	52.8529	2.69629	8.52643	7.77	60.3729	2.78747	8.81476
7.28	52.9984	2.69815	8.53229	7.78	60.5284	2.78927	8.82043
7.29	53.1441	2.70000	8.53815	7.79	60.6841	2.79106	8.82610
7.30	53.2900	2.70185	8.54400	**7.80**	60.8400	2.79285	8.83176
7.31	53.4361	2.70370	8.54985	7.81	60.9961	2.79464	8.83742
7.32	53.5824	2.70555	8.55570	7.82	61.1524	2.79643	8.84308
7.33	53.7289	2.70740	8.56154	7.83	61.3089	2.79821	8.84873
7.34	53.8756	2.70924	8.56738	7.84	61.4656	2.80000	8.85438
7.35	54.0225	2.71109	8.57321	7.85	61.6225	2.80179	8.86002
7.36	54.1696	2.71293	8.57904	7.86	61.7796	2.80357	8.86566
7.37	54.3169	2.71477	8.58487	7.87	61.9369	2.80535	8.87130
7.38	54.4644	2.71662	8.59069	7.88	62.0944	2.80713	8.87694
7.39	54.6121	2.71846	8.59651	7.89	62.2521	2.80891	8.88257
7.40	54.7600	2.72029	8.60233	**7.90**	62.4100	2.81069	8.88819
7.41	54.9081	2.72213	8.60814	7.91	62.5681	2.81247	8.89382
7.42	55.0564	2.72397	8.61394	7.92	62.7264	2.81425	8.89944
7.43	55.2049	2.72580	8.61974	7.93	62.8849	2.81603	8.90505
7.44	55.3536	2.72764	8.62554	7.94	63.0436	2.81780	8.91067
7.45	55.5025	2.72947	8.63134	7.95	63.2025	2.81957	8.91628
7.46	55.6516	2.73130	8.63713	7.96	63.3616	2.82135	8.92188
7.47	55.8009	2.73313	8.64292	7.97	63.5209	2.82312	8.92749
7.48	55.9504	2.73496	8.64870	7.98	63.6804	2.82489	8.93308
7.49	56.1001	2.73679	8.65448	7.99	63.8401	2.82666	8.93868
7.50	56.2500	2.73861	8.66025	**8.00**	64.0000	2.82843	8.94427
N	N²	√N	√10N	N	N²	√N	√10N

N	N²	√N	√10N	N	N²	√N	√10N
8.00	64.0000	2.82843	8.94427	**8.50**	72.2500	2.91548	9.21954
8.01	64.1601	2.83019	8.94986	8.51	72.4201	2.91719	9.22497
8.02	64.3204	2.83196	8.95545	8.52	72.5904	2.91890	9.23038
8.03	64.4809	2.83373	8.96103	8.53	72.7609	2.92062	9.23580
8.04	64.6416	2.83549	8.96660	8.54	72.9316	2.92233	9.24121
8.05	64.8025	2.83725	8.97218	8.55	73.1025	2.92404	9.24662
8.06	64.9636	2.83901	8.97775	8.56	73.2736	2.92575	9.25203
8.07	65.1249	2.84077	8.98332	8.57	73.4449	2.92746	9.25743
8.08	65.2864	2.84253	8.98888	8.58	73.6164	2.92916	9.26283
8.09	65.4481	2.84429	8.99444	8.59	73.7881	2.93087	9.26823
8.10	65.6100	2.84605	9.00000	**8.60**	73.9600	2.93258	9.27362
8.11	65.7721	2.84781	9.00555	8.61	74.1321	2.93428	9.27901
8.12	65.9344	2.84956	9.01110	8.62	74.3044	2.93598	9.28440
8.13	66.0969	2.85132	9.01665	8.63	74.4769	2.93769	9.28978
8.14	66.2596	2.85307	9.02219	8.64	74.6496	2.93939	9.29516
8.15	66.4225	2.85482	9.02774	8.65	74.8225	2.94109	9.30054
8.16	66.5856	2.85657	9.03327	8.66	74.9956	2.94279	9.30591
8.17	66.7489	2.85832	9.03881	8.67	75.1689	2.94449	9.31128
8.18	66.9124	2.86007	9.04434	8.68	75.3424	2.94618	9.31665
8.19	67.0761	2.86182	9.04986	8.69	75.5161	2.94788	9.32202
8.20	67.2400	2.86356	9.05539	**8.70**	75.6900	2.94958	9.32738
8.21	67.4041	2.86531	9.06091	8.71	75.8641	2.95127	9.33274
8.22	67.5684	2.86705	9.06642	8.72	76.0384	2.95296	9.33809
8.23	67.7329	2.86880	9.07193	8.73	76.2129	2.95466	9.34345
8.24	67.8976	2.87054	9.07744	8.74	76.3876	2.95635	9.34880
8.25	68.0625	2.87228	9.08295	8.75	76.5625	2.95804	9.35414
8.26	68.2276	2.87402	9.08845	8.76	76.7376	2.95973	9.35949
8.27	68.3929	2.87576	9.09395	8.77	76.9129	2.96142	9.36483
8.28	68.5584	2.87750	9.09945	8.78	77.0884	2.96311	9.37017
8.29	68.7241	2.87924	9.10494	8.79	77.2641	2.96479	9.37550
8.30	68.8900	2.88097	9.11043	**8.80**	77.4400	2.96648	9.38083
8.31	69.0561	2.88271	9.11592	8.81	77.6161	2.96816	9.38616
8.32	69.2224	2.88444	9.12140	8.82	77.7924	2.96985	9.39149
8.33	69.3889	2.88617	9.12688	8.83	77.9689	2.97153	9.39681
8.34	69.5556	2.88791	9.13236	8.84	78.1456	2.97321	9.40213
8.35	69.7225	2.88964	9.13783	8.85	78.3225	2.97489	9.40744
8.36	69.8896	2.89137	9.14330	8.86	78.4996	2.97658	9.41276
8.37	70.0569	2.89310	9.14877	8.87	78.6769	2.97825	9.41807
8.38	70.2244	2.89482	9.15423	8.88	78.8544	2.97993	9.42338
8.39	70.3921	2.89655	9.15969	8.89	79.0321	2.98161	9.42868
8.40	70.5600	2.89828	9.16515	**8.90**	79.2100	2.98329	9.43398
8.41	70.7281	2.90000	9.17061	8.91	79.3881	2.98496	9.43928
8.42	70.8964	2.90172	9.17606	8.92	79.5664	2.98664	9.44458
8.43	71.0649	2.90345	9.18150	8.93	79.7449	2.98831	9.44987
8.44	71.2336	2.90517	9.18695	8.94	79.9236	2.98998	9.45516
8.45	71.4025	2.90689	9.19239	8.95	80.1025	2.99166	9.46044
8.46	71.5716	2.90861	9.19783	8.96	80.2816	2.99333	9.46573
8.47	71.7409	2.91033	9.20326	8.97	80.4609	2.99500	9.47101
8.48	71.9104	2.91204	9.20869	8.98	80.6404	2.99666	9.47629
8.49	72.0801	2.91376	9.21412	8.99	80.8201	2.99833	9.48156
8.50	72.2500	2.91548	9.21954	**9.00**	81.0000	3.00000	9.48683
N	N²	√N	√10N	N	N²	√N	√10N

N	N²	√N	√10N	N	N²	√N	√10N
9.00	81.0000	3.00000	9.48683	**9.50**	90.2500	3.08221	9.74679
9.01	81.1801	3.00167	9.49210	9.51	90.4401	3.08383	9.75192
9.02	81.3604	3.00333	9.49737	9.52	90.6304	3.08545	9.75705
9.03	81.5409	3.00500	9.50263	9.53	90.8209	3.08707	9.76217
9.04	81.7216	3.00666	9.50789	9.54	91.0116	3.08869	9.76729
9.05	81.9025	3.00832	9.51315	9.55	91.2025	3.09031	9.77241
9.06	82.0836	3.00998	9.51840	9.56	91.3936	3.09192	9.77753
9.07	82.2649	3.01164	9.52365	9.57	91.5849	3.09354	9.78264
9.08	82.4464	3.01330	9.52890	9.58	91.7764	3.09516	9.78775
9.09	82.6281	3.01496	9.53415	9.59	91.9681	3.09677	9.79285
9.10	82.8100	3.01662	9.53939	**9.60**	92.1600	3.09839	9.79796
9.11	82.9921	3.01828	9.54463	9.61	92.3521	3.10000	9.80306
9.12	83.1744	3.01993	9.54987	9.62	92.5444	3.10161	9.80816
9.13	83.3569	3.02159	9.55510	9.63	92.7369	3.10322	9.81326
9.14	83.5396	3.02324	9.56033	9.64	92.9296	3.10483	9.81835
9.15	83.7225	3.02490	9.56556	9.65	93.1225	3.10644	9.82344
9.16	83.9056	3.02655	9.57079	9.66	93.3156	3.10805	9.82853
9.17	84.0889	3.02820	9.57601	9.67	93.5089	3.10966	9.83362
9.18	84.2724	3.02985	9.58123	9.68	93.7024	3.11127	9.83870
9.19	84.4561	3.03150	9.58645	9.69	93.8961	3.11288	9.84378
9.20	84.6400	3.03315	9.59166	**9.70**	94.0900	3.11448	9.84886
9.21	84.8241	3.03480	9.59687	9.71	94.2841	3.11609	9.85393
9.22	85.0084	3.03645	9.60208	9.72	94.4784	3.11769	9.85901
9.23	85.1929	3.03809	9.60729	9.73	94.6729	3.11929	9.86408
9.24	85.3776	3.03974	9.61249	9.74	94.8676	3.12090	9.86914
9.25	85.5625	3.04138	9.61769	9.75	95.0625	3.12250	9.87421
9.26	85.7476	3.04302	9.62289	9.76	95.2576	3.12410	9.87927
9.27	85.9329	3.04467	9.62808	9.77	95.4529	3.12570	9.88433
9.28	86.1184	3.04631	9.63328	9.78	95.6484	3.12730	9.88939
9.29	86.3041	3.04795	9.63846	9.79	95.8441	3.12890	9.89444
9.30	86.4900	3.04959	9.64365	**9.80**	96.0400	3.13050	9.89949
9.31	86.6761	3.05123	9.64883	9.81	96.2361	3.13209	9.90454
9.32	86.8624	3.05287	9.65401	9.82	96.4324	3.13369	9.90959
9.33	87.0489	3.05450	9.65919	9.83	96.6289	3.13528	9.91464
9.34	87.2356	3.05614	9.66437	9.84	96.8256	3.13688	9.91968
9.35	87.4225	3.05778	9.66954	9.85	97.0225	3.13847	9.92472
9.36	87.6096	3.05941	9.67471	9.86	97.2196	3.14006	9.92975
9.37	87.7969	3.06105	9.67988	9.87	97.4169	3.14166	9.93479
9.38	87.9844	3.06268	9.68504	9.88	97.6144	3.14325	9.93982
9.39	88.1721	3.06431	9.69020	9.89	97.8121	3.14484	9.94485
9.40	88.3600	3.06594	9.69536	**9.90**	98.0100	3.14643	9.94987
9.41	88.5481	3.06757	9.70052	9.91	98.2081	3.14802	9.95490
9.42	88.7364	3.06920	9.70567	9.92	98.4064	3.14960	9.95992
9.43	88.9249	3.07083	9.71082	9.93	98.6049	3.15119	9.96494
9.44	89.1136	3.07246	9.71597	9.94	98.8036	3.15278	9.96995
9.45	89.3025	3.07409	9.72111	9.95	99.0025	3.15436	9.97497
9.46	89.4916	3.07571	9.72625	9.96	99.2016	3.15595	9.97998
9.47	89.6809	3.07734	9.73139	9.97	99.4009	3.15753	9.98499
9.48	89.8704	3.07896	9.73653	9.98	99.6004	3.15911	9.98999
9.49	90.0601	3.08058	9.74166	9.99	99.8001	3.16070	9.99500
9.50	90.2500	3.08221	9.74679	**10.00**	100.000	3.16228	10.0000
N	N²	√N	√10N	N	N²	√N	√10N

TABLE II—NORMAL AREAS AND ORDINATES *   243

t	$\phi(t)$	$\int_0^t \phi(t)\,dt$	t	$\phi(t)$	$\int_0^t \phi(t)\,dt$	t	$\phi(t)$	$\int_0^t \phi(t)\,dt$
.00	.39894	.00000	.45	.36053	.17364	.90	.26609	.31594
.01	.39892	.00399	.46	.35889	.17724	.91	.26369	.31859
.02	.39886	.00798	.47	.35723	.18082	.92	.26129	.32121
.03	.39876	.01197	.48	.35553	.18439	.93	.25888	.32381
.04	.39862	.01595	.49	.35381	.18793	.94	.25647	.32639
.05	.39844	.01994	.50	.35207	.19146	.95	.25406	.32894
.06	.39822	.02392	.51	.35029	.19497	.96	.25164	.33147
.07	.39797	.02790	.52	.34849	.19847	.97	.24923	.33398
.08	.39767	.03188	.53	.34667	.20194	.98	.24681	.33646
.09	.39733	.03586	.54	.34482	.20540	.99	.24439	.33891
.10	.39695	.03983	.55	.34294	.20884	1.00	.24197	.34134
.11	.39654	.04380	.56	.34105	.21226	1.01	.23955	.34375
.12	.39608	.04776	.57	.33912	.21566	1.02	.23713	.34614
.13	.39559	.05172	.58	.33718	.21904	1.03	.23471	.34850
.14	.39505	.05567	.59	.33521	.22240	1.04	.23230	.35083
.15	.39448	.05962	.60	.33322	.22575	1.05	.22988	.35314
.16	.39387	.06356	.61	.33121	.22907	1.06	.22747	.35543
.17	.39322	.06749	.62	.32918	.23237	1.07	.22506	.35769
.18	.39253	.07142	.63	.32713	.23565	1.08	.22265	.35993
.19	.39181	.07535	.64	.32506	.23891	1.09	.22025	.36214
.20	.39104	.07926	.65	.32297	.24215	1.10	.21785	.36433
.21	.39024	.08317	.66	.32086	.24537	1.11	.21546	.36650
.22	.38940	.08706	.67	.31874	.24857	1.12	.21307	.36864
.23	.38853	.09095	.68	.31659	.25175	1.13	.21069	.37076
.24	.38762	.09483	.69	.31443	.25490	1.14	.20831	.37286
.25	.38667	.09871	.70	.31225	.25804	1.15	.20594	.37493
.26	.38568	.10257	.71	.31006	.26115	1.16	.20357	.37698
.27	.38466	.10642	.72	.30785	.26424	1.17	.20121	.37900
.28	.38361	.11026	.73	.30563	.26730	1.18	.19886	.38100
.29	.38251	.11409	.74	.30339	.27035	1.19	.19652	.38298
.30	.38139	.11791	.75	.30114	.27337	1.20	.19419	.38493
.31	.38023	.12172	.76	.29887	.27637	1.21	.19186	.38686
.32	.37903	.12552	.77	.29659	.27935	1.22	.18954	.38877
.33	.37780	.12930	.78	.29431	.28230	1.23	.18724	.39065
.34	.37654	.13307	.79	.29200	.28524	1.24	.18494	.39251
.35	.37524	.13683	.80	.28969	.28814	1.25	.18265	.39435
.36	.37391	.14058	.81	.28737	.29103	1.26	.18037	.39617
.37	.37255	.14431	.82	.28504	.29389	1.27	.17810	.39796
.38	.37115	.14803	.83	.28269	.29673	1.28	.17585	.39973
.39	.36973	.15173	.84	.28034	.29955	1.29	.17360	.40147
.40	.36827	.15542	.85	.27798	.30234	1.30	.17137	.40320
.41	.36678	.15910	.86	.27562	.30511	1.31	.16915	.40490
.42	.36526	.16276	.87	.27324	.30785	1.32	.16694	.40658
.43	.36371	.16640	.88	.27086	.31057	1.33	.16474	.40824
.44	.36213	.17003	.89	.26848	.31327	1.34	.16256	.40988

.68268

* Reprinted, by permission, from Kenney, *Mathematics of Statistics*, Part One, pp. 225–227, D Van Nostrand, New York.

t	$\phi(t)$	$\int_0^t \phi(t)\,dt$	t	$\phi(t)$	$\int_0^t \phi(t)\,dt$	t	$\phi(t)$	$\int_0^t \phi(t)\,dt$
1.35	.16038	.41149	1.80	.07895	.46407	2.25	.03174	.48778
1.36	.15822	.41309	1.81	.07754	.46485	2.26	.03103	.48809
1.37	.15608	.41466	1.82	.07614	.46562	2.27	.03034	.48840
1.38	.15395	.41621	1.83	.07477	.46638	2.28	.02965	.48870
1.39	.15183	.41774	1.84	.07341	.46712	2.29	.02898	.48899
1.40	.14973	.41924	1.85	.07206	.46784	2.30	.02833	.48928
1.41	.14764	.42073	1.86	.07074	.46856	2.31	.02768	.48956
1.42	.14556	.42220	1.87	.06943	.46926	2.32	.02705	.48983
1.43	.14350	.42364	1.88	.06814	.46995	2.33	.02643	.49010
1.44	.14146	.42507	1.89	.06687	.47062	2.34	.02582	.49036
1.45	.13943	.42647	1.90	.06562	.47128	2.35	.02522	.49061
1.46	.13742	.42786	1.91	.06439	.47193	2.36	.02463	.49086
1.47	.13542	.42922	1.92	.06316	.47257	2.37	.02406	.49111
1.48	.13344	.43056	1.93	.06195	.47320	2.38	.02349	.49134
1.49	.13147	.43189	1.94	.06077	.47381	2.39	.02294	.49158
1.50	.12952	.43319	1.95	.05959	.47441	2.40	.02239	.49180
1.51	.12758	.43448	1.96	.05844	.47500	2.41	.02186	.49202
1.52	.12566	.43574	1.97	.05730	.47558	2.42	.02134	.49224
1.53	.12376	.43699	1.98	.05618	.47615	2.43	.02083	.49245
1.54	.12188	.43822	1.99	.05508	.47670	2.44	.02033	.49266
1.55	.12001	.43943	2.00	.05399	.47725	2.45	.01984	.49286
1.56	.11816	.44062	2.01	.05292	.47778	2.46	.01936	.49305
1.57	.11632	.44179	2.02	.05186	.47831	2.47	.01889	.49324
1.58	.11450	.44295	2.03	.05082	.47882	2.48	.01842	.49343
1.59	.11270	.44408	2.04	.04980	.47932	2.49	.01797	.49361
1.60	.11092	.44520	2.05	.04879	.47982	2.50	.01753	.49379
1.61	.10915	.44630	2.06	.04780	.48030	2.51	.01709	.49396
1.62	.10741	.44738	2.07	.04682	.48077	2.52	.01667	.49413
1.63	.10567	.44845	2.08	.04586	.48124	2.53	.01625	.49430
1.64	.10396	.44950	2.09	.04491	.48169	2.54	.01585	.49446
1.65	.10226	.45053	2.10	.04398	.48214	2.55	.01545	.49461
1.66	.10059	.45154	2.11	.04307	.48257	2.56	.01506	.49477
1.67	.09893	.45254	2.12	.04217	.48300	2.57	.01468	.49492
1.68	.09728	.45352	2.13	.04128	.48341	2.58	.01431	.49506
1.69	.09566	.45449	2.14	.04041	.48382	2.59	.01394	.49520
1.70	.09405	.45543	2.15	.03955	.48422	2.60	.01358	.49534
1.71	.09246	.45637	2.16	.03871	.48461	2.61	.01323	.49547
1.72	.09089	.45728	2.17	.03788	.48500	2.62	.01289	.49560
1.73	.08933	.45818	2.18	.03706	.48537	2.63	.01256	.49573
1.74	.08780	.45907	2.19	.03626	.48574	2.64	.01223	.49585
1.75	.08628	.45994	2.20	.03547	.48610	2.65	.01191	.49598
1.76	.08478	.46080	2.21	.03470	.48645	2.66	.01160	.49609
1.77	.08329	.46164	2.22	.03394	.48679	2.67	.01130	.49621
1.78	.08183	.46246	2.23	.03319	.48713	2.68	.01100	.49632
1.79	.08038	.46327	2.24	.03246	.48745	2.69	.01071	.49643

t	$\phi(t)$	$\int_0^t \phi(t)\,dt$	t	$\phi(t)$	$\int_0 \phi(t)\,dt$	t	$\phi(t)$	$\int_0^t \phi(t)\,dt$
2.70	.01042	.49653	3.15	.00279	.49918	3.60	.00061	.49984
2.71	.01014	.49664	3.16	.00271	.49921	3.61	.00059	.49985
2.72	.00987	.49674	3.17	.00262	.49924	3.62	.00057	.49985
2.73	.00961	.49683	3.18	.00254	.49926	3.63	.00055	.49986
2.74	.00935	.49693	3.19	.00246	.49929	3.64	.00053	.49986
2.75	.00909	.49702	3.20	.00238	.49931	3.65	.00051	.49987
2.76	.00885	.49711	3.21	.00231	.49934	3.66	.00049	.49987
2.77	.00861	.49720	3.22	.00224	.49936	3.67	.00047	.49988
2.78	.00837	.49728	3.23	.00216	.49938	3.68	.00046	.49988
2.79	.00814	.49736	3.24	.00210	.49940	3.69	.00044	.49989
2.80	.00792	.49744	3.25	.00203	.49942	3.70	.00042	.49989
2.81	.00770	.49752	3.26	.00196	.49944	3.71	.00041	.49990
2.82	.00748	.49760	3.27	.00190	.49946	3.72	.00039	.49990
2.83	.00727	.49767	3.28	.00184	.49948	3.73	.00038	.49990
2.84	.00707	.49774	3.29	.00178	.49950	3.74	.00037	.49991
2.85	.00687	.49781	3.30	.00172	.49952	3.75	.00035	.49991
2.86	.00668	.49788	3.31	.00167	.49953	3.76	.00034	.49992
2.87	.00649	.49795	3.32	.00161	.49955	3.77	.00033	.49992
2.88	.00631	.49801	3.33	.00156	.49957	3.78	.00031	.49992
2.89	.00613	.49807	3.34	.00151	.49958	3.79	.00030	.49992
2.90	.00595	.49813	3.35	.00146	.49960	3.80	.00029	.49993
2.91	.00578	.49819	3.36	.00141	.49961	3.81	.00028	.49993
2.92	.00562	.49825	3.37	.00136	.49962	3.82	.00027	.49993
2.93	.00545	.49831	3.38	.00132	.49964	3.83	.00026	.49994
2.94	.00530	.49836	3.39	.00127	.49965	3.84	.00025	.49994
2.95	.00514	.49841	3.40	.00123	.49966	3.85	.00024	.49994
2.96	.00499	.49846	3.41	.00119	.49968	3.86	.00023	.49994
2.97	.00485	.49851	3.42	.00115	.49969	3.87	.00022	.49995
2.98	.00471	.49856	3.43	.00111	.49970	3.88	.00021	.49995
2.99	.00457	.49861	3.44	.00107	.49971	3.89	.00021	.49995
3.00	.00443	.49865	3.45	.00104	.49972	3.90	.00020	.49995
3.01	.00430	.49869	3.46	.00100	.49973	3.91	.00019	.49995
3.02	.00417	.49874	3.47	.00097	.49974	3.92	.00018	.49996
3.03	.00405	.49878	3.48	.00094	.49975	3.93	.00018	.49996
3.04	.00393	.49882	3.49	.00090	.49976	3.94	.00017	.49996
3.05	.00381	.49886	3.50	.00087	.49977	3.95	.00016	.49996
3.06	.00370	.49889	3.51	.00084	.49978	3.96	.00016	.49996
3.07	.00358	.49893	3.52	.00081	.49978	3.97	.00015	.49996
3.08	.00348	.49897	3.53	.00079	.49979	3.98	.00014	.49997
3.09	.00337	.49900	3.54	.00076	.49980	3.99	.00014	.49997
3.10	.00327	.49903	3.55	.00073	.49981			
3.11	.00317	.49906	3.56	.00071	.49981			
3.12	.00307	.49910	3.57	.00068	.49982			
3.13	.00298	.49913	3.58	.00066	.49983			
3.14	.00288	.49916	3.59	.00063	.49983			

TABLE III—χ² DISTRIBUTION

Degrees of freedom	P = 0.99	0.98	0.95	0.90	0.80	0.70	0.50	0.30	0.20	0.10	0.05	0.02	0.01
1	0.000157	0.000628	0.00393	0.0158	0.0642	0.148	0.455	1.074	1.642	2.706	3.841	5.412	6.635
2	0.0201	0.0404	0.103	0.211	0.446	0.713	1.386	2.408	3.219	4.605	5.991	7.824	9.210
3	0.115	0.185	0.352	0.584	1.005	1.424	2.366	3.665	4.642	6.251	7.815	9.837	11.341
4	0.297	0.429	0.711	1.064	1.649	2.195	3.357	4.878	5.989	7.779	9.488	11.668	13.277
5	0.554	0.752	1.145	1.610	2.343	3.000	4.351	6.064	7.289	9.236	11.070	13.388	15.086
6	0.872	1.134	1.635	2.204	3.070	3.828	5.348	7.231	8.558	10.645	12.592	15.033	16.812
7	1.239	1.564	2.167	2.833	3.822	4.671	6.346	8.383	9.803	12.017	14.067	16.622	18.475
8	1.646	2.032	2.733	3.490	4.594	5.527	7.344	9.524	11.030	13.362	15.507	18.168	20.090
9	2.088	2.532	3.325	4.168	5.380	6.393	8.343	10.656	12.242	14.684	16.919	19.679	21.666
10	2.558	3.059	3.940	4.865	6.179	7.267	9.342	11.781	13.442	15.987	18.307	21.161	23.209
11	3.053	3.609	4.575	5.578	6.989	8.148	10.341	12.899	14.631	17.275	19.675	22.618	24.725
12	3.571	4.178	5.226	6.304	7.807	9.034	11.340	14.011	15.812	18.549	21.026	24.054	26.217
13	4.107	4.765	5.892	7.042	8.634	9.926	12.340	15.119	16.985	19.812	22.362	25.472	27.688
14	4.660	5.368	6.571	7.790	9.467	10.821	13.339	16.222	18.151	21.064	23.685	26.873	29.141
15	5.229	5.985	7.261	8.547	10.307	11.721	14.339	17.322	19.311	22.307	24.996	28.259	30.578
16	5.812	6.614	7.962	9.312	11.152	12.624	15.338	18.418	20.465	23.542	26.296	29.633	32.000
17	6.408	7.255	8.672	10.085	12.002	13.531	16.338	19.511	21.615	24.769	27.587	30.995	33.409
18	7.015	7.906	9.390	10.865	12.857	14.440	17.338	20.601	22.760	25.989	28.869	32.346	34.805
19	7.633	8.567	10.117	11.651	13.716	15.352	18.338	21.689	23.900	27.204	30.144	33.687	36.191
20	8.260	9.237	10.851	12.443	14.578	16.266	19.337	22.775	25.038	28.412	31.410	35.020	37.566
21	8.897	9.915	11.591	13.240	15.445	17.182	20.337	23.858	26.171	29.615	32.671	36.343	38.932
22	9.542	10.600	12.338	14.041	16.314	18.101	21.337	24.939	27.301	30.813	33.924	37.659	40.289
23	10.196	11.293	13.091	14.848	17.187	19.021	22.337	26.018	28.429	32.007	35.172	38.968	41.638
24	10.856	11.992	13.848	15.659	18.062	19.943	23.337	27.096	29.553	33.196	36.415	40.270	42.980
25	11.524	12.697	14.611	16.473	18.940	20.867	24.337	28.172	30.675	34.382	37.652	41.566	44.314
26	12.198	13.409	15.379	17.292	19.820	21.792	25.336	29.246	31.795	35.563	38.885	42.856	45.642
27	12.879	14.125	16.151	18.114	20.703	22.719	26.336	30.319	32.912	36.741	40.113	44.140	46.963
28	13.565	14.847	16.928	18.939	21.588	23.647	27.336	31.391	34.027	37.916	41.337	45.419	48.278
29	14.256	15.574	17.708	19.768	22.475	24.577	28.336	32.461	35.139	39.087	42.557	46.693	49.588
30	14.953	16.306	18.493	20.599	23.364	25.508	29.336	33.530	36.250	40.256	43.773	47.962	50.892

For degrees of freedom greater than 30, the expression $\sqrt{2\chi^2} - \sqrt{2n' - 1}$ may be used as a normal deviate with unit variance, where n' is the number of degrees of freedom.

Reproduced from *Statistical Methods for Research Workers*, 6th ed., with the permission of the author, R. A. Fisher, and his publisher, Oliver and Boyd, Edinburgh.

TABLE IV—STUDENT'S t DISTRIBUTION *

Degrees of freedom n	Probability of a deviation greater than t					
	.005	.01	.025	.05	.1	.15
1	63.657	31.821	12.706	6.314	3.078	1.963
2	9.925	6.965	4.303	2.920	1.886	1.386
3	5.841	4.541	3.182	2.353	1.638	1.250
4	4.604	3.747	2.776	2.132	1.533	1.190
5	4.032	3.365	2.571	2.015	1.476	1.156
6	3.707	3.143	2.447	1.943	1.440	1.134
7	3.499	2.998	2.365	1.895	1.415	1.119
8	3.355	2.896	2.306	1.860	1.397	1.108
9	3.250	2.821	2.262	1.833	1.383	1.100
10	3.169	2.764	2.228	1.812	1.372	1.093
11	3.106	2.718	2.201	1.796	1.363	1.088
12	3.055	2.681	2.179	1.782	1.356	1.083
13	3.012	2.650	2.160	1.771	1.350	1.079
14	2.977	2.624	2.145	1.761	1.345	1.076
15	2.947	2.602	2.131	1.753	1.341	1.074
16	2.921	2.583	2.120	1.746	1.337	1.071
17	2.898	2.567	2.110	1.740	1.333	1.069
18	2.878	2.552	2.101	1.734	1.330	1.067
19	2.861	2.539	2.093	1.729	1.328	1.066
20	2.845	2.528	2.086	1.725	1.325	1.064
21	2.831	2.518	2.080	1.721	1.323	1.063
22	2.819	2.508	2.074	1.717	1.321	1.061
23	2.807	2.500	2.069	1.714	1.319	1.060
24	2.797	2.492	2.064	1.711	1.318	1.059
25	2.787	2.485	2.060	1.708	1.316	1.058
26	2.779	2.479	2.056	1.706	1.315	1.058
27	2.771	2.473	2.052	1.703	1.314	1.057
28	2.763	2.467	2.048	1.701	1.313	1.056
29	2.756	2.462	2.045	1.699	1.311	1.055
30	2.750	2.457	2.042	1.697	1.310	1.055
∞	2.576	2.326	1.960	1.645	1.282	1.036

The probability of a deviation *numerically* greater than t is twice the probability given at the head of the table.

* This table is reproduced from *Statistical Methods for Research Workers*, with the generous permission of the author, Professor R. A. Fisher, and the publishers, Messrs. Oliver and Boyd.

Degrees of freedom *n*	Probability of a deviation greater than *t*					
	.2	.25	.3	.35	.4	.45
1	1.376	1.000	.727	.510	.325	.158
2	1.061	.816	.617	.445	.289	.142
3	.978	.765	.584	.424	.277	.137
4	.941	.741	.569	.414	.271	.134
5	.920	.727	.559	.408	.267	.132
6	.906	.718	.553	.404	.265	.131
7	.896	.711	.549	.402	.263	.130
8	.889	.706	.546	.399	.262	.130
9	.883	.703	.543	.398	.261	.129
10	.879	.700	.542	.397	.260	.129
11	.876	.697	.540	.396	.260	.129
12	.873	.695	.539	.395	.259	.128
13	.870	.694	.538	.394	.259	.128
14	.868	.692	.537	.393	.258	.128
15	.866	.691	.536	.393	.258	.128
16	.865	.690	.535	.392	.258	.128
17	.863	.689	.534	.392	.257	.128
18	.862	.688	.534	.392	.257	.127
19	.861	.688	.533	.391	.257	.127
20	.860	.687	.533	.391	.257	.127
21	.859	.686	.532	.391	.257	.127
22	.858	.686	.532	.390	.256	.127
23	.858	.685	.532	.390	.256	.127
24	.857	.685	.531	.390	.256	.127
25	.856	.684	.531	.390	.256	.127
26	.856	.684	.531	.390	.256	.127
27	.855	.684	.531	.389	.256	.127
28	.855	.683	.530	.389	.256	.127
29	.854	.683	.530	.389	.256	.127
30	.854	.683	.530	.389	.256	.127
∞	.842	.674	.524	.385	.253	.126

The probability of a deviation *numerically* greater than *t* is twice the probability given at the head of the table.

TABLE V—F DISTRIBUTION *

5% (ROMAN TYPE) AND 1% (BOLD-FACE TYPE) POINTS FOR THE DISTRIBUTION OF F

Degrees of freedom for lesser mean square	Degrees of freedom for greater mean square																							
	1	2	3	4	5	6	7	8	9	10	11	12	14	16	20	24	30	40	50	75	100	200	500	∞
1	161 **4052**	200 **4999**	216 **5403**	225 **5625**	230 **5764**	234 **5859**	237 **5928**	239 **5981**	241 **6022**	242 **6056**	243 **6082**	244 **6106**	245 **6142**	246 **6169**	248 **6208**	249 **6234**	250 **6258**	251 **6286**	252 **6302**	253 **6323**	253 **6334**	254 **6352**	254 **6361**	254 **6366**
2	18.51 **98.49**	19.00 **99.01**	19.16 **99.17**	19.25 **99.25**	19.30 **99.30**	19.33 **99.33**	19.36 **99.34**	19.37 **99.36**	19.38 **99.38**	19.39 **99.40**	19.40 **99.41**	19.41 **99.42**	19.42 **99.43**	19.43 **99.44**	19.44 **99.45**	19.45 **99.46**	19.46 **99.47**	19.47 **99.48**	19.47 **99.48**	19.48 **99.49**	19.49 **99.49**	19.49 **99.49**	19.50 **99.50**	19.50 **99.50**
3	10.13 **34.12**	9.55 **30.81**	9.28 **29.46**	9.12 **28.71**	9.01 **28.24**	8.94 **27.91**	8.88 **27.67**	8.84 **27.49**	8.81 **27.34**	8.78 **27.23**	8.76 **27.13**	8.74 **27.05**	8.71 **26.92**	8.69 **26.83**	8.66 **26.69**	8.64 **26.60**	8.62 **26.50**	8.60 **26.41**	8.58 **26.30**	8.57 **26.27**	8.56 **26.23**	8.54 **26.18**	8.54 **26.14**	8.53 **26.12**
4	7.71 **21.20**	6.94 **18.00**	6.59 **16.69**	6.39 **15.98**	6.26 **15.52**	6.16 **15.21**	6.09 **14.98**	6.04 **14.80**	6.00 **14.66**	5.96 **14.54**	5.93 **14.45**	5.91 **14.37**	5.87 **14.24**	5.84 **14.15**	5.80 **14.02**	5.77 **13.93**	5.74 **13.83**	5.71 **13.74**	5.70 **13.69**	5.68 **13.61**	5.66 **13.57**	5.65 **13.52**	5.64 **13.48**	5.63 **13.46**
5	6.61 **16.26**	5.79 **13.27**	5.41 **12.06**	5.19 **11.39**	5.05 **10.97**	4.95 **10.67**	4.88 **10.45**	4.82 **10.27**	4.78 **10.15**	4.74 **10.05**	4.70 **9.96**	4.68 **9.89**	4.64 **9.77**	4.60 **9.68**	4.56 **9.55**	4.53 **9.47**	4.50 **9.38**	4.46 **9.29**	4.44 **9.24**	4.42 **9.17**	4.40 **9.13**	4.38 **9.07**	4.37 **9.04**	4.36 **9.02**
6	5.99 **13.74**	5.14 **10.92**	4.76 **9.78**	4.53 **9.15**	4.39 **8.75**	4.28 **8.47**	4.21 **8.26**	4.15 **8.10**	4.10 **7.98**	4.06 **7.87**	4.03 **7.79**	4.00 **7.72**	3.96 **7.60**	3.92 **7.52**	3.87 **7.39**	3.84 **7.31**	3.81 **7.23**	3.77 **7.14**	3.75 **7.09**	3.72 **7.02**	3.71 **6.99**	3.69 **6.94**	3.68 **6.90**	3.67 **6.88**
7	5.59 **12.25**	4.74 **9.55**	4.35 **8.45**	4.12 **7.85**	3.97 **7.46**	3.87 **7.19**	3.79 **7.00**	3.73 **6.84**	3.68 **6.71**	3.63 **6.62**	3.60 **6.54**	3.57 **6.47**	3.52 **6.35**	3.49 **6.27**	3.44 **6.15**	3.41 **6.07**	3.38 **5.98**	3.34 **5.90**	3.32 **5.85**	3.29 **5.78**	3.28 **5.75**	3.25 **5.70**	3.24 **5.67**	3.23 **5.65**
8	5.32 **11.26**	4.46 **8.65**	4.07 **7.59**	3.84 **7.01**	3.69 **6.63**	3.58 **6.37**	3.50 **6.19**	3.44 **6.03**	3.39 **5.91**	3.34 **5.82**	3.31 **5.74**	3.28 **5.67**	3.23 **5.56**	3.20 **5.48**	3.15 **5.36**	3.12 **5.28**	3.08 **5.20**	3.05 **5.11**	3.03 **5.06**	3.00 **5.00**	2.98 **4.96**	2.96 **4.91**	2.94 **4.88**	2.93 **4.86**
9	5.12 **10.56**	4.26 **8.02**	3.86 **6.99**	3.63 **6.42**	3.48 **6.06**	3.37 **5.80**	3.29 **5.62**	3.23 **5.47**	3.18 **5.35**	3.13 **5.26**	3.10 **5.18**	3.07 **5.11**	3.02 **5.00**	2.98 **4.92**	2.93 **4.80**	2.90 **4.73**	2.86 **4.64**	2.82 **4.56**	2.80 **4.51**	2.77 **4.45**	2.76 **4.41**	2.73 **4.36**	2.72 **4.33**	2.71 **4.31**

* Reprinted, by permission, from Snedecor, *Statistical Methods*, Collegiate Press, Iowa State College, Ames.

df																								
10	2.54 / 3.91	2.55 / 3.93	2.56 / 3.96	2.59 / 4.01	2.61 / 4.05	2.64 / 4.12	2.67 / 4.17	2.70 / 4.25	2.74 / 4.33	2.77 / 4.41	2.82 / 4.52	2.86 / 4.60	2.91 / 4.71	2.94 / 4.78	2.97 / 4.85	3.02 / 4.95	3.07 / 5.06	3.14 / 5.21	3.22 / 5.39	3.33 / 5.64	3.48 / 5.99	3.71 / 6.55	4.10 / 7.56	4.96 / 10.04
11	2.40 / 3.60	2.41 / 3.62	2.42 / 3.66	2.45 / 3.70	2.47 / 3.74	2.50 / 3.80	2.53 / 3.86	2.57 / 3.94	2.61 / 4.02	2.65 / 4.10	2.70 / 4.21	2.74 / 4.29	2.79 / 4.40	2.82 / 4.46	2.86 / 4.54	2.90 / 4.63	2.95 / 4.74	3.01 / 4.88	3.09 / 5.07	3.20 / 5.32	3.36 / 5.67	3.59 / 6.22	3.98 / 7.20	4.84 / 9.65
12	2.30 / 3.36	2.31 / 3.38	2.32 / 3.41	2.35 / 3.46	2.36 / 3.49	2.40 / 3.56	2.42 / 3.61	2.46 / 3.70	2.50 / 3.78	2.54 / 3.86	2.60 / 3.98	2.64 / 4.05	2.69 / 4.16	2.72 / 4.22	2.76 / 4.30	2.80 / 4.39	2.85 / 4.50	2.92 / 4.65	3.00 / 4.82	3.11 / 5.06	3.26 / 5.41	3.49 / 5.95	3.88 / 6.93	4.75 / 9.33
13	2.21 / 3.16	2.22 / 3.18	2.24 / 3.21	2.26 / 3.27	2.28 / 3.30	2.32 / 3.37	2.34 / 3.42	2.38 / 3.51	2.42 / 3.59	2.46 / 3.67	2.51 / 3.78	2.55 / 3.85	2.60 / 3.96	2.63 / 4.02	2.67 / 4.10	2.72 / 4.19	2.77 / 4.30	2.84 / 4.44	2.92 / 4.62	3.02 / 4.86	3.18 / 5.20	3.41 / 5.74	3.80 / 6.70	4.67 / 9.07
14	2.13 / 3.00	2.14 / 3.02	2.16 / 3.06	2.19 / 3.11	2.21 / 3.14	2.24 / 3.21	2.27 / 3.26	2.31 / 3.34	2.35 / 3.43	2.39 / 3.51	2.44 / 3.62	2.48 / 3.70	2.53 / 3.80	2.56 / 3.86	2.60 / 3.94	2.65 / 4.03	2.70 / 4.14	2.77 / 4.28	2.85 / 4.46	2.96 / 4.69	3.11 / 5.03	3.34 / 5.56	3.74 / 6.51	4.60 / 8.86
15	2.07 / 2.87	2.08 / 2.89	2.10 / 2.92	2.12 / 2.97	2.15 / 3.00	2.18 / 3.07	2.21 / 3.12	2.25 / 3.20	2.29 / 3.29	2.33 / 3.36	2.39 / 3.48	2.43 / 3.56	2.48 / 3.67	2.51 / 3.73	2.55 / 3.80	2.59 / 3.89	2.64 / 4.00	2.70 / 4.14	2.79 / 4.32	2.90 / 4.56	3.06 / 4.89	3.29 / 5.42	3.68 / 6.36	4.54 / 8.68
16	2.01 / 2.75	2.02 / 2.77	2.04 / 2.80	2.07 / 2.86	2.09 / 2.89	2.13 / 2.96	2.16 / 3.01	2.20 / 3.10	2.24 / 3.18	2.28 / 3.25	2.33 / 3.37	2.37 / 3.45	2.42 / 3.55	2.45 / 3.61	2.49 / 3.69	2.54 / 3.78	2.59 / 3.89	2.66 / 4.03	2.74 / 4.20	2.85 / 4.44	3.01 / 4.77	3.24 / 5.29	3.63 / 6.23	4.49 / 8.53
17	1.96 / 2.65	1.97 / 2.67	1.99 / 2.70	2.02 / 2.76	2.04 / 2.79	2.08 / 2.86	2.11 / 2.92	2.15 / 3.00	2.19 / 3.08	2.23 / 3.16	2.29 / 3.27	2.33 / 3.35	2.38 / 3.45	2.41 / 3.52	2.45 / 3.59	2.50 / 3.68	2.55 / 3.79	2.62 / 3.93	2.70 / 4.10	2.81 / 4.34	2.96 / 4.67	3.20 / 5.18	3.59 / 6.11	4.45 / 8.40
18	1.92 / 2.57	1.93 / 2.59	1.95 / 2.62	1.98 / 2.68	2.00 / 2.71	2.04 / 2.78	2.07 / 2.83	2.11 / 2.91	2.15 / 3.00	2.19 / 3.07	2.25 / 3.19	2.29 / 3.27	2.34 / 3.37	2.37 / 3.44	2.41 / 3.51	2.46 / 3.60	2.51 / 3.71	2.58 / 3.85	2.66 / 4.01	2.77 / 4.25	2.93 / 4.58	3.16 / 5.09	3.55 / 6.01	4.41 / 8.28
19	1.88 / 2.49	1.90 / 2.51	1.91 / 2.54	1.94 / 2.60	1.96 / 2.63	2.00 / 2.70	2.02 / 2.76	2.07 / 2.84	2.11 / 2.92	2.15 / 3.00	2.21 / 3.12	2.26 / 3.19	2.31 / 3.30	2.34 / 3.36	2.38 / 3.43	2.43 / 3.52	2.48 / 3.63	2.55 / 3.77	2.63 / 3.94	2.74 / 4.17	2.90 / 4.50	3.13 / 5.01	3.52 / 5.93	4.38 / 8.18
20	1.84 / 2.42	1.85 / 2.44	1.87 / 2.47	1.90 / 2.53	1.92 / 2.56	1.96 / 2.63	1.99 / 2.69	2.04 / 2.77	2.08 / 2.86	2.12 / 2.94	2.18 / 3.05	2.23 / 3.13	2.28 / 3.23	2.31 / 3.30	2.35 / 3.37	2.40 / 3.45	2.45 / 3.56	2.52 / 3.71	2.60 / 3.87	2.71 / 4.10	2.87 / 4.43	3.10 / 4.94	3.49 / 5.85	4.35 / 8.10
21	1.81 / 2.36	1.82 / 2.38	1.84 / 2.42	1.87 / 2.47	1.89 / 2.51	1.93 / 2.58	1.96 / 2.63	2.00 / 2.72	2.05 / 2.80	2.09 / 2.88	2.15 / 2.99	2.20 / 3.07	2.25 / 3.17	2.28 / 3.24	2.32 / 3.31	2.37 / 3.40	2.42 / 3.51	2.49 / 3.65	2.57 / 3.81	2.68 / 4.04	2.84 / 4.37	3.07 / 4.87	3.47 / 5.78	4.32 / 8.02
22	1.78 / 2.31	1.80 / 2.33	1.81 / 2.37	1.84 / 2.42	1.87 / 2.46	1.91 / 2.53	1.93 / 2.58	1.98 / 2.67	2.03 / 2.75	2.07 / 2.83	2.13 / 2.94	2.18 / 3.02	2.23 / 3.12	2.26 / 3.18	2.30 / 3.26	2.35 / 3.35	2.40 / 3.45	2.47 / 3.59	2.55 / 3.76	2.66 / 3.99	2.82 / 4.31	3.05 / 4.82	3.44 / 5.72	4.30 / 7.94
23	1.76 / 2.26	1.77 / 2.28	1.79 / 2.32	1.82 / 2.37	1.84 / 2.41	1.88 / 2.48	1.91 / 2.53	1.96 / 2.62	2.00 / 2.70	2.04 / 2.78	2.10 / 2.89	2.14 / 2.97	2.20 / 3.07	2.24 / 3.14	2.28 / 3.21	2.32 / 3.30	2.38 / 3.41	2.45 / 3.54	2.53 / 3.71	2.64 / 3.94	2.80 / 4.26	3.03 / 4.76	3.42 / 5.66	4.28 / 7.88
24	1.73 / 2.21	1.74 / 2.23	1.76 / 2.27	1.80 / 2.33	1.82 / 2.36	1.86 / 2.44	1.89 / 2.49	1.94 / 2.58	1.98 / 2.66	2.02 / 2.74	2.09 / 2.85	2.13 / 2.93	2.18 / 3.03	2.22 / 3.09	2.26 / 3.17	2.30 / 3.25	2.36 / 3.36	2.43 / 3.50	2.51 / 3.67	2.62 / 3.90	2.78 / 4.22	3.01 / 4.72	3.40 / 5.61	4.26 / 7.82
25	1.71 / 2.17	1.72 / 2.19	1.74 / 2.23	1.77 / 2.29	1.80 / 2.32	1.84 / 2.40	1.87 / 2.45	1.92 / 2.54	1.96 / 2.62	2.00 / 2.70	2.06 / 2.81	2.11 / 2.89	2.16 / 2.99	2.20 / 3.05	2.24 / 3.13	2.28 / 3.21	2.34 / 3.32	2.41 / 3.46	2.49 / 3.63	2.60 / 3.86	2.76 / 4.18	2.99 / 4.68	3.38 / 5.57	4.24 / 7.77
26	1.69 / 2.13	1.70 / 2.15	1.72 / 2.19	1.76 / 2.25	1.78 / 2.28	1.82 / 2.36	1.85 / 2.41	1.90 / 2.50	1.95 / 2.58	1.99 / 2.66	2.05 / 2.77	2.10 / 2.86	2.15 / 2.96	2.18 / 3.02	2.22 / 3.09	2.27 / 3.17	2.32 / 3.29	2.39 / 3.42	2.47 / 3.59	2.59 / 3.82	2.74 / 4.14	2.97 / 4.64	3.37 / 5.53	4.22 / 7.72

TABLE V–F DISTRIBUTION—*Continued.*

5% (ROMAN TYPE) AND 1% (BOLD-FACE TYPE) POINTS FOR THE DISTRIBUTION OF *F*

Degrees of freedom for greater mean square

Degrees of freedom for lesser mean square	1	2	3	4	5	6	7	8	9	10	11	12	14	16	20	24	30	40	50	75	100	200	500	∞
27	4.21 / **7.68**	3.35 / **5.49**	2.96 / **4.60**	2.73 / **4.11**	2.57 / **3.79**	2.46 / **3.56**	2.37 / **3.39**	2.30 / **3.26**	2.25 / **3.14**	2.20 / **3.06**	2.16 / **2.98**	2.13 / **2.93**	2.08 / **2.83**	2.03 / **2.74**	1.97 / **2.63**	1.93 / **2.55**	1.88 / **2.47**	1.84 / **2.38**	1.80 / **2.33**	1.76 / **2.25**	1.74 / **2.21**	1.71 / **2.16**	1.68 / **2.12**	1.67 / **2.10**
28	4.20 / **7.64**	3.34 / **5.45**	2.95 / **4.57**	2.71 / **4.07**	2.56 / **3.76**	2.44 / **3.53**	2.36 / **3.36**	2.29 / **3.23**	2.24 / **3.11**	2.19 / **3.03**	2.15 / **2.95**	2.12 / **2.90**	2.06 / **2.80**	2.02 / **2.71**	1.96 / **2.60**	1.91 / **2.52**	1.87 / **2.44**	1.81 / **2.35**	1.78 / **2.30**	1.75 / **2.22**	1.72 / **2.18**	1.69 / **2.13**	1.67 / **2.09**	1.65 / **2.06**
29	4.18 / **7.60**	3.33 / **5.52**	2.93 / **4.54**	2.70 / **4.04**	2.54 / **3.73**	2.43 / **3.50**	2.35 / **3.33**	2.28 / **3.20**	2.22 / **3.08**	2.18 / **3.00**	2.14 / **2.92**	2.10 / **2.87**	2.05 / **2.77**	2.00 / **2.68**	1.94 / **2.57**	1.90 / **2.49**	1.85 / **2.41**	1.80 / **2.32**	1.77 / **2.27**	1.73 / **2.19**	1.71 / **2.15**	1.68 / **2.10**	1.65 / **2.06**	1.64 / **2.03**
30	4.17 / **7.56**	3.32 / **5.39**	2.92 / **4.51**	2.69 / **4.02**	2.53 / **3.70**	2.42 / **3.47**	2.34 / **3.30**	2.27 / **3.17**	2.21 / **3.06**	2.16 / **2.98**	2.12 / **2.90**	2.09 / **2.84**	2.04 / **2.74**	1.99 / **2.66**	1.93 / **2.55**	1.89 / **2.47**	1.84 / **2.38**	1.79 / **2.29**	1.76 / **2.24**	1.72 / **2.16**	1.69 / **2.13**	1.66 / **2.07**	1.64 / **2.03**	1.62 / **2.01**
32	4.15 / **7.50**	3.30 / **5.34**	2.90 / **4.46**	2.67 / **3.97**	2.51 / **3.66**	2.40 / **3.42**	2.32 / **3.25**	2.25 / **3.12**	2.19 / **3.01**	2.14 / **2.94**	2.10 / **2.86**	2.07 / **2.80**	2.02 / **2.70**	1.97 / **2.62**	1.91 / **2.51**	1.86 / **2.42**	1.82 / **2.34**	1.76 / **2.25**	1.74 / **2.20**	1.69 / **2.12**	1.67 / **2.08**	1.64 / **2.02**	1.61 / **1.98**	1.59 / **1.96**
34	4.13 / **7.44**	3.28 / **5.29**	2.88 / **4.42**	2.65 / **3.93**	2.49 / **3.61**	2.38 / **3.38**	2.30 / **3.21**	2.23 / **3.08**	2.17 / **2.97**	2.12 / **2.89**	2.08 / **2.82**	2.05 / **2.76**	2.00 / **2.66**	1.95 / **2.58**	1.89 / **2.47**	1.84 / **2.38**	1.80 / **2.30**	1.74 / **2.21**	1.71 / **2.15**	1.67 / **2.08**	1.64 / **2.04**	1.61 / **1.98**	1.59 / **1.94**	1.57 / **1.91**
36	4.11 / **7.39**	3.26 / **5.25**	2.86 / **4.38**	2.63 / **3.89**	2.48 / **3.58**	2.36 / **3.35**	2.28 / **3.18**	2.21 / **3.04**	2.15 / **2.94**	2.10 / **2.86**	2.06 / **2.78**	2.03 / **2.72**	1.98 / **2.62**	1.93 / **2.54**	1.87 / **2.43**	1.82 / **2.35**	1.78 / **2.26**	1.72 / **2.17**	1.69 / **2.12**	1.65 / **2.04**	1.62 / **2.00**	1.59 / **1.94**	1.56 / **1.90**	1.55 / **1.87**
38	4.10 / **7.35**	3.25 / **5.21**	2.85 / **4.34**	2.62 / **3.86**	2.46 / **3.54**	2.35 / **3.32**	2.26 / **3.15**	2.19 / **3.02**	2.14 / **2.91**	2.09 / **2.82**	2.05 / **2.75**	2.02 / **2.69**	1.96 / **2.59**	1.92 / **2.51**	1.85 / **2.40**	1.80 / **2.32**	1.76 / **2.22**	1.71 / **2.14**	1.67 / **2.08**	1.63 / **2.00**	1.60 / **1.97**	1.57 / **1.90**	1.54 / **1.86**	1.53 / **1.84**
40	4.08 / **7.31**	3.23 / **5.18**	2.84 / **4.31**	2.61 / **3.83**	2.45 / **3.51**	2.34 / **3.29**	2.25 / **3.12**	2.18 / **2.99**	2.12 / **2.88**	2.07 / **2.80**	2.04 / **2.73**	2.00 / **2.66**	1.95 / **2.56**	1.90 / **2.49**	1.84 / **2.37**	1.79 / **2.29**	1.74 / **2.20**	1.69 / **2.11**	1.66 / **2.05**	1.61 / **1.97**	1.59 / **1.94**	1.55 / **1.88**	1.53 / **1.84**	1.51 / **1.81**
42	4.07 / **7.27**	3.22 / **5.15**	2.83 / **4.29**	2.59 / **3.80**	2.44 / **3.49**	2.32 / **3.26**	2.24 / **3.10**	2.17 / **2.96**	2.11 / **2.86**	2.06 / **2.77**	2.02 / **2.70**	1.99 / **2.64**	1.94 / **2.54**	1.89 / **2.46**	1.82 / **2.35**	1.78 / **2.26**	1.73 / **2.17**	1.68 / **2.08**	1.64 / **2.02**	1.60 / **1.94**	1.57 / **1.91**	1.54 / **1.85**	1.51 / **1.80**	1.49 / **1.78**
44	4.06 / **7.24**	3.21 / **5.12**	2.82 / **4.26**	2.58 / **3.78**	2.43 / **3.46**	2.31 / **3.24**	2.23 / **3.07**	2.16 / **2.94**	2.10 / **2.84**	2.05 / **2.75**	2.01 / **2.68**	1.98 / **2.62**	1.92 / **2.52**	1.88 / **2.44**	1.81 / **2.32**	1.76 / **2.24**	1.72 / **2.15**	1.66 / **2.06**	1.63 / **2.00**	1.58 / **1.92**	1.56 / **1.88**	1.52 / **1.82**	1.50 / **1.78**	1.48 / **1.75**
46	4.05 / **7.21**	3.20 / **5.10**	2.81 / **4.24**	2.57 / **3.76**	2.42 / **3.44**	2.30 / **3.22**	2.22 / **3.05**	2.14 / **2.92**	2.09 / **2.82**	2.04 / **2.73**	2.00 / **2.66**	1.97 / **2.60**	1.91 / **2.50**	1.87 / **2.42**	1.80 / **2.30**	1.75 / **2.22**	1.71 / **2.13**	1.65 / **2.04**	1.62 / **1.98**	1.57 / **1.90**	1.54 / **1.86**	1.51 / **1.80**	1.48 / **1.76**	1.46 / **1.72**
48	4.04 / **7.19**	3.19 / **5.08**	2.80 / **4.22**	2.56 / **3.74**	2.41 / **3.42**	2.30 / **3.20**	2.21 / **3.04**	2.14 / **2.90**	2.08 / **2.80**	2.03 / **2.71**	1.99 / **2.64**	1.96 / **2.58**	1.90 / **2.48**	1.86 / **2.40**	1.79 / **2.28**	1.74 / **2.20**	1.70 / **2.11**	1.64 / **2.02**	1.61 / **1.96**	1.56 / **1.88**	1.53 / **1.84**	1.50 / **1.78**	1.47 / **1.73**	1.45 / **1.70**

50	1.44 / 1.68	1.46 / 1.71	1.48 / 1.76	1.52 / 1.82	1.55 / 1.86	1.60 / 1.94	1.63 / 2.00	1.69 / 2.10	1.74 / 2.18	1.78 / 2.26	1.85 / 2.39	1.90 / 2.46	1.95 / 2.56	1.98 / 2.62	2.02 / 2.70	2.07 / 2.78	2.13 / 2.88	2.20 / 3.02	2.29 / 3.18	2.40 / 3.41	2.56 / 3.72	2.79 / 4.20	3.18 / 5.06	4.03 / 7.17
55	1.41 / 1.64	1.43 / 1.66	1.46 / 1.71	1.50 / 1.78	1.52 / 1.82	1.58 / 1.90	1.61 / 1.96	1.67 / 2.06	1.72 / 2.15	1.76 / 2.23	1.83 / 2.35	1.88 / 2.43	1.93 / 2.53	1.97 / 2.59	2.00 / 2.66	2.05 / 2.75	2.11 / 2.85	2.18 / 2.98	2.27 / 3.15	2.38 / 3.37	2.54 / 3.68	2.78 / 4.16	3.17 / 5.01	4.02 / 7.12
60	1.39 / 1.60	1.41 / 1.63	1.44 / 1.68	1.48 / 1.74	1.50 / 1.79	1.56 / 1.87	1.59 / 1.93	1.65 / 2.03	1.70 / 2.12	1.75 / 2.20	1.81 / 2.32	1.86 / 2.40	1.92 / 2.50	1.95 / 2.56	1.99 / 2.63	2.04 / 2.72	2.10 / 2.82	2.17 / 2.95	2.25 / 3.12	2.37 / 3.34	2.52 / 3.65	2.76 / 4.13	3.15 / 4.98	4.00 / 7.08
65	1.37 / 1.56	1.39 / 1.60	1.42 / 1.64	1.46 / 1.71	1.49 / 1.76	1.54 / 1.84	1.57 / 1.90	1.63 / 2.00	1.68 / 2.09	1.73 / 2.18	1.80 / 2.30	1.85 / 2.37	1.90 / 2.47	1.94 / 2.54	1.98 / 2.61	2.02 / 2.70	2.08 / 2.79	2.15 / 2.93	2.24 / 3.09	2.36 / 3.31	2.51 / 3.62	2.75 / 4.10	3.14 / 4.95	3.99 / 7.04
70	1.35 / 1.53	1.37 / 1.56	1.40 / 1.62	1.45 / 1.69	1.47 / 1.74	1.53 / 1.82	1.56 / 1.88	1.62 / 1.98	1.67 / 2.07	1.72 / 2.15	1.79 / 2.28	1.84 / 2.35	1.89 / 2.45	1.93 / 2.51	1.97 / 2.59	2.01 / 2.67	2.07 / 2.77	2.14 / 2.91	2.22 / 3.07	2.35 / 3.29	2.50 / 3.60	2.74 / 4.08	3.13 / 4.92	3.98 / 7.01
80	1.32 / 1.49	1.35 / 1.52	1.38 / 1.57	1.42 / 1.65	1.45 / 1.70	1.51 / 1.78	1.54 / 1.84	1.60 / 1.94	1.65 / 2.03	1.70 / 2.11	1.77 / 2.24	1.82 / 2.32	1.88 / 2.41	1.91 / 2.48	1.95 / 2.55	1.99 / 2.64	2.05 / 2.74	2.12 / 2.87	2.21 / 3.04	2.33 / 3.25	2.48 / 3.56	2.72 / 4.04	3.11 / 4.88	3.96 / 6.96
100	1.28 / 1.43	1.30 / 1.46	1.34 / 1.51	1.39 / 1.59	1.42 / 1.64	1.48 / 1.73	1.51 / 1.79	1.57 / 1.89	1.63 / 1.98	1.68 / 2.06	1.75 / 2.19	1.79 / 2.26	1.85 / 2.36	1.88 / 2.43	1.92 / 2.51	1.97 / 2.59	2.03 / 2.69	2.10 / 2.82	2.19 / 2.99	2.30 / 3.20	2.46 / 3.51	2.70 / 3.98	3.09 / 4.82	3.94 / 6.90
125	1.25 / 1.37	1.27 / 1.40	1.31 / 1.46	1.36 / 1.54	1.39 / 1.59	1.45 / 1.68	1.49 / 1.75	1.55 / 1.85	1.60 / 1.94	1.65 / 2.03	1.72 / 2.15	1.77 / 2.23	1.83 / 2.33	1.86 / 2.40	1.90 / 2.47	1.95 / 2.56	2.01 / 2.65	2.08 / 2.79	2.17 / 2.95	2.29 / 3.17	2.44 / 3.47	2.68 / 3.94	3.07 / 4.78	3.92 / 6.84
150	1.22 / 1.33	1.25 / 1.37	1.29 / 1.43	1.34 / 1.51	1.37 / 1.56	1.44 / 1.66	1.47 / 1.72	1.54 / 1.83	1.59 / 1.91	1.64 / 2.00	1.71 / 2.12	1.76 / 2.20	1.82 / 2.30	1.85 / 2.37	1.89 / 2.44	1.94 / 2.53	2.00 / 2.62	2.07 / 2.76	2.16 / 2.92	2.27 / 3.13	2.43 / 3.44	2.67 / 3.91	3.06 / 4.75	3.91 / 6.81
200	1.19 / 1.28	1.22 / 1.33	1.26 / 1.39	1.32 / 1.48	1.35 / 1.53	1.42 / 1.62	1.45 / 1.69	1.52 / 1.79	1.57 / 1.88	1.62 / 1.97	1.69 / 2.09	1.74 / 2.17	1.80 / 2.28	1.83 / 2.34	1.87 / 2.41	1.92 / 2.50	1.98 / 2.60	2.05 / 2.73	2.14 / 2.90	2.26 / 3.11	2.41 / 3.41	2.65 / 3.88	3.04 / 4.71	3.89 / 6.76
400	1.13 / 1.19	1.16 / 1.24	1.22 / 1.32	1.28 / 1.42	1.32 / 1.47	1.38 / 1.57	1.42 / 1.64	1.49 / 1.74	1.54 / 1.84	1.60 / 1.92	1.67 / 2.04	1.72 / 2.12	1.78 / 2.23	1.81 / 2.29	1.85 / 2.37	1.90 / 2.46	1.96 / 2.55	2.03 / 2.69	2.12 / 2.85	2.23 / 3.06	2.39 / 3.36	2.62 / 3.83	3.02 / 4.66	3.86 / 6.70
1000	1.08 / 1.11	1.13 / 1.19	1.19 / 1.28	1.26 / 1.38	1.30 / 1.44	1.36 / 1.54	1.41 / 1.61	1.47 / 1.71	1.53 / 1.81	1.58 / 1.89	1.65 / 2.01	1.71 / 2.09	1.76 / 2.20	1.80 / 2.26	1.84 / 2.34	1.89 / 2.43	1.95 / 2.53	2.02 / 2.66	2.10 / 2.82	2.22 / 3.04	2.38 / 3.34	2.61 / 3.80	3.00 / 4.62	3.85 / 6.66
∞	1.00 / 1.00	1.11 / 1.15	1.17 / 1.25	1.24 / 1.36	1.28 / 1.41	1.35 / 1.52	1.40 / 1.59	1.46 / 1.69	1.52 / 1.79	1.57 / 1.87	1.64 / 1.99	1.69 / 2.07	1.75 / 2.18	1.79 / 2.24	1.83 / 2.32	1.88 / 2.41	1.94 / 2.51	2.01 / 2.64	2.09 / 2.80	2.21 / 3.02	2.37 / 3.32	2.60 / 3.78	2.99 / 4.60	3.84 / 6.64

INDEX